WHAT'S THE ANSWER?

WHAT'S THE ANSWER?

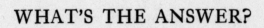

WHAT'S
the
ANSWER?

A book that entertains and instructs
Classify your mind, and give your friends a
chance to know their own minds

BY

FRED GARRIGUS

Boston   BOOKS, INC.   New York

WHAT'S
the
ANSWER
?

A book that entertains and instructs.
Classify your mind, and give your friends
a chance to know their own minds.

BY

FRED GARRIGUS

Boston   BOOKS, INC.   New York

THIS BOOK IS DEDICATED TO MY SON, DAVID, WHOSE YOUTHFUL
QUESTIONINGS BID FAIR TO MAKE THOSE CONTAINED IN
THIS VOLUME SEEM VERY SIMPLE INDEED.

FOREWORD

"What's the Answer?" is designed primarily for entertainment. If something new is learned in the process of answering these questions so much the better.

In many instances we have gone into rather more detail than is absolutely necessary to answer the given question with this thought in mind. Many a serious minded soul is going to be taken aback by the levity of some of our answers, for we have scattered the lighter touch throughout. Since one of Webster's definitions of the word quiz is to "mock with pretended seriousness" there is some authority for this mixing of fact and fancy.

These questions, like any others, are all easy if you know the answers; but no one can be expected to know them all. In giving this series of quizzes to many people we have found that 70 or 75 for a general quiz is very good, while specialists usually get about 80 in their own field. The average person may expect to fare very well, even in the special quizzes, because the information needed is of the type that is general information rather than purely academic.

One form of quiz included in this book is, we believe, a new variation of the question and answer technique. We refer to the two sets in which we have given you the answers and your problem is the reverse of the usual procedure inasmuch as you supply the missing question. In these sets there is only one question that could have received this answer. Of course it is unimportant that you phrase the questions exactly as we have; the thought and general accuracy is the important element.

In editing a book of this type it is impossible to mention by name all who have contributed to its set up and accuracy. There is one in this instance, however, without whose hard work, encouragement, and organizing genius this book would not have been completed. The name of my wife, Elizabeth Reed Garrigus, is more deserving of a place on the cover than is my own, for without her close cooperation I should long ago have failed in this project. Whatever of good entertainment and skillful arrangement there is in this book may safely be attributed to her, and the inadequacies which are bound to appear, are my own.

To my publisher, the hundreds of friends and acquaintances who have suggested questions and submitted themselves to the process of being quizzed, and assisted in research, go the author's thanks.

In using this book for party games, we suggest that one point be allowed for each correct answer if 100 questions are used. To facilitate the use of parts of different quizzes the sets are divided into groups of 25 each. In the event that only 25 questions are used at one time the scoring for each question should, of course, be four.

In every instance we have strived to check the accuracy of the answers to these questions, but even so, we find, there are many who will discover some opening for argument or disagreement. The person who gives the answers to the questions contained herein will, at least, be sure of an authority to quote when the party's master of ceremonies asks: "What's the Answer?"

FRED GARRIGUS

CONTENTS

WHAT'S THE ANSWER?

DON'T CONFUSE 'EM QUIZ NUMBER I-A

Answers on page 221

1. What is the difference between gross weight, tare weight, and net weight?
2. If an introduction to a book is a preface, and a prelude is an introduction to a musical work, what is a prologue?
3. What is the difference between the Fahrenheit and Centigrade thermometers?
4. What is the difference between a tabor and a tabard?
5. What is a gob? What is a goblet?
6. Distinguish between eminent and imminent.
7. What is a philatelist, a somnambulist, a polygamist?
8. What is the difference between amnesia and asthenia?
9. When we are hopeful or confident we are sanguine; what are we when we are consanguineous?
10. What is the difference between stalactites and stalagmites?
11. What is the meaning of introspection and retrospection?
12. What is the difference between rhodium and radium?
13. If a gnome is a fabulous person, what is a gnomon?
14. Give the definitions of the following words: alembic, ceramics, and polemics.
15. What is a howdah, and a hookah?
16. If speculate means to invest where a risk is involved, what is peculate?
17. What is the difference between maternity and husbandry?
18. What is the difference between a skipper and a scupper on a ship?
19. What is the difference between transparent, translucent, and opaque?
20. What is an inn? What is an inlet?
21. What is the difference between plurality and majority?
22. What is the difference between bingo, dingo, and lingo?
23. What is the difference between convey and convoy?
24. What is the difference between a gourmet and a gourmand?
25. What is the difference between a relic and a relict?

DON'T CONFUSE 'EM QUIZ NUMBER I-B

Answers on page 222

1. What is the difference between a bridge, a viaduct, and an aqueduct?

2. If a barrier is something which hinders or obstructs, what is a farrier?
3. What is the difference between a misogamist and a misogynist?
4. Define: tycoon, cocoon, monsoon.
5. What is the difference between a convex and a concave lens?
6. If a python is a large non-venomous serpent, what is a Pythoness?
7. What is the difference between selvage and salvage?
8. If avert means to avoid or shun, what does overt mean?
9. What is the difference between a replica and a reproduction?
10. If a squid is a fish, what is a quid?
11. What is the difference between izard and izzard?
12. What is the meaning of the words auger and augur?
13. If a Republican is a member of that party which favors the principles of a republic, what is a publican?
14. If a baboon is an ape, what is a lagoon?
15. What is the difference between a polygon and a polypod?
16. What are the following: lute, jute, Ute?
17. What is the difference between erode and corrode?
18. If a crypt is à subterranean cell, what is cryptography?
19. What is the difference between a cornucopia and a cornopean?
20. If gargle means to wash the throat and mouth, what is the meaning of the word gargoyle?
21. What is the difference between interstate and intrastate?
22. If quince is a pear shaped fruit, what is squince?
23. What is the difference between terra cotta, terra firma, and terrapin?
24. If errant means roving or wandering, what does arrant mean?
25. What is the difference between a disinfectant and an antiseptic?

DON'T CONFUSE 'EM QUIZ NUMBER I-C

Answers on page 222

1. What is the difference between terminal and terminus?
2. If a fiesta is a gay holiday, what is a siesta?

3. What is the difference between polygon, hexagon, and lexicon?
4. Distinguish between timber and lumber.
5. What is the difference between amnesia and aphasia?
6. If a hippodrome is an arena, and an airdrome is an airport, what is a palindrome?
7. Although pronounced alike, what is the difference between indict and indite?
8. What is the meaning of firkin, gherkin, and jerkin?
9. What is the difference between a lama and a llama?
10. If a cheater is a person who deceives or defrauds, what is a cheetah?
11. What is the difference between a picaroon, a picador, and a piccolo?
12. What is a chateau, a bando, and a plateau?
13. What is the difference between caddie, caddy, and cadi?
14. What is the difference between a hallmark, a water mark, and a land mark?
15. What is the difference between an audience and a spectator?
16. What is the difference between parsimonious and persimmons?
17. What is the difference between a scapegoat, a scapegrace, and a scapula?
18. If compulsion means to compel, what does compunction mean?
19. What is the difference between an aviary and an apiary?
20. What is the difference between adhesion and cohesion?
21. What is the difference between martial law and military law?
22. What is the difference between a papoose and a porpoise?
23. What is the difference between a surplus and a surplice?
24. Distinguish between carat, caret, carrot.
25. If a cousin is a relative, what is a cuisine?

DON'T CONFUSE 'EM QUIZ NUMBER I-D

Answers on page 223

1. What is the difference between an esophagus and a sarcophagus?

2. What is the difference between the words specie and species?

3. What is the difference between the words ravel and unravel?

4. If a currycomb is a comb used to groom horses, what is a catacomb?

5. If an epitaph is an inscription on a tomb stone, what is a cenotaph?

6. What is the difference between a valedictorian and a valetudinarian?

7. If a chandelier is a hanging frame for a light, what is a bandoleer?

8. Distinguish between a bell buoy, a highboy, and a breeches buoy?

9. What is the difference between a derelict and a dialect?

10. If a greenhouse is a conservatory for flowers, what is a green room?

11. What is the difference between a patricide and a parasite?

12. If a wharf is a place for discharging freight or passengers, what is a wharfinger?

13. What is the difference between counterfoil and counterpoint?

14. If an argot is a form of slang, what is an ingot?

15. What is the difference between explode and implode?

16. What is an octave? An octant? An octopod?

17. If a short story is a small story, what is a tall story?

18. What is the difference between liniment and lineament?

19. If a latch is a kind of lock, what is a latchet?

20. You know what a Yale lock and a canal lock are used for; but what is a fetlock?

21. Can you differentiate between Samuel Taylor Coleridge and Samuel Coleridge Taylor?

22. You know what a fire escape is; what is an airscape?

23. What would you expect to find in a crow's nest? In a mare's nest?

24. What is the difference between a tundra, a savanna, and a pampas?

25. Distinguish between dido, dado, dodo.

ARE YOU MUSICALLY INCLINED? I-A.

Answers on page 224

1. From what language do we get most of our musical terms?
2. Give the characteristics of the following heroines of song: Annie Laurie, Clementine, Juanita, Alice Ben Bolt.
3. Who wrote "Believe Me If All Those Endearing Young Charms" and " 'Tis the Last Rose of Summer"?
4. What is the difference between a cantata and an opera?
5. What event does the song "Marching Through Georgia" commemorate?
6. How many times does the word "America" appear in the stanzas of "My Country 'Tis of Thee"?
7. Who wrote "Lead Kindly Light"?
8. Who wrote the following lines and to what do they refer:
"On the shore dimly seen, through the mists of the deep,
Where the foe's haughty host, in dread silence reposes,
What is that which the breeze, o'er the towering steep
As it fitfully blows, half conceals, half discloses?"
9. Who was the siren of the Rhine who lured boatmen to shipwreck by her singing?
10. How many strings has a violin? What are they?
11. Who were the three famous "B's" of music?
12. How old was Billy Boy's girl friend in the song "Billy Boy"?
13. In what opera was John Howard Payne's song "Home Sweet Home" first sung?
14. From what song are these lines taken:
" 'Tis you who makes my friends and foes,
'Tis you who makes me wear old clothes"?
15. "The Chocolate Soldier" is a musical version of what play by George Bernard Shaw?
16. Which of the following is a musical term: mezzanine, mezzotint, intermezzo?
17. What article of dress is frequently used in a jazz band to mute a trumpet?
18. Is it true that the national anthem of this country has the same tune as the national anthem of another country?
19. Where and what is "Tin Pan Alley"?
20. What Prince Consort of a Queen of England composed songs, church music, and an opera?

13

21. What is a lyre?
22. What is the name of the National hymn of Canada?
23. Name five United States' rivers that have had songs written about them.
24. To play an harmonica one uses the hands and mouth. To play an harmonium one uses what?
25. What type of musical instrument is a bombardon?

MUSIC QUIZ NUMBER I-B

Answers on page 225

1. What does a swing musician mean when he refers to "schmalz"?
2. Which does not belong in the following group: "Rose of Washington Square", "How I Hate to Get Up In The Morning", "Swanee River", and "God Bless America"?
3. Name five different kinds of "moon" found in songs.
4. Name five song titles containing the names of women.
5. Which is the larger: a bass drum or a kettle drum?
6. Why was Beethoven unable to finish the "Unfinished Symphony"?
7. What type of music is described by the word "polyphony"?
8. If Bo-Peep is the little lady who lost her sheep, who is Peep-Bo?
9. "Readin' and writin' and 'rithmetic, taught to the tune of a hickory stick" is a line from what song?
10. When was the Star-Spangled Banner made the national anthem?
11. From what does the tune for the song "Hail, hail the gang's all here" come?
12. In what opera would you find the "Anvil Chorus"?
13. What is meant by the words "grand diapason"?
14. How would you go "roamin' in the gloamin' "?
15. In the song "Comin' through the Rye" to what does the word Rye refer?
16. In what opera is the "Toreador Song" sung?
17. Where is the land of the sky blue water, glorified in song?
18. Name the titles of three songs which contain the word "waltz".
19. Complete the following lines: "On my arm a soft hand

rested, rested light as ocean foam," and tell what song it is from.

20. Who composed each of the following: "Narcissus", "Liebestraum", "Clair de Lune", "Hungarian Rhapsody Number Eight", and "The Gold and Silver Waltz"?

21. Name three song titles which mention a bird in them.

22. By whom were the two most popular wedding marches composed?

23. Name the four component parts of an orchestra.

24. Who wrote the march "The Stars and Stripes Forever"?

25. "Corn on the cob" is a swing term for what musical instrument?

MUSIC QUIZ NUMBER I-C

Answers on page 226

1. In a pipe organ do the long or short pipes produce the high notes?

2. How many notes are there in an octave? How many are there in two octaves?

3. Fill in the missing words in this song and give it's title: "Of all the days that's in the week, I dearly love but one, and that's the day that comes betwixt the —— and ——."

4. From what song do these lines come: "The horse was lean and lank, misfortune was his lot, he got into a drifted bank and we, we got upsot"?

5. From what song are these lines taken: "I have seen him in the watchfires of a thousand circling camps, they have builded him an altar in the evening dews and damps"?

6. Name three musical instruments the playing of which requires the use of both the feet and hands.

7. How many strings has: a banjo? a guitar?

8. Where do "they do such things and they say such things"?

9. What song was sung "when the lights were low and the flickering shadows moved around"?

10. What is an a cappella choir?

11. Name three orchestra leaders whose first and last names begin with the same letters?

12. Give three song titles containing the names of articles of clothing.

15

13. From what song are the following lines: "I gaze on the moon as I tread the drear wild, and feel that my mother now thinks of her child"?
14. "The girl of my dreams is the sweetest girl of all the girls I know." Who is she?
15. Give three song titles containing a color in them.
16. Name three operas composed by Giuseppe Verdi.
17. Who was the author of "Auld Lang Syne"?
18. Who wrote the verse "Drink to Me Only With Thine Eyes"?
19. According to a popular song what is a good substitute for an umbrella?
20. What is an elegy?
21. Name five songs written by Stephen Foster.
22. What is the name of Ludwig van Beethoven's only opera?
23. What is the correct name for the musical instrument known as the "cello"?
24. What is a luthier?
25. The following are all what type of musical instruments: ophicleide, bombardon, sackbut?

MUSIC QUIZ NUMBER I-D

Answers on page 227

1. Who wrote "Carry Me Back to Old Virginny"?
2. Where would you go to see a horse opera?
3. What is the difference between a pianoforte and a piano?
4. The English horn is misnamed on two points. What are they?
5. What was the nationality of Aida, the heroine of Verdi's opera of the same name?
6. What have the words diatonic and chromatic in common?
7. What is the only musical instrument represented on a national flag?
8. What is a metronome?
9. Name three well known composers whose last names begin with the letter "S".
10. What is the steam piano of the circus called?
11. What four orchestra leaders of popular music have names that contain royal titles?

12. What is a hemidemisemiquaver?
13. "Oh, Promise Me" is from what operetta by what composer?
14. What type of musical instrument is the balalaika?
15. What is a barcarolle?
16. What is the difference between a melody and a harmony?
17. In what comic opera by Rossini is Figaro a character?
18. Richard Wagner was married to the daughter of what pianist?
19. What musical instrument did Benjamin Franklin invent?
20. Where does the "long, long trail" end?
21. Of what musical suite is Anitra's Dance a part?
22. Who composed the "Moonlight Sonata"?
23. Who was cautioned not to cry by her lover as he left for Alabama with a banjo on his knee?
24. What is chamber music?
25. What grand opera is truly Biblical in its theme?

BIBLE QUIZ NUMBER ONE

Answers on page 227

1. What is the Mosaic Law of retaliation?
2. Who was the father of Cain and Abel?
3. What Biblical character symbolized lying?
4. Who was the oldest man mentioned in the Bible and how old was he?
5. How many Psalms are there in the Bible?
6. What Biblical character symbolized patience?
7. Who said: "A good name is rather to be chosen than great riches"?
8. What Biblical inscription is on the Liberty Bell?
9. What does the Bible say is the root of all evil?
10. In the Genesis account of the creation, on what day was the land made?
11. What two birds did Noah send out of the Ark to search for land?
12. "My cup runneth over", is in what Psalm?
13. Name the traditional resting place of Noah's Ark after the flood.
14. What part of the Bible is referred to as the Decalogue?

15. Is the Torah a part of the Bible?
16. What was the foot covering worn in Bible times called?
17. What hero was betrayed by Delilah?
18. What character in the Old Testament had a coat of many colors?
19. Which apostle was a physician?
20. How many books are there in the Old Testament? How many in the New Testament?
21. Why did Joseph's brothers throw him into the pit?
22. How high was the Tower of Babel?
23. What was the name of the shepherd boy in the Bible who killed the giant Goliath?
24. In the Bible, which one of the following was Matthew: carpenter, shepherd, tax collector, or priest?
25. What unusual weapon did Samson use in his fight against the Philistines?

BIBLE QUIZ NUMBER TWO
Answers on page 228

1. What Biblical king ate grass like an ox?
2. At what king's feast did the handwriting appear on the wall?
3. Which contains the Law of Moses, the Talmud or the Torah?
4. What Biblical man has become a symbol for wisdom?
5. What Biblical character sold his birthright for a mess of pottage?
6. Who were the parents and grand-parents of Esau and Jacob?
7. Through what sea did the Israelites walk dry-shod?
8. The Queen of what country paid a visit to Solomon?
9. What was the language used by Christ during his life?
10. What is that part of the Bible between the Old and the New Testament called?
11. How did Joshua break down the walls of Jericho?
12. In the Bible, what man killed one-fourth of the world's population?
13. Name three of the five books of the Bible that begin with the letter "E".

14. What does the word "Gospel" mean?
15. What is the shortest verse in the Bible?
16. Why is it doubtful that the Bible story of Joseph's coat of many colors is wholly accurate?
17. Finish these Biblical quotations: "Do not cast ————". "Train a child ————". "Spare the rod ————".
18. Who translated the Bible for the American Indians?
19. Where is the quotation "down to the sea in ships" found?
20. What is a cubit?
21. The man cast into the lion's den was: Daniel, Jonah, or Joseph?
22. Who asked "Am I my brother's keeper?"
23. Who wrote the four gospels?
24. What Biblical leader ordered the sun to stand still in its course?
25. Who was sorry when the prodigal son returned?

BIBLE QUIZ NUMBER THREE
Answers on page 228

1. From what physical defect did Moses suffer?
2. What is meant by the Pentateuch?
3. What character in the Bible is never mentioned by name, yet suffered a death different from that of any other person?
4. When the Queen of Sheba sent 500 boys and 500 girls, dressed alike, to King Solomon, what was the test by which he determined which were boys and which were girls?
5. Who was the most successful financier mentioned in the Bible?
6. In what lay the secret of Samson's great strength?
7. In what book of the Bible is the battle of Armageddon mentioned?
8. To what Old Testament characters might these terms apply: most soluble? Most indigestible?
9. In which book of the Bible are the Ten Commandments found?
10. There are eight books in the King James version of the Bible which contain only four letters. Can you name five of them?
11. If all of the children killed by Herod were buried in the

sand with just their hands showing, how could you tell the boys from the girls?

12. Does the word "girl" appear in the King James version?
13. Would it be possible to open the Vulgate?
14. Who was the original doubting Thomas?
15. What was the relationship between the following Biblical characters: Adam and Eve; Cain and Abel; Ruth and Naomi; Solomon and David; Saul of Tarsus and Paul?
16. Where did the slang expression "by the skin of your teeth" originate?
17. Who was Shadrach?
18. What was the name of the loose flowing outer garment worn by the citizens of Rome in Bible days?
19. Name the principal river of Palestine and tell in what direction it flows.
20. Name five of the twelve apostles.
21. What country was referred to as the "land of bondage"?
22. Who were the Wise Men?
23. How did the angels speak of Jesus to the shepherds?
24. In what province was the town of Bethlehem?
25. Where is Mount Ararat, and for what is it noted?

BIBLE QUIZ NUMBER FOUR

Answers on page 229

1. When the three wise men came to Judea on the first Christmas they were following which of the following: an angel, a caravan, or a star?
2. Why were Joseph and Mary in Bethlehem the night Jesus was born?
3. What were the gifts brought to the manger by the wise men?
4. Give the next line after "Glory to God in the highest and on earth . . . .".
5. What famous town is five miles south of Jerusalem?
6. Give exactly the Golden Rule.
7. Name three of the famous Johns of the New Testament.
8. What general sacrificed his daughter to fulfill a vow?
9. Complete the proverb "A wise son maketh . . . .".
10. Who was David's close friend?
11. Who was the first King of Israel?

12. What is the Hexateuch?
13. What book of the Bible means the "going forth"?
14. Who was the daughter of Jezebel?
15. What was the name of the King of Judea at the time of Christ's birth?
16. What is the meaning of "El" as used in Hebrew names such as Daniel, Elisha, Elisabeth?
17. Who was "the voice of one crying in the wilderness"?
18. What baby was hidden in a basket of rushes?
19. What is the shortest book of the Bible?
20. What does "Selah" mean in the Psalms?
21. What characterized the laws of the Medes and the Persians?
22. What book of the Bible has the largest number of chapters?
23. What living creatures did Noah take into the Ark?
24. How long a rain made Noah's flood?
25. What common symbol of peace is connected with the Flood?

LITERARY QUIZ NUMBER I-A
Answers on page 229

1. Using the titles of Shakespeare's plays, answer the following questions: Who were the famous lovers? What was their courtship like? What day of the month were they married? Of whom did he buy the ring?
2. What two famous poems were written by Homer?
3. In "The Charge of the Light Brigade" the poet Tennyson commemorated an episode in what war?
4. In whose honor did Walt Whitman write the poem "O Captain, My Captain"?
5. What is the next line after "Young Lochinvar has come out of the West"?
6. In Dickens's "Tale of Two Cities", what was the salient characteristic of Madame de Farge?
7. Who wrote the "School for Scandal"?
8. What one word did Poe's Raven say?
9. What did Daniel Defoe do to make him famous in literature?

21

10. What woman had "the face that launched a thousand ships"?

11. In what novel by Charles Dickens does a pet raven play an important part?

12. How many ages of man are mentioned by Shakespeare?

13. Who on a summer's day "raked the meadows sweet with hay"?

14. Who wrote "There was a little girl and she had a little curl, right in the middle of her forehead"?

15. From what story do the following lines come:
"The time has come, the Walrus said,
To talk of many things:
Of shoes and ships and sealing wax,
And cabbages and kings"?

16. What famous character in a book was carved from wood?

17. In what famous literary work did three caskets figure prominently in the wooing of a woman's hand in marriage?

18. Complete this quotation: "Let me live in a house by the side of the road ....".

19. From what poem and by what author does the following come: "This is the forest primeval, the murmuring pines and the hemlocks ...."?

20. Name five great tragedies of Shakespeare.

21. Name three characters of fiction whose names include a color.

22. Give the line of the poem preceding this: "And never the twain shall meet".

23. In what book by what author does the character of Jean Valjean appear?

24. With what literary figure do you associate Sherwood Forest?

25. Who was Launcelot Gobbo?

LITERARY QUIZ NUMBER I-B

Answers on page 230

1. What author used the following pen names: Toby, Quiz, The Uncommercial Traveler, and Timothy Sparks?

2. What is the next line after "How far that little candle throws its beams"?

3. How many ghosts of Christmas did Ebenezer Scrooge see in Dickens's Christmas Carol?
4. Who wrote "Twenty Thousand Leagues Under the Sea"?
5. By what name is Eva St. Clair better known?
6. Who wrote the famous poem about the one hoss shay?
7. Who were the brothers Karamazov?
8. What was Mr. Micawber always waiting for?
9. Who wrote the "Little Minister"?
10. Who tamed the shrew?
11. What novel of Charles Dickens's was never finished?
12. In what famous book does a footprint play an important part?
13. Name three books whose titles have numbers in them.
14. Longfellow had three daughters and wrote about them in his poem, "The Children's Hour". Name them and describe them in the words of the poem.
15. What are the first and last names of the four girls in Louisa May Alcott's "Little Women"?
16. Evangeline found Gabriel dying, she never found him at all, or she found him married?
17. The Bridge of San Luis Rey was on the road to Lima, Mexico City, or Madrid?
18. Was Lear King of England or France in the fourteenth century?
19. What book was the world's best seller in 1922?
20. In what famous American short story does a headless horseman appear?
21. Who is responsible for the origin of the phrase "sweets to the sweet"?
22. In what literary work does an albatross play an important part?
23. In the "Murders in the Rue Morgue", by Poe, who was the murderer?
24. In what historical novel was there a famous chariot race?
25. Give the next line after "Blessings on thee, little man".

LITERARY QUIZ NUMBER I-C

Answers on page 230

1. On what river did Huckleberry Finn's adventures take place?

2. In what story by what author does the character of Ellen Douglas appear?
3. What was the name of Lorna Doone's lover in Blackmore's novel of the same name?
4. Who wrote the quotation "From Judy O'Grady to the Colonel's Lady, they're sisters under the skin"?
5. In what book does the phrase "Fifteen men on a dead man's chest" play an important part?
6. Who wrote "The paths of glory lead but to the grave"?
7. Who was Becky Sharp?
8. Sir Launfal sought which the following: the Golden Fleece, Holy Grail, Silver Buddha?
9. What was the name of the white scout in the "Last of the Mohicans"?
10. In what state is the great stone face of Hawthorne's tale located?
11. Who was Ichabod Crane's rival in love?
12. Philo Vance, the detective, was a character created by what author of detective fiction?
13. Give the next line after "I am the master of my fate".
14. In which of his books did Charles Dickens feature these characters: Little Em'ly, Little Nell, Little Dorrit?
15. Who first asked, in literature, "what is so rare as a day in June?"?
16. In Shakespeare's Julius Caesar, Calpurnia was: A poet, Caesar's friend, or Caesar's wife?
17. In what book will you find the expression: "When you call me that, smile"?
18. In what play is the line "A rose by any other name would smell as sweet"?
19. What play has for its subtitle "The Moor of Venice"?
20. Who was the Chevalier Raoul?
21. What was the Deacon's masterpiece, and how long did it last?
22. From what poem do the following lines come: "In the spring a young man's fancy lightly turns to thoughts of love"?
23. In what book were submarines spoken of long before their invention?
24. Who wrote the "Scarlet Letter" and what letter was it?
25. In what country was Hamlet supposedly a Prince?

LITERARY QUIZ NUMBER I-D

Answers on page 231

1. What are the two longest sleeps mentioned in literature?
2. What was the last name of Tiny Tim in Dickens's Christmas Carol?
3. Only one of Shakespeare's plays has a dog in it. What is the name of that play?
4. Who was the last of the Mohicans?
5. What event is referred to in the following Longfellow quotation: "On the eighteenth of April, in Seventy-five, hardly a man is now alive, who remembers that famous day and year"?
6. What were the last names of Romeo and Juliet?
7. Who was the best known actress in Shakespeare's time?
8. Where is the Poets' Corner?
9. Who was Gunga Din?
10. Who was Sarah Gamp?
11. Was Shakespeare's character of Macbeth real or imagnary?
12. Jim Hawkins is a character in what book?
13. Give the next line after "Tomorrow will be of all the year, the maddest, merriest day ....".
14. "Hail to thee, blithe Spirit!" opens what poem?
15. Name three prominent American authors who lived in Concord, Massachusetts.
16. The character of Ophelia appears in what play by Shakespeare?
17. From what poem and by whom is the following a quotation: "Water, water everywhere
Nor any drop to drink"?
18. For what characteristic was Trilby famous?
19. What famous character of modern fiction lived in Baker Street, London?
20. What author is responsible for the following line: "None but the brave deserve the fair"?
21. In what famous play did Banquo make his appearance?
22. What two cities are referred to in Dickens's story "The Tale of Two Cities"?
23. In Shakespeare's play were Romeo and Juliet finally married?

24. In what novel does the character of Sancho Panza appear?
25. Finish this stanza: "And the night shall be filled with music, and the cares that infest the day ....".

GENERAL QUIZ NUMBER I-A
Answers on page 232

1. Name three seas beginning with the letter 'B'?
2. On what Italian island is the famous Blue Grotto?
3. What is the largest Spanish speaking city in the world?
4. Where are these baseball parks located: Polo Grounds; Sportsman's Park; Wrigley Field; Brigg's Stadium; Shibe Park?
5. What two presidents of the United States have had the longest full names?
6. Fill in these blanks:
   A .... is burned in the fireplace at Christmas.
   A .... is worn on St. Patrick's Day.
   .... decorate churches on the Sunday before Easter.
7. Where is Cape Horn?
8. What is the capital of Missouri?
9. When is Hogmanay Night?
10. Give the first names of the following presidents: Coolidge, Wilson, Cleveland.
11. If you wanted to drop a box into the deepest part of the ocean, where would you go to do it?
12. Is Bermuda part of the West Indies?
13. What group of islands lie north of the mainland of Scotland?
14. What is the correct name of Santa Claus?
15. What cheese is *made* backwards?
16. How many islands comprise the West Indies group, and can you name them?
17. What does Adeste Fidelis mean?
18. Where is the Calvin Coolidge Memorial bridge?
19. Where was the birth place of Mahomet?
20. Where are the Ozark Mountains?
21. What is an atoll, and where is it chiefly found?
22. Who invented the revolver?
23. What is hob-nobbing?

24. Name the capital of North Carolina?
25. An imaginary trip down South. Fill in the blanks with names of well known cities and in the correct states: I jumped on my bicycle and started .... in West Virginia, and when hungry I ate a .... in Kentucky, but preferring fruit, I found the best place to get .... in Maryland. Going further south, I met the girl friend..... in North Carolina, and made a .... Beach in Florida. Charlotte was all right in Florida, but I had much rather .... in Cuba.

GENERAL QUIZ NUMBER I-B
Answers on page 232

1. Can you give the following sentence without sounding the R's: Robert gave Richard a rap in the ribs for roasting the rabbit so rare.
2. Name three cities in the United States ending in 'polis', and tell what state each is in?
3. What famous New England dishes did the Indians teach the Pilgrims to make?
4. What have the following in common: cicada, mantis, dor, scarab, emmet, and miller?
5. What South American countries are bounded by both the Atlantic and Pacific Oceans?
6. What berry has its seeds on the outside. What berry has the name of a fowl?
7. What single acquisition of territory almost doubled the size of the United States?
8. What American city gave its name to the fastest type of commercial sailing ship?
9. What famous building in Boston was erected from lottery money?
10. How high is the Rock of Gibraltar?
11. The Red River, Wisconsin River, and the St. Croix River all flow into what river?
12. To kiss the Blarney Stone, which would you do: walk up twelve steps, wade through water, or hang by your feet?
13. What southern state has an Indian name meaning "river of the great bend"?

27

14. If someone gave you some frijoles would you eat them, wear them, smoke them or preserve them?
15. If you had a Cheddar would you wear it, throw it away, or eat it?
16. What is the literal meaning of the word Christmas?
17. What was the origin of the word novel, meaning a book?
18. What New England state compares in size to Albania?
19. In what country is Christmas celebrated on New Years?
20. In what ocean is the island of Ceylon?
21. In what country is the ancient city of Antioch?
22. Was January first always the first day of the year?
23. What are the official languages of the League of Nations?
24. How many presidents have died in office?
25. Did you ever eat any canned pilchards?

GENERAL QUIZ NUMBER I-C

Answers on page 233

1. Radio advertising is not allowed on what type of United States radio stations?
2. Which is farther south, the tip of Africa or the tip of South America?
3. Does a Dutch youngster hang up his stocking on Christmas Eve?
4. In what cities are the following streets: Wall Street; Downing Street; Champs Elysées; Ponte di Rialto?
5. What is the meaning of the beginning of a new year?
6. If you look at a world map, how can you tell the British possessions?
7. To what sports do the following terms apply: eagle, chukker, bunt, face off?
8. What is "first footing", and in what country is it a custom?
9. When you say that a man is glabrous, is he handsome, disagreeable, bald, talkative, or morose?
10. How many reindeer did Saint Nicholas have, and what were their names?
11. Of what common colors are the following variations: azure, jade, saffron?
12. With what countries or continents do you associate the fol-

lowing: zebras, llamas, gorillas, armadillos, mongoose, Polar bear?

13. Of the 50 highest mountain peaks in the United States, which state has the greatest number?
14. The island off the coast of France which is famous for its cows is Holstein, Jersey, Durham, or Hereford?
15. If you were presented with a large amount of pelf, would you plant it, give it away, or eat it?
16. Name three cities in the United States that begin with a man's first name.
17. In what manner are maple sugar and rubber alike?
18. What male bird takes his turn setting on eggs to hatch them?
19. Where would one go to see the Spirit of St. Louis?
20. Pan was the Greek god of what?
21. What is the difference between commute and compute?
22. What does 'working for a dead horse' mean?
23. What is an emporium?
24. What is a carol?
25. Which word does not belong in the following group: carrots, cabbage, onions, beets, potatoes?

GENERAL QUIZ NUMBER I-D

Answers on page 233

1. If someone told you that you had a face that would stop a clock, would you feel hurt or complimented?
2. "Slaps", "nerve rolls", and "pickups" are units in what stage routine?
3. Answer these questions by naming a part of the body:
   When you want to make a good impression, you put your best . . . . forward.
   When you want applause for a lady, you say: "Give the little girl a great big . . . .
   When a person is touchy, he has a chip on his . . . .
   Napoleon said that an army travels on its . . . .
4. What is the difference between commendation and condemnation?
5. What famous patriot was born on January 1, 1735?
6. Who wrote "A Visit from Saint Nicholas"?
7. What is the hottest spot on earth?

29

8. Do England and France celebrate Thanksgiving day?
9. What are the "Pillars of Hercules"?
10. When is Candlemas day?
11. In what state is East Chicago?
12. How many legal national holidays are there?
13. Where is the island of Corfu?
14. Where are the two towns of Santa Claus and Christmas located?
15. How long does it take a bomb dropped from an airplane a mile high to reach the earth?
16. What is the distinctive characteristic of the opossum?
17. What is a Yule log?
18. In which river are the famous Whirlpool Rapids?
19. What do we mean by crossing the Rubicon?
20. When a person travels incognito, how does he travel?
21. What is a cotillion?
22. What is a collet?
23. Where is the city of Montevideo?
24. What country is noted for its windmills?
25. What is the difference between the North and the South poles?

GENERAL QUIZ NUMBER II-A

Answers on page 234

1. What is always the last unit of each of the following: a freight train; a circus parade?
2. For what is Harley Street, in London, especially known?
3. What did the American Indians call heaven?
4. Why do soldiers break their step when crossing a bridge?
5. What is the highest officer of a regiment called?
6. What country calls its flag the tricolor?
7. What is the opposite of Deism?
8. What type of store would be indicated by the following signs: a striped pole, a wooden Indian, three balls, a mortar and pestle?
9. Articles such as chinaware and pottery are called which of the following: alembics, polemics, ceramics, or quadratics?
10. What general word is used to denote a graduate from a man's college? From a woman's college?

11. Which of the following is a stirrup cup: hunting horn, fitting for a saddle, farewell drink, a prize award?
12. What is the name given to the science which traces the history of the origin and descent of a family?
13. Who wrote "There's a divinity that shapes our ends, rough hew them how we will"?
14. For whom was the Taj Mahal in Agra, India, erected?
15. What are the five recognized precious stones?
16. Give the meaning of the following colloquialisms: Old Nick, Old Maid, Old Salt, Old Glory.
17. Why is cotton so often a contraband of war?
18. Who has the authority to call out the National Guard?
19. Where are Panama hats made?
20. What are "Piccadilly weepers"?
21. How many masts has a brig?
22. What postal stamp of the United States, in common use, has no picture on it?
23. What three things are West Point cadets forbidden?
24. What is the ordinary name for solidified carbon dioxide?
25. What is the name applied to female warriors?

GENERAL QUIZ NUMBER II-B

Answers on page 234

1. If a farmer plants a kernel of corn two inches deep and it grows one half the distance to the surface the first night, and continues to grow one half the remaining distance each night following, how long will it take to reach the surface?
2. What is the difference between audience and spectator?
3. What part of a mile is a furlong?
4. What is a samisen?
5. What is a plebe?
6. Who won the historic duel which Alexander Hamilton lost?
7. What are the following things collectively: books, maps, poems, and hymns?
8. Express the word "Mister" in French, German, and Spanish.
9. What is a lapidary?
10. To what does polyandry refer?

31

11. Does the oak tree have a rough or smooth bark?
12. What three one syllable words rhyme with the word "work" and mean, respectively, darkness, a dagger, and to lie in wait?
13. What imaginary island did Sir Thomas More picture as an ideal commonwealth?
14. What did Robin Hood, William Tell, Diana, and Cupid have in common?
15. In speaking of a vessel's speed is it correct to say it travels twenty knots or it travels twenty knots per hour?
16. What is the difference in meaning of the following words: duplicate, facsimile, and replica?
17. What is the usual color for mourning in: China; Turkey; Egypt?
18. If a nail is driven into a tree four feet above the ground today how far above ground will it be in twenty years, if the tree grows six inches taller each year?
19. What is the singular of the word dice?
20. What is an incandescent light?
21. When do the highest tides occur?
22. Who was the King who requested that everything he touched be turned to gold?
23. If you peeled the paint off the White House in Washington, what would you find?
24. What branch of medicine is known as pediatrics?
25. In what theater were most of Shakespeare's plays first performed?

GENERAL QUIZ NUMBER II-C

Answers on page 235

1. In what religions are the following places of worship used: mosque, synagogue, pagoda, cathedral?
2. What did the Governor of North Carolina say to the Governor of South Carolina?
3. What honorary title is frequently given to a retired clergyman or college professor?

4. What was the water-filled ditch around an ancient castle called?
5. What is the most widely known address in the British Empire?
6. Name the months of the year in their alphabetical order.
7. In what shape is the floor plan of most of the world's great cathedrals?
8. What is meant by a jury of your peers?
9. How hard must the wind blow to be called a hurricane?
10. What is the name of the instrument you pass the thread with in weaving?
11. What is the name given to a painting done on a wall?
12. In what state is each of the following colleges located: Brown, Johns Hopkins, Notre Dame, Columbia?
13. What word can be used to mean both an English coin and a king?
14. At what age does a colt officially become a horse?
15. What distinguishes a hunting watch from the ordinary kind?
16. What is the form of execution used in the following countries: France, Germany, Russia?
17. If you stepped off an elevator on the fifth floor of a building and were in the middle of the building, how many floors high would it be?
18. Where is the Norfolk Navy Yard? Where is the Portsmouth Navy Yard?
19. Name a color for each one of these characteristics: embarrassment, anger, cowardice, loyalty, honest or straight, ignorance.
20. Don't look now, but how many spaces have you between the fingers of your two hands?
21. Snuff is really pulverized what?
22. When can you: jump while sitting still, crawl while off the ground, pass without moving around?
23. In the well-known poem, "Casey at the Bat", how many fans were present to see great Casey strike out?
24. When a consignment is sent by train what is it called? When it is sent by boat what is it called?
25. What is one half of a sphere called?

GENERAL QUIZ NUMBER II-D

Answers on page 235

1. Pure gold contains how many carats?
2. One Webster was a famous orator, another compiled a dictionary. What was the first name of each?
3. Give four weather proverbs.
4. What is the difference between the way a horse and a cow get up?
5. What commonly used vehicle has only one wheel?
6. What is the London residence of the King of England called?
7. Give three definitions for the word "jersey".
8. Who were the legendary founders of Rome?
9. How many times does the minute hand pass the hour hand on a clock from twelve noon to twelve midnight?
10. Which is the heavier, platinum or lead?
11. Give five common expressions, which, if taken literally, would be lamentable.
12. What surgical operation is performed more often than any other?
13. Name four "insane" objects.
14. What does the word diurnal mean?
15. Name five categories of persons or things which are grouped in sevens.
16. What is the meaning of the Latin expression "E pluribus unum"?
17. Is a ghost writer one who writes ghost stories?
18. What are the two most famous Universities of England?
19. Give the names of four fruits that are also the names of colors.
20. Give the correct denominations of the following slang references to money: grand, fin, century, sawbuck.
21. What was the cause of the wreck of the Titanic? Of the Lusitania?
22. Can you name three characters in history or fiction famous for their hair?
23. What is the term used to describe a policeman on a passenger liner?
24. What do you call the distance between the front and rear axles of a car?

25. In England what is the name of the body of men who advise the King?

GENERAL QUIZ NUMBER III-A

Answers on page 236

1. What is a widow's watch?
2. When does Christmas begin and end in Scandinavian countries?
3. Identify the following countries by their insignia: the dragon, the lion, the thistle, the crescent.
4. What was Coxey's Army?
5. Do Christmas and New Year ever come in the same year?
6. In what sports would you find each of the following terms: eagle, chukker, advantage, parry, half-gainer?
7. When an army routs its enemy by means of nitrous oxide it has used which of the following: tear gas, laughing gas, high explosives, or shrapnel?
8. What is the most common breed of sheep?
9. When and where was George Washington inaugurated President of the United States?
10. If you had a genuine Cremona would you play a tune on it, write a letter on it, or wear it?
11. What do the auk and the dodo have in common?
12. What one word could you place in front of each of the following words to make sense: skin, iron, headed, pen?
13. What is a gnu?
14. How is it possible for a man to become president of the United States without being elected?
15. Why is the Red Sea so called?
16. What pole, fish, and mountain have the same name?
17. Which side of a boat is the port side?
18. Why did the wise men of old choose gold, frankincense, and myrrh as their gifts to the Christ child?
19. What are frankincense and myrrh?
20. Douglas, a city of more than sixty thousand, is the capital of what island?
21. Name the seven seas.
22. Who was the last bearded president of the United States?
23. In Parliamentary rule, to favor a motion you say what?

How does a sailor answer an officer when spoken to?
If someone gave you an aye-aye what would you do with it?
24. If you had an okapi would you eat it, put it out to pasture, or throw it away?
25. What is a creche?

GENERAL QUIZ NUMBER III-B

Answers on page 237

1. Distinguish between a beetle, a beadle, and a beagle.
2. Whose death is it that is celebrated every year on the stroke of midnight of December thirty-first?
3. Who wrote the "Ode on the Morning of Christ's Nativity?"
4. How did a quarter become known as two bits?
5. After what Scotch engineer is a type of road or pavement named?
6. What are the Arabic equivalents of the following Roman numerals: L, D, M?
7. Name at least three of the four islands in the English Channel.
8. What is meant by each of the following expressions: a fall guy, a fagin?
9. Is a chalet something you ride in, live in, or wear?
10. Where are the Aleutian Islands?
11. What is the next line after: "But I heard him exclaim, ere he drove out of sight, ...?"
12. Name the New England states and their capitals.
13. Pediatrics is mainly concerned with: the feet, fireworks, children, or bicycling?
14. What is the name of the only state in the union whose capital city is the same name as the state?
15. Name the section of Palestine where Bethlehem is located.
16. What New England state has an Indian name meaning "Long River?"
17. What American city, located on neither ocean, lake, nor river, is a busy maritime port?
18. What are two other names for Santa Claus?
19. If you visited the famous Cathedral of St. Mark, would you be in Rome, Paris, Venice, or London?
20. What is the capital of the state of Nevada?

21. Why is the letter X substituted for Christ in the word Christmas, to make Xmas?
22. On board ship, what does "splice the main brace" mean?
23. How did the saxophone get its name?
24. How did the expression "a flash in the pan" originate?
25. Is the dance called the fox trot so called because it resembles the trot of a fox?

GENERAL QUIZ NUMBER III-C
Answers on page 237

1. Give the capitals of the following South American countries: Republic of Argentine, Brazil, Chile, Peru.
2. What is the literal meaning of the word "mortgage"?
3. Which is the wider at its widest point, North or South America?
4. Who invented the banjo?
5. Is it true that the Hudson river empties into Hudson Bay?
6. In what ocean are the Polynesian Islands?
7. What's wrong with this headline: "South Carolina heiress wins divorce in Charleston"?
8. What is the oldest city in the United States?
9. Who made the following famous remarks: "When you call me that, smile"; "Who touches a hair of yon gray head, dies like a dog"; "What this country needs is a good five cent cigar"; "Everybody talks about the weather, but nobody does anything about it"?
10. Panama was formerly a part of: Colombia, Costa Rica, or Nicaragua?
11. Is Ben Nevis a popular song writer, a Canadian cartoonist, or the name of the highest mountain in Great Britain?
12. What was the former name of Oslo, Norway?
13. Perry, Maine, is halfway between what two points?
14. Name three states of the United States in which there are rivers of the same name.
15. Which of the great lakes is entirely within the United States?
16. Name three plants which are associated only with the Christmas season.

17. In what state is the petrified forest?
18. In what state is Yellowstone National Park?
19. What is known as the Continental Divide of the United States?
20. A man with histrionic ability would make a good: farmer, actor, plumber, or athlete?
21. What is the name of the highest mountain range in the world? What is the name of the highest peak in this range?
22. Name five birds beginning with the letter G.
23. What is a labyrinth?
24. What is it that is filled every morning and emptied every night except for one day when it is filled at night and emptied in the morning?
25. How many states in the union have no capital punishment?

GENERAL QUIZ NUMBER III-D

Answers on page 238

1. Where is the Island of Bali?
2. Name four states beginning with the letter "W".
3. Of what are the following officers in charge in the United States Army: Lieutenant, Captain, Major, Colonel, Brigadier General, Major General?
4. What is the capital of Kansas?
5. What are the six important natural wonders of the United States?
6. For what do the three initials, T, B, and I above the lens of a camera stand?
7. Where was the statue of Liberty made?
8. Give within one thousand the number of different languages there are in the world.
9. If you lost your hat, what would be the first thing you'd do after you found it?
10. Where are the Himalayas located?
11. Name a famous Christmas story by an American author.
12. What is the capital of Kentucky?
13. Are the Hawaiian Islands nearer San Francisco or Yokohama, Japan?
14. Give three uses for the word peel.
15. In what city is the Bank of France located?

38

16. What is the height of Niagara Falls?
17. What nursery rhyme character is famed for having eaten his Christmas pie?
18. What nationality was the composer of "Silent Night"?
19. Spanish is the language spoken in all parts of South America save one. What is the name of that country?
20. Through what four New England states does the Connecticut River flow?
21. What happens to most barbers' chairs after they have served their usefulness?
22. From what poem are these lines taken: "Ring out wild bells to the wild sky, the flying cloud, the frosty light, the year is dying in the night, ring out wild bells and let him die."?
23. On Christmas of what year did Washington cross the Delaware?
24. What great city was once known as Byzantium?
25. Where are the Grand Banks?

HERE ARE THE ANSWERS........YOU ASK THE QUESTIONS....I-A

Answers on page 239

1. It's a mixture of English, French, and Portuguese.
2. It's located at Fort Riley, in Kansas.
3. You'd use a howdah.
4. That's just another name for the Rocky Mountain Water Shed.
5. That happened on February 15, 1898, in Havana Harbor.
6. That's a case for carrying arrows.
7. The first is a long gown worn by clergymen under a surplice, and the second a skillful horseman of southern Russia.
8. We'd say: pansy, petunia, peony, and phlox.
9. It's made up of strings, wood winds, brasses, and the percussion group.
10. It means that the animal goes into hiding and sleeps all winter.
11. General John Burgoyne received this sobriquet.
12. She's called a Maharanee.
13. Their official burying place is Westminster Abbey.
14. It was named the Spirit of St. Louis.

15. The humming bird possesses this rare ability.
16. Mahogany trees are cut at this peculiar time.
17. It's an old fashioned counting board made with a series of beads strung on wires.
18. It's called an oasis.
19. Spring time starts with this occurrence.
20. You would be talking to a French soldier, an English soldier, and an American sailor respectively.
21. It is the literary language of old India.
22. They take the oath of Hippocrates.
23. It's the medical term for nearsightedness.
24. That is the name for a cup of wine or liquor taken before the hunt.
25. The term is applied to the process of combing wool, flax, or cotton.

HERE ARE THE ANSWERS........YOU ASK THE QUESTIONS....I-B

Answers on page 239

1. It's Latin for "time flies".
2. Those were the names of the original Siamese twins.
3. A good one will carry a load of five hundred pounds a distance of seventy miles a day.
4. It is a small blue flag with a white square in the center used as a signal for sailing.
5. Two windows very close together, separated by one casing.
6. This is a person who draws maps.
7. It's a high sounding term for a fee for professional services.
8. A straight line answers this question.
9. Admiral Peary's daughter, Marie, who was born in the Arctic circle received this sobriquet.
10. It's an instrument used in music for marking time.
11. This word describes a broad, flexible knife used for spreading purposes.
12. It's the black flag of piracy.
13. Violet, indigo, blue, green, yellow, orange, and red.
14. It is a body of floating seaweed in the North Atlantic.
15. Because they are the only part of the body which do not repair themselves.

16. Francois Marie Arouet was his real name.
17. It's the anatomical name for the kneecap.
18. It extends across the East River in New York at Hell Gate.
19. They unite at Pittsburgh, Pennsylvania, to form the Ohio.
20. They are riding breeches which require no riding boots.
21. Walter Raleigh and Francis Drake received this honor from her.
22. Both these cities of the same name are famous for their iron works.
23. He may vote in the United States Senate to break a tie.
24. The name is applied to a native of Egypt who cultivates the soil.
25. The poinsettia.

HERE ARE THE ANSWERS........YOU ASK THE QUESTIONS....I-C

Answers on page 240

1. This carpenter's implement most closely resembles a hoe.
2. Samson managed to carry off these famous gates.
3. Zythum is the word; it's an ancient beverage made from malted wheat.
4. Judas did it for thirty pieces of silver.
5. Because the rib is the only bone in the body which has blood in it, and blood is essential to life in the body.
6. Cape Horn is the nearer of these two famous capes.
7. It's an archangel.
8. It's between Africa and Europe.
9. Massachusetts, Pennsylvania, Kentucky, and Virginia are the only four.
10. Here are their ancient Celtic names: Hibernia, Caledonia, and Cambria.
11. This name is applied to an apprentice in the printer's trade.
12. The Hague is its capital.
13. He made that famous ride from Winchester to Cedar Creek, Virginia.
14. It lies between New York and Vermont.
15. In English it means January River.
16. The state of Wisconsin has this nickname.
17. Quito is its capital.

18. It's the stick used by painters as a rest for the hand while painting.
19. Elizabeth was the Queen's name and Globe was the name of the theater.
20. They were born on May 28, 1934.
21. It connects the Atlantic Ocean and the North Sea.
22. Richard I of England was so called.
23. Tiny Tim Cratchit was his name.
24. Because the land is lower than sea level and without them it would be flooded.
25. It's a narrow strip of land, bordered by water and connecting two larger strips of land.

HERE ARE THE ANSWERS........YOU ASK THE QUESTIONS....I-D

Answers on page 240

1. It's called the premium.
2. It's the scientific study of birds.
3. They are measured by candle power.
4. The correct name for this procedure is a pedicure.
5. "Fourscore and seven years ago ....".
6. He's called a Manxman.
7. There were one hundred and fifty at this famous table.
8. This term is used to describe a church yard or burying ground.
9. Toby is this dog's name.
10. It's English slang for a pickpocket or thief.
11. Tradition has it he was searching for an honest man.
12. It means "Ireland forever".
13. They are Nova Scotia, New Brunswick, and the Prince Edward Islands.
14. It's most beautiful characteristic, and perhaps its only one, is its extremely long eyelashes.
15. Taylor was this famous showman's middle name.
16. Opus is its singular.
17. This term applies to lovers of archery.
18. It's called a dodecahedron.
19. This word in the song refers to a river in Scotland.

20. It wouldn't have been possible, because he invented the rocking chair.
21. The cross, anchor, and heart are used as symbols.
22. Their patron Saint is Saint Crispin and they are sometimes called crispins.
23. It's the word used to designate a polygon with an indefinite number of sides.
24. It's a real unit of measurement and is one forty-eighth of an inch.
25. You couldn't get a copy of this anywhere; it's an unwritten constitution.

SO YOU READ THE SPORTS SECTION?

Answers on page 241

1. The infield of a baseball ground is: oblong, square, triangular, or diamond in shape?
2. Curling is a game that is played on what surface?
3. In boxing, where is a rabbit punch delivered?
4. The following are nicknames for what college football teams: the Tartans, the Panthers, and the Wolverines?
5. What is a "dead heat"?
6. In golf what does the word "stymied" mean?
7. Who is the patron Saint of winter sports?
8. What game is frequently referred to as "barnyard golf"?
9. In what country does the sport of pigeon racing compare with the American game of baseball as a national sport?
10. With what sport is Wimbledon associated?
11. How many cards are used in playing euchre?
12. What is the name given to a period of play in polo?
13. "Dusting 'em off" in baseball parlance means: throwing the bat at the umpire, brushing off home plate, pitching at the batter's head, or kibitzing from the bleachers?
14. What sound device is used to start each of the following sports: a prizefight, a footrace, a football game?
15. American football is a form of what English game?
16. What are the official dimensions of a baseball base?
17. How many outs in an inning of baseball?
18. With what popular amusement is the name of Edmund Hoyle associated?

19. Locate the following famous football "bowls": Rose, Cotton, Sugar, Orange?
20. Where is a Charlie Horse usually found?
21. Hockey is known by what name in Ireland?
22. What is the English national game?
23. In what sport does the winning team move backward?
24. What event in sports do the figures 4.4.4. suggest to you?
25. In what sport is the Davis Cup an International trophy?

SPORTS QUIZ........SET NUMBER TWO
Answers on page 242

1. Which one of these royal persons is famous for playing tennis: the Duke of Windsor, the King of Sweden, the Nizam of Hyderabad, the Crown Princess Juliana?
2. With what sport do you associate each of the following phrases: sacrifice hit, drop kick, and cross check?
3. List in their ascending order the winning hands in a poker game.
4. In baseball what is meant by a nightcap?
5. In a fifteen round bout of boxing, with three minutes for each round and a one minute rest period between rounds, how many minutes are consumed?
6. Why is a football field called a gridiron?
7. Why do jockeys stand up in their stirrups?
8. Red has crossed the bar to his outer and inner table and is attempting to bear off his men by throwing dice. What game is he playing?
9. Name five games in which a sphere is used.
10. What other college athlete besides a cheer leader uses a megaphone?
11. Name six of the ten events that comprise the decathlon.
12. What is the regulation length of a bowling alley?
13. When a bowler bowls three hundred, how many balls does he bowl?
14. How many umpires are there on the field during a world series baseball game?
15. Explain these bridge terms: small slam, grand slam, the rank of cards, the rank of the suits.
16. What sporting event has been run every May since 1875?

44

17. In baseball what is the dish?
18. In bowling how many balls are used in a box?
19. Standard baseball bats are made from what wood?
20. Differentiate between a professional, an amateur, and a novice.
21. How many major baseball leagues are there in the United States and what are their names?
22. What are the three gaits of a three-gaited horse?
23. A caddie is associated with what game?
24. How many seams has a baseball?
25. What method is used for handicapping a horse in a race?

SPORTS QUIZ........SET NUMBER THREE
Answers on page 242

1. Name the six pieces used in the game of chess.
2. How long does a chukker of polo last?
3. Of what is the center of a standard baseball made?
4. What heavyweight boxers are or were known by the following nicknames: Manassa Mauler, Brown Bomber, Boston Strong Boy, Gentleman Jim, Ruddy Robert?
5. What words are used in horseracing to describe the horses that come in in second and third place?
6. Which baseball league is the older; the National or the American league?
7. Name the eight weight classes in boxing.
8. What substance is placed on the floor of prize fighting rings to give the battlers a firm footing?
9. To what sport does tally-ho refer?
10. What was the former name of the Boston Bees?
11. What is a half nelson?
12. In what game does one peg sixty-one holes to win?
13. What are the races called in which the horses are entered before they are born?
14. Exclusive of ties, what is the largest number of games that can be played in a world series?
15. In golf what is the difference between match play and medal play?
16. What sport is referred to as "the manly art of self-defense"?

45

17. In amateur boxing do the gloves used weigh more or less than the ones used in a professional bout?
18. Identify the following football teams: Cornhuskers, Middies, Fighting Irish, Wildcats.
19. For what class of boxers is there no weight limit?
20. The ten periods in bowling are called what?
21. How many men are there on an ice hockey team?
22. In what sport is each of the following cries used: yoicks, hold 'em, slide, break?
23. In rowing is the stroke oar nearest the bow or the stern of the boat?
24. What are the divisions of the following games called: baseball, football, basket ball, races, prize fighting, bowling, tennis, bridge, hockey, golf?
25. What ball game does not permit the use of the hands?

SPORTS QUIZ........SET NUMBER FOUR
Answers on page 243

1. What are the three types of swords used in fencing?
2. If you were buying a line for salt water fishing would you select one of silk or linen thread?
3. What is a perfect score in bowling?
4. What is a "southpaw" pitcher?
5. Is horse racing in the United States run clockwise or count : clockwise?
6. What game is played on the following: gridiron, diamond, rink, and court?
7. Explain these slang baseball terms: a can of corn, a banana stalk, a hind snatcher.
8. At what inning of a ball game do many people stand up, and why?
9. What do the letters K.O. stand for in sporting circles?
10. In baseball a pitcher and catcher are known jointly as what?
11. To what sport or game do each of the following apply: luff, huff, ruff, buff?
12. What is a stalemate?
13. What have the following in common, alley, court, diamond, and ring?
14. How many furlongs are there in a mile?

46

15. What is the oldest college sport?
16. What game is called the "game of Kings"?
17. What sportsman calls "track" when he wants others to get out of his way?
18. What American game is the same as the British game of draughts?
19. What race is twenty-six miles, three hundred and eighty-five yards in length?
20. What colleges do the following mascots represent: bulldog, eagle, tiger, Indian, ram, crusaders?
21. What is the measurement of a "hand" used in giving the height of a horse? How much is a span?
22. Name a college in the United States that has no athletic activities of any kind.
23. In what sports are the following terms used: stymie, foot-fault, squeeze play, and puck?
24. How many players are there on a side in lacrosse? How many are there on a side in rugby football?
25. Name two of the New England colleges that constitute the "Little Three".

JUNGLE LIFE
Answers on page 244

1. What breed of dogs has black tongues?
2. What two animals are said to be unable to swim?
3. What is a dromedary?
4. Give the titles of three comic strips that have animals as their subject.
5. Are the zebra's stripes black on white or white on black?
6. Does coral belong to the animal, vegetable, or mineral kingdom?
7. What common wild animal washes its food before eating it?
8. Do elephants use their trunks for drinking?
9. What is a pinto?
10. Is it true that there is a large savage baboon with a light blue nose, orange and yellow beard, and a forehead crest of greenish hair?
11. If kid gloves are made from the leather of young goats, what are kid shoes made of?

47

12. What is a glutton, besides one who eats to excess?
13. What country is represented by the lion and what one by the eagle?
14. Is a rat an adult mouse?
15. What rodent animal, with completely webbed hind feet, is renowned as an engineer?
16. Give three of the early ragtime dance forms that were named after a bear, a rabbit, and a fowl respectively.
17. Are polar bears found in the North or South polar regions?
18. What animals are referred to by the following adjectives: bovine, canine, equine, and feline?
19. In fiction who was the master of a famous cat that was of great assistance to a foreign country?
20. Which of these animals can come down a tree head first: monkey, porcupine, bear, or chipmunk?
21. Does a rabbit run faster uphill or downhill?
22. What well known man made a fortune out of a mouse and three pigs?
23. Does a horse pull or push in his harness?
24. What one animal's name, added to each of the following words, forms a new word: sea, watch, hot, sun?
25. What member of the cat family is used in India for hunting?

ABOUT ANIMALS........SET NUMBER TWO

Answers on page 244

1. Name four kinds of horses that neither eat hay nor race.
2. How many stomachs has the cow?
3. What is another name for an elephant's trunk?
4. Give four common sayings that mention animals.
5. What animals would you expect to find in the following different types of enclosures: corral, warren, sty, and fold?
6. What monetary values are suggested by the following: lamb, frog, horse, skunk, and bronco?
7. What animal can see to the rear without turning its head?
8. What do these words have in common: Manx, Siamese, Persian, and Angora?
9. To which of the following animals does the word lupine refer: dog, lion, wolf, or walrus?

48

10. What type of animal is classified as a zoophyte?
11. What is the name of the dog in each of these comic strips: "Blondie", "Annie Rooney", and "Orphan Annie"?
12. What do we mean when we say that an animal hibernates?
13. Vellum is made from the skin of what animal?
14. In what country is the cow worshipped as a sacred animal?
15. What are firedogs?
16. What does the Alaskan term "mush" mean?
17. What do a kangaroo and an opossum have in common?
18. What is the name of the dog star?
19. What is the nearest living relative of the hippopotamus?
20. What animal does the Teddy bear represent and of what country is he a native?
21. Name a common characteristic of the bactrian camel and the llama, and describe the difference in their backs.
22. Taurus, one of the twelve signs of the zodiac, is represented by which of these animals: man, fish, bull, or dog?
23. Hudson seal fur comes chiefly from which of these: rat, muskrat, wolf, or bear?
24. Name four animals that have only three letters in their name.
25. What two animals are closely associated with the month of March?

ABOUT ANIMALS........SET NUMBER THREE
Answers on page 245

1. When does a fox sit upon a stump?
2. Two shepherds with their flocks met at a crossroad. One said: "Stand back, sir, while I pass with my large flock!" The other questioned "Is your flock so large? If I had one of your sheep I would have as many as you." The other replied: "I still say my large flock, sir! If I had one of your sheep I would have twice as many sheep as you." How many sheep were there in each flock?
3. If swine is a source of lard, from what does tallow come?
4. Which feet of a horse touch the ground together as it walks?
5. What are the setae of a feline?
6. If you were sent to Norway, Lapland, Siberia, or the Hud-

son Bay region to hunt for ermine what would you have to bear in mind in searching for the animal?

7. Tell the name of the breed of dog that most closely answers these descriptions: a pious dog, a thrifty dog, an old hen of a dog, a good chaperon, a noble protector, pride of the Hub, always in a pickle.

8. What is the classic advice of the monkeys of Nikko?

9. What is a camelopard?

10. What are the following live-stock: a barrow, a wether, a gelding, and a ewe?

11. Besides the elephant what three animals provide us with ivory?

12. What is a mulley cow?

13. Is a cosset something in which to keep an animal or the name of the animal?

14. What animal does the phrase "cave canum" warn one against?

15. Name seven Shakespearean plays with the names of animals in the title.

16. If a lion roars what do the elephant and the hyena do?

17. If a friend asked you to come and see his mangur what would you expect to see?

18. Give three breeds of dogs whose names suggest a country.

19. If you had a moke would you eat it, ride it, or cage it?

20. How many legs does a mongoose have?

21. What are little black cats called in England?

22. What is the special characteristic that determines a rodent?

23. Give three slang phrases used in speaking of persons, which contain the names of animals.

24. What is a dogie?

25. Is it true that it's bad luck to be followed by a black cat?

ABOUT ANIMALS........SET NUMBER FOUR

Answers on page 246

1. Give the females of the following: bull, rooster, deer, sheep, hog, lion, horse, gander, drake, fox, ram, stag, and buck.

2. Can you give three slang phrases which include the name of an animal?

3. What are the young of the following called: frogs, geese, bears, deer, elephant, seal, cat, hare, fox, trout, horse, hog, zebra?
4. What name is given to a hog or ox roasted whole?
5. What is the distinguishing characteristic of a Manx cat?
6. What do you call the hide of a fur bearing animal?
7. What animals are commonly used as beasts of burden in the following countries: Alaska, Sahara Desert, India, Lapland, Peru?
8. Does a cow have teeth?
9. What animals are usually referred to by the following: Reynard, Peter, Leo, Jumbo, and Donald?
10. What is the name that was given to a mythological flying horse?
11. What are the fleshy pieces of skin that hang from a rooster's throat called?
12. Are a cow's horns in front or behind its ears?
13. What animal walks upside down, never drinks water, and whose hair grows opposite to that of any other animal?
14. A hunter saw a bear 100 feet to the East of him, walked 100 feet to the North and shot due South, killing the bear, which had not moved. What color was the bear?
15. At what party would you welcome a black grimalkin as guest?
16. Name three animals with names ending in "X".
17. Two sheep are standing in a field. One faces due North, the other due South. Can they see each other?
18. What are animals called that carry their young in their pouch?
19. Give the collective noun (as "herd of cattle") for each of the following: sheep, partridges, wolves, bees, fish.
20. Is the backbone of a camel humped or straight?
21. What was the ultimate fate of the fabled Kilkenny cats?
22. What are the young of these called: turkeys, hens, and roosters?
23. What is there about the joints of an elephant's hind legs that are different from those of the horse and most other animals?
24. Why does a dog stick out his tongue when it pants?
25. What's wrong with the name Donald Duck?

ENGLISH QUIZ I-A

Answers on page 246

1. In poetry a sonnet has how many lines?
2. What is the meaning of the suffix "-ous"?
3. What is mnemonics?
4. What common English word means both a noise and a color?
5. Give the comparative and superlative of "little".
6. What word may be added to each of the following to form another word: fear, toil, lone, tire?
7. If stenography is the art of writing in shorthand, what is orthography?
8. What is the meaning of the prefix "demo-" as in democratic, etc.?
9. What is the longest non-scientific word in the English language?
10. What six letter English word means to stick together and to part?
11. What does the word "franking" mean?
12. What is a palindrome?
13. In a poem, what is the envoi?
14. Of what is the following an example: "Fanny Finch fried floundering fish for Francis Forbe's father."?
15. What is onomatopoeia?
16. Which is a cipher, aught or naught?
17. Name four pronouns that have only three letters.
18. Legally, does "alibi" mean excuse?
19. What is the difference between "among" and "between"?
20. For what does the abbreviation Mrs. stand?
21. Can you give four different spellings and variations of the word "right"?
22. What four letter word is pronounced the same but spelled three different ways?
23. What is the proper form to use in addressing: the President, a Cardinal, an Ambassador?
24. What is meant by the letters R.S.V.P. on an invitation?
25. What is the difference between a verse and a stanza?

ENGLISH QUIZ NUMBER I-B

Answers on page 247

1. What word unquestionably contains all of the vowels?
2. Give a long word for a short one.
3. Is Washington, D.C. the capitol or the capital of the United States?
4. What is the technical name to describe a play on words which have the same sound but different meanings?
5. If you were taking a course in philology, what branch of study would you be pursuing?
6. What are homephones?
7. What is the meaning of the term "hors de combat"?
8. For what three common words does the abbreviation St. stand?
9. Name at least nine of the thirteen punctuation marks.
10. Can you use the words "I is" correctly in a sentence?
11. If you were to pay a dollar a line for a limerick, how much would one cost you?
12. If you went into a drug store and asked for five grains of acetyl salicylic acid, what would the clerk give you?
13. What country is referred to as Albion, in poetry?
14. Approximately how many words are there in the English language?
15. If you committed a faux pas, what did you do?
16. What is a catchword?
17. What is the difference in pronunciation between fiance and fiancée?
18. What is the antonym of synonym?
19. When is a person said to be gauche?
20. Define the words verso and recto?
21. What is the meaning of the word philoprogenitiveness?
22. Is data singular or plural?
23. Name three words with more than three letters, which end in "oo".
24. What is a book called that is made up of the following number of pages: two, four, eight, twelve?
25. What common word has three sets of double letters in succession?

53

ENGLISH QUIZ NUMBER I-C

Answers on page 247

1. Explain the names "perisphere and trylon", as symbolic of the New York World's Fair.
2. What is the correct pronunciation of the word "chic"?
3. What word in the English language rhymes with orange?
4. What is the name of the symbol that is used for the word "and"?
5. A Baron is addressed as "My Lord", how is a baronet addressed?
6. The people of what ancient country first introduced the alphabet into Europe?
7. How many syllables are there in the word Niagara?
8. Why are teeth like verbs?
9. Translate this phrase into plain English: "Pulchritude ceases to exist below the integument".
10. What have the words gaucho and sinister in common?
11. Name three words in the English language which end in the letters "-cion".
12. What is the meaning of the following: a la mode, apropos, bona fide?
13. Give three meanings for the word cue.
14. What is a four letter word ending in "-eny"?
15. What letter of the alphabet has the least number of words beginning with it?
16. Of which verb is wrought the past participle?
17. If a person's language were euphuistic he would be guilty of which of the following: use of swear words, slang, or flowery speech?
18. What does the verb ricochet mean?
19. Name three words in the English language ending in "-ous".
20. What word or words rhyme with month?
21. If the fire in the furnace were not burning properly you would create a draft by opening the flaw, fleet, flue, or flu?
22. What six common words beginning with the letter "g" mean a brightness or to shine?
23. Translate: "Malignant depredations, penalized by incarceration, involuntary servitude, or execution are in no degree conducive to lucrative emolument."

54

24. If A, E, I, O, and U are vowels, what are the other letters of the alphabet called?
25. What word of five letters is never pronounced right?

ENGLISH QUIZ NUMBER I-D

Answers on page 248

1. What is the British equivalent of the American word gasoline?
2. Several words in the English language end with "ough". There are five separate ways of pronouncing this "ough". Give a word or words for at least three of these different pronunciations.
3. What word of three syllables has twenty-six letters in it?
4. What is illiteracy?
5. Give four meanings for the word "fast".
6. If a newspaper story said that a man was an octogenarian would it refer to his age, diet, or occupation?
7. What have the prefixes Fitz, Ben, and Mac in common?
8. Unscramble the following sentence to make sense: "She wore a toga on her head, a topaz on her back, a toupee on her finger, and a toque on top of that."
9. What does alma mater mean?
10. What is nepotism?
11. Name the length of time designated by the following: a score of years, a decade, a fortnight.
12. What is the meaning of the phrase "coup de grace"?
13. How do you spell the name of the pigtail the Chinese formerly wore?
14. What is the meaning of the title "Il Duce"?
15. What is a homonym?
16. What color goes with each of the following words: tape, laws, smith, standard?
17. Give three words which begin with the letter G in which the initial G is silent.
18. Which word does NOT belong in the following list: galatea, chintz, percale, serge, cretonne?
19. Is it true that George Washington owned a set of the Encyclopaedia Britannica?

55

20. What have the following words in common: fight, lamb, written, gnome?
21. If an ancient Greek had found the little yellow basket, what would he have been likely to say?
22. Did Homer write the Odyssey or the Iliad?
23. What common word is spelled incorrectly in the dictionary?
24. What is the study of paleography?
25. What is a poetaster?

GENERAL QUIZ NUMBER IV—A

Answers on page 249

1. What French holiday corresponds to our Fourth of July?
2. How many cabinet members were there in the first president's cabinet?
3. What one man on an American football team is restricted from carrying the ball?
4. Which is farther south, Melbourne, Australia, or the Cape of Good Hope?
5. Why does England in approximately the same latitude as Labrador enjoy a so much milder climate?
6. What symbol, frequently in today's news, is a fylfot?
7. What is the opposite of the reverse side of a coin called?
8. Where is the Red Sea?
9. What state in the Union holds the greatest amount of refined gold?
10. Napoleon died on the island of Corsica, St. Helena, Waterloo, or Devil's Island?
11. Where are a boar's head and a Yule log a typical part of the Christmas celebration?
12. What city with a hot climate never has flies, insects, or mosquitoes?
13. Why is the color red associated with the Christmas season?
14. What is the usual color of the following: Sapphires, rubies, emeralds?
15. Who was the first United States president to speak over the radio?
16. Name an automobile whose name recalls: an Indian chief, a president, a French explorer, a Spanish explorer.

17. A pullet is: a young hen, an old rooster, a male duck, a young goose?
18. What is a hackmatack?
19. Can you locate these bridges: Hell Gate Bridge, Golden Gate Bridge, Wheatstone Bridge?
20. An important holiday falls on every day of the week except Saturday. Can you name them?
21. Who introduced the Christmas tree into England?
22. How many states are there along the Pacific coast of the United States?
23. How many balls do you have to bowl to make a perfect score?
24. What caused the decline of the whiffletree?
25. Who first used the word "normalcy"?

GENERAL QUIZ NUMBER IV-B

Answers on page 249

1. What is another title for Yahweh?
2. Recite the second verse of the "Night before Christmas."
3. Name four states whose capital begins with the letter "B".
4. What is a tetrahedron?
5. The late Madame Schumann-Heink sang what famous Christmas carol every Christmas Eve?
6. Can you name three states whose names contain a double N as the third and fourth letters?
7. Is the word "schnapps" applied to a fastener for women's dresses, a strong Holland gin, or a large spicy cookie?
8. What is the other name given to the old man with the scythe?
9. What do you use to shoot a birdie? To shoot the chutes? To shoot a glance? To shoot the works?
10. Why is a mother with four sons, all sailors, like a year?
11. If it is 360 degrees around the earth, and the earth is nearly four times the diameter of the moon, how many degrees is it around the moon?
12. What did Delilah cut? What did Alexander the Great cut?
13. What three presidents of the United States have died on the Fourth of July?

14. What famous dance was made popular in America by George and Martha Washington?
15. Has an elephant the same number of toes on the fore and hind feet?
16. Is a hagiographer an older woman?
17. What is the difference between the way a cat, a camel, and a cow sit down as compared with the way a dog sits down?
18. In what state is Walla Walla?
19. Name the rivers on which these cities are located: Paris; Budapest; London; Montreal.
20. There are eight states beginning with the letter "M". Can you name four of them?
21. In what state, if any, is Christmas not a legal holiday?
22. What is the second largest state in the United States?
23. Unscramble this: themselves God that them helps help.
24. Red and green are to Christmas as orange and black are to . . . . ?
25. Can you give the correct pronunciation of "precedent"?

GENERAL QUIZ NUMBER IV-C

Answers on page 250

1. How many states in the union begin with the word 'North'?
2. What is a young swan called?
3. What continent contains practically half of the world's population?
4. The Erie Canal connects what two bodies of water?
5. In what American city, once the capital of the United States, are the streets named as in this old refrain:
   "Market, Arch, Race and Vine,
   Chestnut, Walnut, Spruce and Pine."?
6. New England people make a delicious syrup by boiling down the sap of a tree. What is the name of the tree?
7. From what plant is linen made?
8. What presidents of the United States were married while holding that office?
9. In what state is Mount Greylock the highest peak?
10. What is the name of the statue at the Naval Academy to which the students offer alms?

11. Who was the first Harvard graduate to become president of the United States?
12. What is known as the ambulant treatment?
13. What is a dudeen?
14. What is an orphan car?
15. What are adult female seals called?
16. Name two presidents who were born in April.
17. What was Lincoln's occupation before he became president?
18. Would you feel badly if you were guilty of cacography?
19. Name two ill omens, in which an animal is the chief character.
20. What are the chief methods of defense of: boa constrictor, dog, cow, ostrich, porcupine, skunk?
21. Which president was at one time president of Princeton University, Governor of New Jersey, and Nobel Prize winner in 1919?
22. Who discovered the law of gravity?
23. Can you explain the custom of why people make New Year's resolutions?
24. During which president's administration was the Lewis and Clark expedition sent out?
25. What is the state flower of Kansas?

GENERAL QUIZ NUMBER IV-D

Answers on page 250

1. What have these three in common: giraffe, toy dog, catnip?
2. It is said that dragonflies are perfectly innocuous. Does that mean that they are liable to sting, to bite, to poison, or that they are generally harmless?
3. Can you name two presidents whose last names contain only four letters?
4. If you were a native of the country of the Jura and Vosges Mountains, what nationality would you be?
5. If someone called you a "scaramouche", would you feel hurt or flattered?
6. What human organ appears on the back of a dollar bill?
7. Is New Year's Day a legal holiday in all states of the Union?

8. What kind of evergreen tree is the ordinary Christmas tree?
9. From what people are the mistletoe and the Yule log relics?
10. A horse 16 hands high, measures how many inches?
11. What island in the South Pacific was colonized by mutineers from the H.M.S. Bounty?
12. What song is sung on New Year's Eve?
13. What five travel ways are there that end in '—way'?
14. Niagara Falls are between what two great lakes?
15. Where is the Kennebec River?
16. Where is Madagascar?
17. What is the capital of Pennsylvania?
18. What is allspice?
19. What major game originated in Springfield, Massachusetts?
20. Where is Pitcairn Island?
21. What did a stadium originally mean?
22. On a railroad, what does a gondola carry?
23. What is a felly?
24. What is arithmania?
25. If a critic called someone "chauvinistic", would he mean that the person was affected, overpatriotic, or a charlatan?

GENERAL QUIZ NUMBER V-A

Answers on page 251

1. The shortest distance between any two points on the surface of a sphere is which of the following: A straight line, a parabola, a great circle, or a hyperbola?
2. Can you give three meanings for the word 'slug'?
3. With what colors are the following words associated: oyster, jet, burnt, battleship, navy, shell, hunter, royal, canary, vermilion?
4. How does a carpenter's hip differ from a plumber's elbow?
5. What is the inside margin of the pages of a book called, where they are bound?
6. The following terms are identified with the newspaper industry. What is the meaning of each: banner, tops, by-line?
7. A galliard is an old French .... what?
8. Could a pitcher throw a ball in a straight line, have it come to a full stop and return it to his hand?
9. A ring stamped 18k contains how much gold?

10. Where and when was Pine Tree money used?
11. What is the name for the solid portion of the earth?
12. Is a termite a blonde or a brunette?
13. Mrs. Brown has three yards of white cloth; she pinks it, and then she blues it. What color is it now?
14. For what purpose is litmus paper used?
15. What is a dormer?
16. A record book kept at a police station is called what?
17. The American flag has eight rows of six stars, or six rows of eight stars?
18. If you were a potentate, would you be handsome, possess great power, be extremely tall, or be mentally deficient?
19. What is the meaning of the world 'bilk'?
20. What have the following in common, besides being names of cities, Burlington, Erie, Milwaukee, New Haven, Santa Fe?
21. What is a breeches buoy?
22. Which of the following comic strip characters has grown up with the years: Skippy, Skeezix, Smitty, Popeye?
23. The ore known as pitchblende yields aluminum, radium, iron, or mercury?
24. Name six famous women who never lived.
25. Give the table of dry measure.

GENERAL QUIZ NUMBER V-B

Answers on page 251

1. How hard must the wind blow to be called a hurricane?
2. How is dynamite detonated?
3. What is the Roman numeral for 500?
4. Which is the largest cathedral in the world: Notre Dame in Paris, St. John the Divine in New York, the Duomo in Milan, or St. Peter's in Rome?
5. What liquid is used on the back of plate glass to make mirrors?
6. What is a sepoy?
7. For what is the Baume scale used?
8. The well known Flirtation Walk is located at what school?
9. Name five words containing a silent 'B'?
10. Can you name six Indian tribes?

11. Which of these three styles is found in the Parthenon of Athens: Doric, Ionic, Corinthian?
12. Is Mauna Loa the name of a movie actress, a race horse, a volcano, or a river in Africa?
13. If you were taken to Dartmoor, Newgate, or Dannemora, where would you be?
14. If an attitude is a position of the body, what is a Beatitude?
15. What is a herpetologist?
16. What large boats are shaped the same at both ends?
17. Is a shibboleth one who stutters, a password, or a totem pole?
18. Astrology is to astronomy as .... is to chemistry.
19. If you are going on a littoral trip, are you going to the seashore or to the mountains?
20. What is a sabbatical year?
21. What do the letters O.N.T. mean on a spool of thread?
22. What three lamps or lanterns are famous in literature or history?
23. What is an intaglio? What is a cameo?
24. Is it easier to swim in deep water than in shallow water?
25. What part of your name is the patronymic?

GENERAL QUIZ NUMBER V-C

Answers on page 252

1. Name six famous men who never lived.
2. What is an infant's wardrobe called? A bride's wardrobe?
3. What is a man called who practices magic? What is a woman called who practices magic?
4. Why does thunder follow lightning?
5. Which of the following is out of place: Daytona Beach, Rye Beach, Rex Beach, Long Beach?
6. What is the outstanding difference between a schooner and a sloop?
7. Polygamy means plurality of wives. What is the term for plurality of husbands?
8. Which item does not belong in this list: hail, rain, snow, sleet, frost?
9. What is the meaning of "al fresco"?
10. What is attar?

11. How many rooms has the vatican in Rome?
12. What keeps an arch from falling?
13. What is the meaning of the expression "white haired boy"?
14. Why is the Rosetta stone famous?
15. What atmospheric change does an asterisk indicate on a weather chart?
16. What name is given to the states in the Swiss confederacy?
17. What language has the most letters in its alphabet?
18. Would a mine be worth prospecting if it were auriferous?
19. A pavane is a Polish count, a portable chair, a dance, or a piece of furniture?
20. Which of the following methods of execution are used in the United States Army today: firing squad, electrocution, hanging?
21. What are the profits earned by a corporation and paid out to its stockholders called?
22. Is a nabob an animal, bird, or man?
23. Can you name an animal, a fruit, and an article of warfare, all beginning with the word 'musk'?
24. What would you call a plot of land devoted entirely to the growth of the following: apples, oranges, watermelons, grapes?
25. What is the distaff side of the family?

GENERAL QUIZ NUMBER V-D

Answers on page 252

1. What is a sphygmometer?
2. What is a farad?
3. What kind of motion, the dream of inventors, is defeated by friction?
4. What was the Russian form of the title Kaiser?
5. What have the following words in common: cruet, decanter, carboy?
6. A demoiselle is a young girl, a bird, or a fly?
7. What is the meaning of the word finical?
8. How many wheels on a freight car?
9. What is the smallest number of hooks required to string a clothesline across a yard five times?

10. Which of these words means the same as omnipotent: arrant, infinite, almighty, worthy?

11. What language is reputed to have the largest vocabulary?

12. What is a pyrrhic victory?

13. In what year in American history was the Stamp Act passed?

14. When a farmer says he has cut his rowen, what does he mean?

15. When a man is knighted in England he becomes Sir So-and-So. When the same honor is bestowed upon a woman, what is her title?

16. Electric current flows readily through mica, porcelain, mercury, or pure distilled water?

17. How many hearts on the nine of hearts?

18. Why are concrete roads built in sections, instead of one solid strip?

19. Vilify means to praise, to beat harshly, to debase, or to pay in full?

20. Would you start putting shingles on a building from the ridgepole down or the eaves up?

21. What is a hobbledehoy?

22. What is the difference between a pigeon and a widgeon?

23. Whose ships were the following: Golden Hind? Mayflower? Santa Maria? Half Moon? Pinta?

24. Name three Mother Goose rhymes or jingles that refer to shoes, stockings, or hose?

25. If a python is a big snake, what is a pylon?

GENERAL QUIZ NUMBER VI-A

Answers on page 253

1. Is a stogie a walking stick, a stoker on an oil tanker, or a slender cigar?

2. What point on the earth's surface has neither longitude, latitude, nor altitude?

3. What are halyards?

4. If a pecan is a nut, and a pelican is a bird, what is pemmican?

5. If an incubator is a device for hatching eggs, what is an incubus?

6. What is the distinction between a platoon and a poltroon?
7. Define the following words: argot, ergot, and ingot.
8. What is the difference between a facet and a faucet?
9. Would a person who is peccable and peccant be inclined to peculate?
10. A ute tied a newt with jute. Who did what to whom?
11. Name two states which include a woman's name.
12. When and where was the first Christmas celebrated in North America?
13. What are the young of each of the following called: Chickens, ducks, geese, turkeys, guinea hens?
14. If a barber is a person who cuts hair, what is a barbette?
15. What is the difference between a bassoon and a monsoon?
16. From what name did the familiar Santa Claus derive?
17. If sin is moral evil, what is a sinecure?
18. What is the distinction between a gallon and a galleon?
19. What is beri beri?
20. If a typhoon is a hurricane, what is a tycoon?
21. In Dickens's Christmas Carol, what was the name of the close fisted miser?
22. What is the difference between genealogy and geology?
23. If an aquarium is a place for keeping fish, what is a ranarium?
24. If a squid is a fish, what is a quid?
25. If you were on a boat and were told to get a barnacle and a binnacle, would you know what to get?

GENERAL QUIZ NUMBER VI-B

Answers on page 254

1. What is the opposite of philanthropy?
2. Define: tom-tom, can-can, haw-haw, and Sing-Sing.
3. Give three meanings for the word bolt.
4. Define fantan, fandango, and fanfare.
5. What girl's name has more variations than any other?
6. Why does one cry when he peels onions?
7. Give the English equivalent of the American word suspenders?
8. Which is more, six dozen dozen, or one-half dozen dozen?
9. Do fixed stars move?

10. To whom is the Lion of Lucerne a memorial?
11. What is the greatest water power in the world?
12. What is the sole industry of the antarctic region?
13. To determine how deep the water is, sailors do which of the following: open the sea cocks, shoot the sun, heave the lead, or splice the main brace?
14. Can you name four animals whose normal life span is one hundred years or over?
15. If a shoe cobbler is one who fixes shoes, what is a peach cobbler?
16. Why does the pitch of a train whistle sound higher as the train approaches?
17. Answer the following with the names of fruits: a good sport, a bargain that's not a bargain, father's favorite daughter?
18. In what business were the Wright brothers when they built their first airplane?
19. Give within ten the number of yards there are in the average package of spaghetti?
20. What is meant by trading on a shoestring?
21. Who is the only cabinet officer who does not have to make an annual report to the President of the United States?
22. What does A.W.O.L. mean?
23. If you leave California when it's summer and proceed directly to China what season will you find there?
24. If a galley is a ship's kitchen is a galley slave a ship's cook?
25. What is a sutler?

GENERAL QUIZ NUMBER VI-C

Answers on page 254

1. What is the oldest branch of the armed service of the United States?
2. Where does the so-called English walnut come from?
3. What is the science of reasoning called?
4. What is the next line after: "He said to his friend, if the British march by land or sea from the town tonight?"
5. How many are there in a gross?
6. What country has the longest miles?
7. Remove the letter B from bananas and what fruit have you?

8. Satinette is which of these things: a breed of pigeon, a kind of dress material, or a reddish wood of French Guiana?
9. What is an amphor?
10. If you had a plaice, would you wear it, eat it, or paint it?
11. What is the distinction between ordnance and ordinance?
12. If a chapter is a division of a book, what is a chaplet?
13. If you had a manatee where would you keep it?
14. If you had a bream would you eat it, wear it, or plant it?
15. What is chicanery?
16. What is a timbrel?
17. If you had a calot, a jabot, and a sabot, what would you do with each of them?
18. What is the difference between a faker and a fakir?
19. If a tart is a small pie, what is a Tartar?
20. What is the difference between a vial and a phial?
21. If a dingy is a small boat, what is a dingo?
22. What is a blind advertisement?
23. Distinguish between whoopee and rupee?
24. Where did the Holland Tunnel get its name?
25. If a cat's eye is a stone, what is a cat's paw?

GENERAL QUIZ NUMBER VI-D

Answers on page 255

1. Was Benjamin Franklin an only child?
2. With what subject does the science of acoustics deal?
3. What is the name of the stand on which an artist sets his painting?
4. If you were given a pail of water and two eggs, one bad and one good, how could you determine which was which?
5. How many justices are there on the bench of the United States Supreme Court?
6. Why do we blink our eyes?
7. Why is the Dead Sea dead?
8. What book is necessary to every trial court room?
9. What is the definition of nothing?
10. Charlie Noble is a traditional name for what?
11. How many of the seven dwarfs in "Snow White" had beards?

12. Are red flannels warmer than white ones?
13. What is peat?
14. Odometers measure: angles, smells, or mileage?
15. What river has an entrance about two hundred miles wide?
16. In the following, what part of the plant is used for food: asparagus, potato, tomato?
17. If you were given a flitch would you eat it, sell it, or put it in a zoo?
18. If you had a case of odontalgia would you go to a mechanic, a doctor, a dentist, or a policeman?
19. Was any member of the present United States Supreme Court ever a candidate for the presidency?
20. If you lived on the shore of the Sea of Marmora what nationality would you be?
21. What state is nicknamed the Sunflower State?
22. What is the capital of Newfoundland?
23. Name four states smaller in area than Massachusetts.
24. What city in the United States gets its water supply from a foreign country?
25. Of what states are the following cities the capitals: Concord, Augusta, Salem?

ARISTOLOGY QUIZ FOR THE BON VIVANT

Answers on page 256

1. Nine animals give milk for human consumption. What are they?
2. The song Yankee Doodle refers to "hasty pudding." What is it?
3. Do grape fruit grow singly or in clusters?
4. What is finnan haddie?
5. What causes the holes in Swiss cheese?
6. If you invited the following people to dinner what would you serve them: Popeye, Wimpy, and Jack Horner?
7. Supply these missing words by using an article of food: As cool as a ....; As alike as ....; As bald as ....?
8. What distinguishes a kermess from other meals?
9. What is the chief ingredient of red-flannel hash?

68

10. The following animals are called what when you see them on the dinner table: ox, sheep, calf, and deer?
11. When does a chicken become a fowl?
12. Separate the apples from the pears in the following list: Baldwin, Bartlett, pippin, Seckel, Gravenstein.
13. What is caviar?
14. Name five fruits with seeds which we eat without removing the seeds.
15. What underground fungi are highly prized by French chefs?
16. What meat do we associate with Yorkshire pudding?
17. What fish is part of a shoe?
    What fish is always complaining?
    What fish is used in a duel?
    What fish is inclined to be melancholy?
    What fish is a communist?
18. Of what is mock turtle soup usually made?
19. What are "curds and whey"?
20. What were these before they were what they are: sauerkraut, hominy, and prunes?
21. There are ten varieties of tea. Name eight of them.
22. Why are sardines packed so closely in a can?
23. What nation comes to mind when you mention the following: chowmein, vodka, sake, and haggis?
24. Name four natural coverings of vegetables.
25. Give the missing ingredient in the following list: Boston Baked Beans contain: pea beans, salt pork, salt and pepper, sugar, mustard, boiling water, and ....?

FOOD QUIZ NUMBER TWO

Answers on page 256

1. What is the principal food of one-third of the world?
2. When you order a dish of "bubble and squeak" what do you get?
3. Biscuits in England are what in the United States?
4. What is a pennyroyal?
5. What is the color of the inside of a ripe watermelon before it is cut open?
6. What is the common name for sodium chloride?

7. Which is correct: welsh rabbit or welsh rarebit?
8. Garlic is a member of what plant family?
9. If you served a fried alevin what would you be serving?
10. What is the meaning of the word calorie?
11. What kind of cake would you buy for: a sculptor, an idler, and one who lives on his friends?
12. If you mixed the following what would you be making: 18 ounces of scalded milk, 18 ounces of boiled water, five tablespoons of corn syrup. Serve lukewarm.
13. What, besides the color, is the difference between white pepper and black?
14. Can acetic acid safely be used on food and eaten?
15. What are prawns?
16. What do statistics show to be the most popular beverage in the world?
17. Limburger cheese is named after a town in what country?
18. From what do we obtain gelatin?
19. Swiss chard is a variety of: apple, beet, cabbage, or squash?
20. What is a crouton?
21. If you ordered a braised leg of lamb at a restaurant it would have been cooked on a grate over red hot coals, in a covered dish with scant water, in a casserole at a low temperature, or in fat?
22. Name three apples famous in history.
23. How many *legs* of lamb can a butcher get from a lamb?
24. There are eight edible grains. Name six of them.
25. If you asked for an order of pettitoes what would you get?

FOOD QUIZ NUMBER THREE
Answers on page 257

1. With what country do you associate each of the following: tamale, antipasto, goulash, mutton chops, frog's legs?
2. What is the difference between a seeded raisin and a seedless raisin?
3. What is the meaning of the following words often found on menus: puree, fondant, roti, souffle?
4. Name three kinds of edible butter that have nothing to do with a cow.

5. What do the following have in common: anise, hyssop, rue, and basil?
6. Name three important foreign cities that your butcher might feature.
7. The answers to the following questions can all be found in a garden. Where does money originate? What is a symbol of bereavement? What is a popular pipe? What is frequently seen from the coast?
8. Classify the following: tomato, cocoanut, cauliflower, and cucumber.
9. Does tapioca grow in the same form we find it in the package?
10. Name four vegetables grown underground.
11. If you were in England and asked for a glass of lemon squash, what would you get?
12. What kind of food is chow chow?
13. What sauce is usually served with roast lamb?
14. What Boston hotel has won a world wide renown for its rolls?
15. What type of food is a tumble rose?
16. Does the free end of a banana point upward or downward when it's growing?
17. Why does a doughnut have a hole in the center?
18. The state of Washington is famed for which of the following: avocadoes, apples, pears, tangerines, or breadfruit?
19. If you were served a steak that was coriaceous, could you eat it?
20. Among ordinary foodstuffs what is the rarest vitamin?
21. If you bought a basket of damsons would they be fruits or vegetables?
22. What fruit tree has leaves ten feet long?
23. Of what three vegetables do we eat only the seeds?
24. How many holes are there in a pretzel?
25. Would it be proper to serve pinders and goobers at the same time?

FOOD QUIZ NUMBER FOUR
Answers on page 258

1. How many standard cups of granulated sugar are there in one pound?

2. What part of the plant do we eat in each of the following foods: broccoli, cauliflower, salsify, endive?
3. From what vegetable family does the caraway seed come?
4. What's the difference between American and European plans of hotel operation?
5. Would you eat or drink a "scotch haggis"?
6. Sardines are the young of what fish?
7. What is the chief ingredient of angel cake?
8. What is the white of an egg called?
9. Is a ramekin a young sheep, an earthen baking dish, or a cut of mutton?
10. What are the usual ingredients of a New England boiled dinner?
11. In which of the following beverages is caffeine found: tea, coffee, cocoa?
12. Is the kumquat a vegetable, a fruit, or a nut?
13. What type of food is kohlrabi?
14. What country is the source of each of the following cheeses: Stilton, Edam, Roquefort, and Parmesan?
15. What four methods might you use to preserve meat?
16. Under what classification are oranges, watermelons, and lemons?
17. From what does chocolate come?
18. What is a cluster of bananas called?
19. Does an average ear of corn have an odd or even number of rows or do the ears vary?
20. A griskin was originally part of what animal?
21. What is the difference between a minimum charge and a cover charge at a hotel?
22. Name three fish which are also colors.
23. The filbert nut is the fruit of what tree?
24. Is an olive a fruit or a vegetable?
25. Shaddock is another name for what?

NURSERY QUIZ

Answers on page 258

1. Who kept his wife in a pumpkin shell?
2. What famous character in Alice In Wonderland was forever shouting "off with his head"?

3. Give four nursery rhymes with the name Jack in the rhyme.
4. What did Jill do for Jack when he fell down?
5. Who went to bed with his stockings on?
6. In the rhyme "Hi Diddle Diddle," what did the dish do?
7. In the old nursery rhyme what was the Queen doing while the King was in his counting house counting out his money?
8. Who were the three men in a tub as mentioned in the nursery rhyme?
9. Who exchanged a cow for a bag of beans?
10. Who or what frightened Miss Muffet away?
11. Who did a lot of "huffing and puffing" to blow a house down?
12. According to Mother Goose, what are little boys made of?
13. What princess was given the poisoned apple?
14. Who were the diet faddists of Mother Goose rhymes?
15. What did Simple Simon fish in, and for what?
16. What were the names of the three sisters of Peter Rabbit?
17. Who is associated with the prospect of picking a peck of pickled peppers?
18. Who was the clerk at Cock Robin's wedding?
19. Who milked the cow with the crumpled horn?
20. On what did Mother Goose ride through the air?
21. What did the crooked man find beside the crooked stile?
22. What bachelor in Mother Goose sang, and what was his reward?
23. Who met the pieman?
24. What time was it when the mouse ran up the clock?
25. Who kissed the girls and made them cry?

NURSERY QUIZ NUMBER TWO

Answers on page 259

1. What little girl found herself in a house inhabited by three bears?
2. How many bags of wool did baa-baa black sheep have?
3. What was it that Little Jack Horner ate in the corner?
4. How many blackbirds were baked in a pie?
5. What bridge is still falling, and will probably continue to fall until the end of childhood?

6. In nursery land what three sailors sailed off in a wooden shoe?

7. What did the farmer's wife do to the three blind mice?

8. Which of the Mother Goose characters enjoyed a smoke and the music of a string trio?

9. According to Mother Goose, what are little girls made of?

10. What did the following steal: Taffy, the Welshman; the Jack of Hearts; Tom, Tom, the piper's son?

11. Who was the famous shepherdess?

12. What did Bobby Shaftoe wear when he went to sea?

13. What was Humpty Dumpty?

14. Who runs through the town, upstairs and downstairs, in his nightgown?

15. What little animal went to school?

16. Name three fairy tale characters who are associated with shoes.

17. Who killed Cock Robin?

18. In what did the three Wise Men of Gotham go to sea?

19. Name three of the things mentioned in the garden of Mary, Mary, quite contrary.

20. What were the materials used by each of the three little pigs in building their houses?

21. What little girl was nearly devoured by a wolf who impersonated her grandmother?

22. Who went to fetch a pail of water?

23. What was the dainty dish set before the king?

24. Who was a merry old soul?

25. Why did the old woman who was tossed up in a basket carry a broom in her hand?

NURSERY QUIZ NUMBER THREE

Answers on page 259

1. What were the chief characteristics of the following nursery rhyme characters: Mary, Mary; Simon; Ten O'Clock Scholar; Three Little Kittens?

2. Where was Little Boy Blue?

3. Give the two lines following these: "Fee fi fo fum, I smell the blood of an Englishman ...."

4. Who laughed when the cow jumped over the moon?

5. Who saw Cock Robin die?
6. What nursery rhymes signify the following: fright, thievery, starvation, accident, music, bravery?
7. Name three Mother Goose rhymes where a specific amount of money is mentioned.
8. Who ate the Little Bear's porridge, broke his chair, and fell asleep in his bed?
9. Why did the Pussycat go to London?
10. How many tailors went to kill a snail?
11. Give four nursery rhymes that refer to music, either instrumental or vocal.
12. How late did Richard and Robin lie in bed?
13. Give the first verse of the poem of which this is the last:
"And you each gentle animal
To you for life may bind,
And make it follow at your call,
If you are always kind."
14. Name three "little boys" mentioned in Mother Goose.
15. Was there a real Mother Goose?
16. The nursery rhyme says that "the man of words and not of deeds" is like what?
17. What member of royalty was interested in cooking?
18. For whom were the three bags of wool?
19. Who said "I'll dress you like a gold finch or a peacock gay"?
20. What did the cow with the crumpled horn do to the dog in the house that Jack built?
21. In the story of the old woman and the pig, what was it that the pig wanted to do?
22. Who fell off the wall?
23. Where did the Cock Horse ride to?
24. Where did Goosey, Goosey Gander wander?
25. Give the first line of three nursery rhymes which mention mutton, pork, and beef respectively.

NURSERY QUIZ NUMBER FOUR

Answers on page 260

1. Who owned a hungry dog?
2. How many mice ran after the farmer's wife?
3. What did the teacher throw at Mary's little lamb?

4. Name the nursery rhymes that mention the following foods: pudding and pie, roast beef, water, tarts, pie, white bread and butter, broth and bread?

5. A certain type of shoe changed the entire life of a well known girl. What was her name and what type of shoe was it?

6. In the poem "The Night before Christmas" what creature was not stirring?

7. In what book was Ali Baba a character?

8. The piping of what musician was equally appealing to rats, mice, and children?

9. What question was asked of the fly?

10. Who fell asleep in his teacup?

11. How did Ali Baba gain admittance to the cave of the forty thieves?

12. Where is the Land of Nod?

13. What well known poem contains these lines:
"Rats! They fought the dogs and they killed the cats,
And bit the babies in their cradles"?

14. What boy, whose cat brought him fortune, later became Lord Mayor of London?

15. What kind of a cat gave Alice In Wonderland advice, and then disappeared?

16. Name the eight reindeer in the poem "A Visit From St. Nicholas."

17. Where was Red Riding Hood going when she met the wolf?

18. What did the blackbird do to the maid who was "in the garden hanging out the clothes"?

19. According to Mother Goose where does one ride a cock-horse?

20. What nursery rhyme character proclaimed "my dame has lost her shoe: my master's lost his fiddlestick"?

21. Where was little Polly Flinders sitting?

22. For what were the lion and the unicorn fighting?

23. How many crooked things are mentioned in the verse about the crooked man?

24. In the Mother Goose tale of good King Arthur, what did the Queen do with the bag-pudding that was left?

25. What color was Bobby Shaftoe's hair?

Answers on page 260

1. Where is the largest desert in the world and where is it?
2. What is the Holy City of the Mohammedans?
3. Where would you go to see the great tulip growing country?
4. To what part of what country would you go to see the Mammoth Cave?
5. Why is Oberammergau famous?
6. To what country does Greenland belong?
7. Name the five great lakes.
8. Is there land at the North or South pole?
9. In what countries would you find the people spending: the franc? lira? pound?
10. To what country would you go to see the Matterhorn?
11. In what countries are the following lakes located: Lucerne, Lomond?
12. Name the five oceans.
13. On what sea is Venice located?
14. What is the capital of Canada?
15. Name the countries that border France.
16. Is Canada larger or smaller than continental America?
17. What three states of the United States are more properly called "Commonwealths"?
18. What is the name of the capital of Puerto Rico?
19. What is the name of the Indiana city that contains a famous automobile race track?
20. What three nations begin with the letter "E"?
21. In what province of Canada were the Dionne quintuplets born?
22. What city would you visit to see the original portrait of Mona Lisa?
23. Where and what is the Jungfrau?
24. Is Brittany in France, England, or Scotland?
25. In South America, it's the United States of what?

WHERE HAVE YOU BEEN? QUIZ NUMBER I-B

Answers on page 261

1. Where is the Carlsbad Cavern?

2. What is the Golden Gate?
3. On what river is Budapest located?
4. Where do the Hottentots live?
5. If you were a philatelist and had stamps from Helvetia, Eire, and Hispana, where would they have come from?
6. What countries do these words suggest to your mind: steppe, pampas, veldt?
7. What is the capital of Peru?
8. In passing through the Panama Canal from the Atlantic to the Pacific, in what direction does one travel?
9. What was the former name of the country now called Iran?
10. What is the most famous cave in the world?
11. Between what two seaports is the passage of the English Channel?
12. On which continent are the Andes mountains?
13. Name four geographical points along the New England coast which bear feminine names.
14. Where is the white sea?
15. If you wanted to visit the city of Smyrna you would go to which of these countries: Turkey, Syria, or Algeria?
16. Where are the Thousand Islands?
17. In which mountain range are the Green Mountains?
18. What is the most important river in Brazil?
19. Where is the George Washington Bridge?
20. Give within one hundred miles the length of the Great Wall of China.
21. In what part of the world does the wind always blow from the North?
22. In the address Honolulu, T.H., what does the T.H. stand for?
23. Where is the Yukon River?
24. Why are dykes used in the Netherlands?
25. Where are the Ural Mountains?

WHERE HAVE YOU BEEN? QUIZ NUMBER I-C

Answers on page 261

1. In what part of the world would you find the following: Death Valley, Everglades, Grand Banks, Roof of the World, Giant's Causeway?

2. What is the oldest city in the United States?
3. What novel by Dickens deals with the French Revolution?
4. What country is due east of New York city?
5. What is the name of the island on which the Statue of Liberty is located?
6. What is the largest lake in North America?
7. Where is Mandalay?
8. Name four seas bearing the name of colors.
9. Geographically speaking what do the letters B.W.I. stand for?
10. Is the Arctic Ocean at the North or South pole?
11. If you took a trip from India to Australia, you would cross what ocean?
12. What and where is the Bois de Boulogne?
13. In what country is Monte Carlo?
14. What two seas are connected by the Suez Canal?
15. What is the capital of Haiti?
16. Porto Ricans are citizens of what country?
17. What United States city is known as the Queen City of the Lake?
18. In what forest in the United States could one freeze before getting a wood fire built there?
19. What is the capital of the Hawaiian Islands?
20. Give the six New England states with their nicknames.
21. If you visited Muscovy and Nippon, where would you have been?
22. When you go to the West Indies what sea do you sail on?
23. In going through the Panama Canal how many miles would you travel?
24. What are the three largest countries by population?
25. What are the names of the five Republics that comprise Central America?

WHERE HAVE YOU BEEN? QUIZ NUMBER I-D

Answers on page 262

1. Everyone knows that "It's a long way to Tipperary", but just where is Tipperary?
2. In what country is Waterloo, where Napoleon met his defeat?

3. Where would you look for: the Coliseum, the Blarney Stone, and the Taj Mahal?
4. Name the only one of the seven ancient wonders of the world that is still in existence.
5. What is the capital of Alaska?
6. Name four countries ending in "-land".
7. In what towns are the following places located: the House of the Seven Gables, the Wayside Inn, the Manning Manse?
8. What is the largest island of the West Indies?
9. Where are the "Plains of Abraham"?
10. Is Japan flat or mountainous?
11. Finish the following geographical names: Martha's ———, Malay ———, Philippine ———, Hot ———, and Mammoth ———.
12. To which countries do the following Islands belong: Azores, Java, Trinidad, Madagascar, Tasmania?
13. In what cities are the following streets located: Wall, Downing, Champs Elysees, Ponte di Rialto?
14. Which countries use the following monetary terms: dollar, rupee, tael, ruble, mark, yen?
15. A Hottentot is a native of what country?
16. Identify the following places by these phrases: Land of the Midnight Sun, Land of the Rising Sun, Dark Continent, Gift of the Nile, Eternal City, Land of Opportunity.
17. If, on a tour of the United States, you visited the Athens of America, the Empire City, the Windy City, the Automobile City, the Smoky City, the City of Brotherly Love, the Twin Cities, and the City of the Golden Gate, where would you have been?
18. What inland body of water in Asia is saltier than the ocean?
19. In what states are these mountain ranges located: Catskill, White, Green, Great Smoky, Sierra Nevada?
20. What six states have names which, when abbreviated, spell a word?
21. What are the boundaries of Hawaii?
22. What single state touches four of the five Great Lakes?
23. Through what national capitals do the following rivers flow: Thames, Potomac, Tiber, and Seine?
24. Give the states for which these are the nicknames: Lone Star State, Buckeye State, and Palmetto State.
25. For what is the Rue de la Paix famous?

KNOW YOUR PRESIDENTS?

Answers on page 262

1. Who was the only president elected from a state west of the Mississippi?
2. What president of the United States was sworn into office by his father?
3. Which state is known as the "Mother of Presidents"?
4. What three presidents of the United States were assassinated?
5. Who was the first vice-president of the United States?
6. What president of the United States wore the largest hat?
7. In whose administration as president was the Panama Canal built?
8. What man ran for president of the United States three times and was elected twice?
9. Which president was a soldier in the Black Hawk war?
10. Who was the first president born in the United States of America?
11. What two signers of the Declaration of Independence later became presidents of the United States?
12. What animal was the symbol of the Progressive Party which was led by Theodore Roosevelt?
13. Under what president was Louisiana purchased?
14. Which president was nicknamed "Old Hickory"?
15. In what state did Abraham Lincoln deliver his famous Gettysburg address?
16. What president lived to be the oldest and who died the youngest?
17. What must a president do to qualify for having his likeness on a postage stamp?
18. What president of the United States had a son who also became president?
19. For what do the letters "U" and "S" in U. S. Grant's name stand?
20. Where is George Washington buried?
21. What president declared war in 1917?
22. Name four of the six army generals who lived to become Presidents of the United States.
23. How long did George Washington occupy the White House?

24. What was the profession, in private life, of each of the following presidents: Abraham Lincoln, Woodrow Wilson, Warren G. Harding, Herbert Hoover?

25. Do ex-presidents of the United States receive pensions?

PRESIDENTS QUIZ NUMBER TWO

Answers on page 263

1. How many presidential electors is the District of Columbia allowed?

2. What president was known as the "rail splitter"?

3. If a president of the United States were impeached, who would try him?

4. Who was president of the United States when the "Star-Spangled Banner" became our national anthem?

5. What United States political party has had the least number of candidates elected president?

6. Who was president of the United States during the World War?

7. Can the president pardon anyone who has been convicted of a crime?

8. Who ran against George Washington in his first and second terms?

9. What three presidents served in the Mexican War of 1845-1848?

10. Did any signers of the United States Constitution become presidents of the United States?

11. When were there two presidents at the same time in this country?

12. Name three presidents from New York state besides Franklin D. Roosevelt.

13. If all of our presidents up to 1897 stood side by side how far would the line reach?

14. What are the requirements for president of the United States?

15. During what president's administration did the expression "big stick" originate?

16. Every fourth man elected president since Taylor has died in office. Can you name them?

17. What president was born in Hodgenville, Kentucky?

18. Queen Victoria ascended the English throne in June of 1837. Who was president then?
19. Why was there originally a lapse of four months between the presidential election and the time the winner assumed his official duties?
20. Who was the first president to toss out the ball at the beginning of the baseball season in Washington?
21. Of what trade were all of the presidents?
22. Which president came from New Hampshire?
23. What president of the United States had the largest family?
24. How is the president's salary paid to him?
25. Thanksgiving day has been proclaimed ever since the term of office of what president?

PRESIDENTS QUIZ NUMBER THREE

Answers on page 264

1. If Washington was the father of his country what was he to his wife's children?
2. Name three presidents whose first name was "James".
3. What president popularized the slogan "America First"?
4. What president was the grandfather of another president?
5. To what political party did George Washington belong when he was elected president?
6. What president of the United States is sometimes referred to as "Sir Veto"?
7. What was the shortest length of time served by any president of the United States, and who was he?
8. Can the president of the United States be arrested?
9. At social functions who enters the rooms first, the president or his wife?
10. Who was the first president to be inaugurated at Washington D. C.?
11. Who was the only bachelor president?
12. What were the names of the homes of George Washington, Thomas Jefferson, and Andrew Jackson?
13. Why didn't George Washington have his picture taken?
14. Name six vice presidents of the United States who later became presidents.

83

15. Who was the first president to ride to his inaugural in an automobile?
16. What president was called the "great emancipator"?
17. Was George Washington born in the United States?
18. From what colleges did these presidents graduate: F. D. Roosevelt, Woodrow Wilson, and Calvin Coolidge?
19. Who is the only man the president has to take his hat off to?
20. Which president was a tailor by profession?
21. What president organized the Rough Riders during the Spanish American War?
22. Who was the only American president to go to Europe during his term of office?
23. How many states are named after presidents?
24. In what city was the first president of the United States inaugurated?
25. What president issued the first mother's day proclamation?

PRESIDENTS QUIZ NUMBER FOUR

Answers on page 265

1. What president was known as "old rough and ready"?
2. What two presidents of the United States were awarded the Nobel peace prize?
3. What was George Washington's middle name?
4. Who was the first president of the forty-eight states?
5. Who was the last bearded president of the United States?
6. What is the name of the selection played upon the entrance of the president?
7. Eight presidents were born in the state of Virginia, which is called "the mother of presidents". Name five of them.
8. How many presidents of the United States had last names ending in "son"? Name them.
9. Carved in the stone face of the mountain at Mount Rushmore National Memorial at Rapid City, South Dakota, are the stone faces of what four presidents?
10. What was the color of George Washington's hair?
11. What did the "G" stand for in president Warren G. Harding's name?
12. Who was the first president to address the American public over the radio?

13. Name the president and the war that go with the following dates: 1861, 1898, 1914.

14. Name two state capitals that derive their name from former presidents of the United States.

15. What three presidents were born in the month of February?

16. What ex-president swore one of his successors into office?

17. Of what presidents of the United States were these the first names: Millard, Franklin, Chester?

18. Quakers are also called Friends; how many Friends have been presidents of the United States?

19. Who was the richest president the United States ever had?

20. Name the first five presidents of the United States in the order of their inauguration.

21. What is the salary of the president of the United States? Who was the first president to receive this amount?

22. Here are the names of four presidents with the vowels omitted. Fill them in. T-ft; T-l-r; P--rc-; H--v-r.

23. Who was president when egg rolling was introduced on the White House lawn?

24. What was the name of the theater Abraham Lincoln was attending when he was shot?

25. What are names of the five presidents memorialized in the Presidential Range in the White Mountains?

GENERAL QUIZ NUMBER VII-A

Answers on page 265

1. What have the following in common: chaise, buckboard, barouche, brougham?

2. If an explosion occurs near enough a building to break the glass by concussion, will the broken glass be found inside or outside the building?

3. What is wrong with this sentence: The slaves were given the right to vote by the Fifteenth Amendment?

4. How much would a man, whose normal weight is 150 pounds, weigh if all the water in his system were dried up?

5. In Colonial days, what was a cordwainer?

6. How many pence in a shilling?

7. How high is the Washington Monument at Washington, D. C.?

8. What is the world's most common family name?

9. If a duke asked you to come and see his duchy, would you reply: "I've already met your wife." "How much territory do you control?" "Isn't your mother too ill to have visitors?" "Do you call your father that to his face?"?

10. Give within five years the time it took Noah Webster to write the dictionary.

11. If you were hunting for the Maginot Line, would you be apt to find it in a fishing tackle box, in France, on a ruler, in Germany, or in China?

12. How many ciphers are required after the figure 1 to make a quintillion?

13. The Jack of Spades, Hearts, Diamonds, and Clubs went to enlist in the army; two of them were rejected. Who, and why?

14. What is epistaxis?

15. If a mining engineer, a jeweler, a marble worker, an archaeologist, and a European painter were to examine the Rosetta Stone, which one would be most likely to show the greatest interest?

16. How many pennies do you think it would take stacked to equal the height of one penny standing on its side?

17. Which of the five senses does a pantomimist neglect?

18. Would you expect to find a clavicle in the sky, in the ocean, or in your Sunday dinner?

19. For what do the following chemical formulae stand: HCL; H_2O; H_2SO_4; $NaCL$?

20. What are the following babies called: an Indian baby, an Italian baby, a cowboy's baby?

21. In the language of a used car dealer, a tomato is a car with the speedometer set back, a stolen car, an oil eater, a junky used car, or a repaint job?

22. What multiplies by dividing?

23. Angina pectoris is a very painful disease usually affecting the lungs, the liver, the heart, teeth, or the backbone?

24. Name three slang expressions using the name of a fruit.

25. Why did gold certificate No. A7397664A go down in history?

GENERAL QUIZ NUMBER VII-B

Answers on page 266

1. If you were told to go get a besom and use it in the kitchen, what would you do?
2. What is a chinook?
3. With what day does the month have to start in order to have a Friday the 13th?
4. Name three pairs of husbands and wives in the comic strips.
5. From which of the following material is worsted made: flax, cotton, or wool?
6. Is your scapula above or below your femur?
7. If it costs 30 cents to cut and weld one ring, how much will it cost to make a chain from five rings?
8. From what does cork come? (Not out of a bottle).
9. What would you call one who takes no part in a card game, but who gives unasked for advice?
10. Has a horse ever won the English derby twice? Why?
11. Does the human heart ever rest?
12. How many years did Jack Dempsey hold the heavyweight boxing crown?
13. With what sports are the following trophies associated: Davis cup; Childs cup; Walker cup; Astor cup?
14. On what two days of the year are day and night of equal duration in every part of the world?
15. A burnoose is a knot tied by boy scouts, the hangman's noose, or a headdress to protect the head from the sun?
16. Where did the saying originate "........ according to Hoyle"?
17. In 1930, what condensed outdoor sport became popular almost overnight and faded as quickly?
18. If the Olympics are the athletic games held in various countries every so often, what is the Olympiad?
19. What have the following in common: cradle, flail, scythe?
20. What implement is used in hitting the ball in tennis, baseball, and croquet?
21. What have the whale and the bat in common?
22. What is the largest bird that flies?
23. In what country was modern polo developed?
24. From what is saccharin derived?

25. When was the last time Babe Ruth played in a World Series?

GENERAL QUIZ NUMBER VII-C
Answers on page 267

1. Is the caber eaten, thrown, or smoked?
2. Which of the following is the best definition of a dodo: a fabulous bird of the Arabian Nights; a large, clumsy flightless bird now extinct; a prehistoric bird with giant wings, or a person who is not very intelligent?
3. Are long or short mallets used in water polo?
4. In golf, what is a birdie?
5. Is a sparling a bird, a fish, or part of a ship?
6. On what race track is the Kentucky Derby annually run?
7. How far is a league?
8. The emu, kiwi, and ostrich (poor birds!) can't do what?
9. In what particular sport is the goal referred to as a cage: soccer, basketball, ice hockey, or lacrosse?
10. What is the name of the oil obtained from flaxseed?
11. With what sport are the following terms associated: lunge, button, thrust, parry, and tierce?
12. What word in the following list is out of place: mound, nightcap, hit and run play, goal posts, squeeze play?
13. What have the following in common: coon-can, snip-snap-snorem, Earl of Coventry?
14. Which of the following is out of place: Cheviot, Dorset, Aberdeen-Angus, Southdown?
15. Name four presidents who were commanders-in-chief of the Army and Navy during a war?
16. What foreign capital is named for a former president of the United States?
17. Where would you look for a saber-toothed tiger?
18. Name three crackers that cannot be eaten.
19. Are there any tigers in Africa?
20. What term is used in measuring the fuel value of a food?
21. Name three coverings of vegetables.
22. If you had a nectarine would you eat it, wear it, or play it?
23. Classify the following as plants or animals: coral, seaweed, sponge.

24. What is a goober?
25. Are the following statements true or false:
The monsoon is employed in India to kill cobras.
The skunk is a carnivorous quadruped.

GENERAL QUIZ NUMBER VII-D
Answers on page 267

1. A campanile is a girls' camp, a bell tower, a French prison, or a medieval ship?
2. Name two animals whose coats resemble that of the leopard.
3. What is a herbivorous animal?
4. How many players on an ice hockey team; a football team; a baseball team; a basketball team?
5. Is the expression 'stalemate' commonly used in stables, chess, golf, or polo?
6. How do chickens close their eyes?
7. In boxing, how many minutes are there in a round fought under Queensberry rules?
8. What are cattle thieves called in the west?
9. What golf term applies to one stroke better than par?
10. A game called battledore, and then shuttlecock, is now called what?
11. What are the mascots of the West Point cadets, Yale, Navy?
12. What breed of goats and cats have the same name?
13. What fruit do you think of when you look at a calendar?
14. How many pelts can you get from a fox in two years?
15. What are the male, female, and young of deer called?
16. To what animals do the following names refer: Reynard, Bruin, Leo, Dobbin?
17. Name three games in which a sphere is not used.
18. What country has a picture of a dog of the same name on one of its postage stamps?
19. Where would you go if you wished to see a heath hen or a passenger pigeon?
20. Name five of the well-known and commonly used spices.
21. Is the tiger spotted or striped?
22. Four important things happened to George Washington in the month of December. Can you name two of them?
23. What is a young salmon called?

24. What two plants furnish most of our granulated sugar?
25. Are the following statements true or false:
Tomatoes were once considered poisonous and inedible.
The scientist Einstein plays the violin.
A tepee is a wig for a bald-headed man.

GENERAL QUIZ NUMBER VIII-A
Answers on page 268

1. What is the chief food of baby whales?
2. Does a cat scratch its head with its front or rear paw?
3. Is the sun a planet? satellite? star or comet?
4. What would be the outstanding feature of Christopher Columbus if he were alive today?
5. In the game of golf, what is a divot?
6. Using the name of an animal, complete the following: John ....; Charley ....; Peter ....; Cheshire .....
7. With what fruit do you associate the following names: Baldwin, Elberta, Bartlett, Blackheart?
8. La cucaracha is a Mexican dancing girl, a Mexican doll, or a cockroach?
9. When are the terms "gee" and "haw" used, and what do they mean?
10. Can you name three historical or legendary incidents in which an apple figures?
11. Is this true or false: A truffle is a table delicacy?
12. What is the difference in the billing of a star and a featured player in movie and stage productions?
13. An enrober works in what kind of a factory?
14. How many blocks would a full rigged ship need?
15. How full should your fountain pen be when you start on an airplane trip?
16. If an eagle and a seagull staged a race from the United States to Australia which do you think would win?
17. Name four trees that have only three letters in their name.
18. Is baculine punishment sitting in the stocks, torture on the rack, or flogging with rods?
19. Name five things that turn without moving.
20. What is the antonym of hibernation?
21. Name three movie stars who are unable to sign their names?

22. Gold is the most ductile of all metals. What does ductile mean?
23. What household articles do the following words suggest: Haviland, Sterling, Fostoria?
24. Does the earth travel around the sun, or the sun around the earth?
25. In yachting what is indicated by two red flags with black squares flying from the weather station?

GENERAL QUIZ NUMBER VIII-B
Answers on page 268

1. If you had a pair of pinking shears, would you cut grass, hedges, cloth, roses, or hair with them?
2. Is a sponge a fungus, a fossil, a plant or an animal?
3. Name three radio comedy teams of husband and wife.
4. What do you associate cumulus, stratus, and cirrus with?
5. Give the common nickname for the instrument through which a radio announcer speaks.
6. How many words can you give beginning with the letter "k", in which the "k" is not sounded?
7. If hens are kept in a hen house, and dogs in a dog house, what is kept in a round house?
8. The wives of Lot, Bluebeard, and Adam had at least one thing in common; they were senile, slap-happy, curious, or spendthrifts?
9. If you had a nimbus, would you wear it, eat it, spend it, or plant it?
10. What New England college grants free tuition to selected Indian youths?
11. What term describes a victory that is as disastrous to the victor as to the vanquished?
12. If you had a fillet, would you wear it, eat it, or hang it on the wall?
13. If the Equator is the imaginary line across the earth, what is the imaginary line across the sky?
14. Which of the five senses would be affected by something that is noisome?
15. Is a shamrock a flower, a vine, a bush, or a species of grass?

16. Name five days of the week without naming Monday, Tuesday, Wednesday, Thursday, Friday.
17. What do they call a student of the United States Naval Academy?
18. Define pappous, and name two pappous plants.
19. What is a young goose called?
20. Is an amulet a plant, a charm, an animal, or a fish?
21. What are Assizes?
22. What kind of leaves do silkworms prefer?
23. What is an incendiary?
24. Is a jerboa a neck scarf?
25. Who was Moby Dick?

GENERAL QUIZ NUMBER VIII-C

Answers on page 269

1. If you had a "White Holland" would you eat it, take it to the theatre, or drink coffee from it?
2. Is aconite a flower, a piece of furniture, a person, or an animal?
3. What is the number and street address of the White House in Washington, D.C.?
4. Identify the following men: Man of Destiny; Man of Iron; Man of Straw?
5. If you had a siskin, would you put in it a cage, wear it, cook it, or tie a package with it?
6. Which has the larger antler spread, the reindeer or the killdeer?
7. Why is helium, which is heavier than hydrogen, preferred in aircraft?
8. What do you think the human body would be worth if sold for the value of its chemical elements?
9. Would you describe a person lying on his back as being in a prone or a supine position?
10. Supposing that you have an ordinary window that opens at top and bottom. If you open both parts as far as they will go, how much of the window is open?
11. Who owned the following famous coats: the coat of many colors; a coat half yellow and half red; a coat trod upon by a queen?

92

12. What are meant by the following: Vanishing American? Thundering herd? Prairie schooner?
13. What race would you belong to if you called a baby by the name of papoose, bairn, bambino, pickaninny?
14. Would aluminum, iron, or lead float in mercury?
15. What is the trunk or stem of a tree called?
16. What kind of a store would be indicated by: a striped pole; an Indian; three balls; mortar and pestle?
17. What have the following in common: ketch, felucca, dhow?
18. If olive oil comes from the olive, what does linseed oil come from?
19. When is the penultimate day of the month?
20. For what is the house of Rothschild known?
21. How many letters are there in the Hawaiian alphabet?
22. What is a yellow hammer?
23. What is a banshee?
24. Does tobacco grow on a bush, vine, or stalk?
25. What is the name of the fruit of an oak tree?

GENERAL QUIZ NUMBER VIII-D

Answers on page 269

1. What do the following signify: orange blossoms, mistletoe, olive branch?
2. Medications that kill germs are called anaesthetics, narcotics, antiseptics, or histrionics?
3. What have the following in common: Great Mogul, Kohinoor, Southern Star?
4. How does a Diesel engine differ from a gasoline engine?
5. Complete the following using the name of some kind of footwear: Puss in ....? Dem Golden ....?
6. If you hold a thermometer in front of an electric fan, will the mercury drop, remain the same, or rise?
7. With what industry are the words Cheltenham, Gothic, and Caslon associated?
8. Which of the following words means the same as cranesbill: sea gull, derrick, geranium, or pelican?
9. In rendering first aid to a person who has fainted, should the head be placed lower or higher than the rest of the body?

93

10. Which one of the following is the meaning of fiscal: political, calendar, financial, or nautical?
11. If you had a caliper, would you eat it, sew with it, measure with it, or shoot with it?
12. What have the following words in common: caravel, corvette, umiak, shuyt?
13. What is a comet?
14. A window built out from a sloping roof is called what?
15. With what branch of learning were Galen and Hippocrates associated?
16. For what reason would you visit a horological shop?
17. Where is pewter mined?
18. What marked similarity exists between fingerprints and snow flakes?
19. Does a vane or weathercock show the direction *to* or *from* which the wind is blowing?
20. A salver is a serving tray, a Mexican coin, or an instrument for spreading salve?
21. What is the proper name for the halfmoons on a person's fingernails?
22. If somebody should speak to you in Esperanto, what country would you say he was from?
23. Which has the larger capacity, a liter or a quart?
24. What causes knots in boards?
25. What public building in London is the King of England not allowed to enter?

GENERAL QUIZ NUMBER IX-A

Answers on page 270

1. What familiar proverb is this: Employ visual faculties before engaging in propulsive exertion?
2. What coin minted by the United States bore the motto "Mind your business"; and when was it minted?
3. Which of the planets is inhabited beyond a doubt?
4. What American animal that once numbered in the millions is now nearly extinct?
5. Would a rabbit's hind feet or front feet make the first track on snow?

6. What is the color of a dishonorable discharge in the United States army?
7. What is the next step up from a Major in the army?
8. Who first announced the belief that the world is round?
9. What event is generally considered to mark the beginning of the French Revolution?
10. What is the name of the poem which contains these lines: "Poems are made by fools like me."?
11. What, in sea-going language, is the meaning of doldrums?
12. What happens when a boomerang is thrown?
13. Before ironwork is painted, it receives a protective coat of which of the following: blue vitriol, red lead, salt of magnus, or yellow potash?
14. What living creatures have the greatest number of ribs?
15. What is the popular name for the people of Massachusetts?
16. Which of the following would you say is the average weight of the human brain: 32 ounces, 16 ounces, 48 ounces, or 12 ounces?
17. If you were listening to a broadcast from London and the time there was 5 P.M., what time would it be in Boston?
18. Which is saltier, the Atlantic or the Pacific Ocean?
19. What is a kelly? A benny? A brogue? A poncho?
20. If the solid figure which has squares on all sides is called a cube, and one which has circles on all sides is called a sphere, what solid figure has triangles on all sides?
21. What is a moratorium?
22. What is an amanuensis?
23. What were the Princess Pats?
24. Is an oboe a tramp, a musical instrument, or the name of an electrical appliance?
25. If you had a canvasback, would you wear it, eat it, or frame it?

GENERAL QUIZ NUMBER IX-B

Answers on page 270

1. Is any officer of the United States government ever permitted to accept any title of nobility or order of honor from another country?
2. In what figurative bed of ease does one never sleep?
3. What is a baboushka?

4. Commercially speaking, what tree is considered the most valuable?

5. Finish the following phrases: A penny for your ....
All that glitters is not .... Too many cooks spoil the ....

6. Is a peccadillo a South American animal, a London thoroughfare, a trifling affair or misdemeanor, or a highly seasoned pickle?

7. What four words starting with the letter "S" mean a grin or a chuckle?

8. Name five words starting with the word "butter".

9. What makes soap float?

10. What is a centaur?

11. What is a golliwog?

12. In what kind of advertisements do you find the word "cellophane"? What is it, and what is it made from?

13. Which of these animals can see most clearly in total darkness: owl, bat, or leopard?

14. Which national flag is nearest in design and coloring to that of the United States?

15. What famous explorer went on an expedition and didn't know where he was going. When he got there, he didn't know where he was, and when he got back he didn't know where he had been?

16. What line of type is almost always to be found on a book of matches?

17. Where does the water go at low tide?

18. What precious metal can be salvaged from old movie films?

19. Name a democratic nation in which women may not vote?

20. How long does it take to bring orchids from seed to maturity?

21. How many stars in the Big Dipper?

22. If lemonade is a beverage, what is a colonnade?

23. Finish this line: " 'Tis the last rose of summer ....".

24. What used to be the sign outside a cigar store?

25. Name three dogs whose breed begins with the letter "D".

GENERAL QUIZ NUMBER IX-C
Answers on page 271

1. From what are camel hair brushes made?

2. Which two cities did the first telegraph line connect?

3. What is a Rathskeller?
4. How much is 2½ times 2½?
5. Can you complete the following proverb: "Many go out for wool ...."?
6. If you had to sweep the horizon while out sailing, what would you use?
7. What is the name given to the man at the wheel of a steamship at sea?
8. Name three fruits beginning with the letter "P"?
9. What is it that works when it plays and plays only when it works?
10. Who was the celebrated possessor of a glass slipper?
11. Who was the inventor of the cotton gin?
12. Would you find a unicorn in the sea or in the jungle?
13. Was William Tell a real person or a legendary hero?
14. Name five evergreen trees.
15. What implements are used in crocheting, knitting, and tatting?
16. What was the chief problem of the alchemists of the Middle Ages?
17. Give the common names of the two stellar constellations known to astronomers as Ursa Major and Ursa Minor.
18. What is the business of the man on a ship who is called "Chips"?
19. What are the three "R's"?
20. Name the three leading United States imports according to value.
21. Name four varieties of apples.
22. How many shoes will it take to shoe a pair of oxen?
23. Give five musical terms that are also common to baseball.
24. If the Commander in Chief of the United States army should die, who would take his place?
25. Is coal animal, vegetable, or mineral?

GENERAL QUIZ NUMBER IX-D
Answers on page 271

1. Name the countries that comprise Scandinavia.
2. What is the official diplomatic language of the world?
3. Lloyd's of London writes all forms of insurance policies but one; which is that?

4. Does the President of the United States pay income tax on his salary?
5. What is a heliograph?
6. What agency of the United States has the power to declare war?
7. What does pure radium resemble?
8. Traveling from New York to Chicago by the shortest route, you must pass through six states. Can you name them?
9. Which is the highest order of English knighthood?
10. What degrees do the following abbreviations stand for: A.B.; D.D.; Ph.D.?
11. If a clock takes six seconds to strike six, how long will it take to strike eleven?
12. What bird is the symbol of supremacy in at least ten countries, and can you name any of these countries?
13. What is meant by a custom made garment?
14. Where and what is The Hague?
15. What European monarch succeeded his own son to the throne?
16. If someone gave you a canterbury, what would you do with it?
17. In dueling, what is the usual distance for pistols?
18. If a bride is a newly married woman, and a well is a hole full of water, what is a bridewell?
19. Name the only state flag bearing a coat of arms.
20. Give three definitions for the word "band".
21. Who is the father of the American public school system?
22. What is a Nantucket sleigh ride?
23. How many legs has a Zulu?
24. Who was the star of the old serial thriller of the movies, "The Perils of Pauline"?
25. What was Robert Fulton's profession before he became an inventor?

TRUE—OR FALSE? YOU'VE GOT A FIFTY-FIFTY CHANCE ANYWAY!

Answers on page 272

Is it true or false that:
1. The U.S. Marines are known as "Devil dogs"?

2. Zero is the freezing point of water on the Centigrade thermometer?
3. Five thousand dollars is the largest denomination of currency issued by the United States?
4. Gold is the most malleable of all the metals?
5. A necrologist is one who practices a mystic art?
6. Pocahontas married John Smith?
7. An archipelago is a collection of mountains?
8. The berries on the mistletoe are waxy white?
9. It is colder at the arctic than at the antarctic?
10. The Pacific ocean is larger than the Atlantic ocean?
11. Hyperbole is an astronomical term?
12. Rome is farther north than New York City?
13. A soubrette is an actress who plays pert parts?
14. There are ten feet in one fathom?
15. "Il Duce" means "The Leader"?
16. An anchorite is a hermit?
17. The mule is a domestic animal that cannot ordinarily reproduce itself?
18. Excalibur was the name of King Arthur's sword?
19. Wampum is another name for Indian money?
20. A peruke is a small bow used as a hair ornament?
21. Icebergs are sometimes formed of salt water?
22. Honolulu is the capital of the Hawaiian Islands?
23. The Sahara Desert is in Northern India?
24. John Hancock was the last to sign the Declaration of Independence?
25. Carat is the unit of weight used by jewelers?

TRUE OR FALSE? NUMBER TWO

Answers on page 272

Is it true or false that:
1. New Amsterdam was the original name of New York?
2. The common house fly has seven legs?
3. There are 5280 feet to the mile?
4. The top and bottom stripes on the American flag are red?
5. A fortnight means ten days?
6. A hogshead is a measure of sixty-five gallons?
7. Water boils at 212 degrees Fahrenheit?

8. A cornucopia is another word for the horn of plenty?
9. A bibliophile is another word for a bibliography?
10. In England molasses is called treacle?
11. An amanuensis is a loss of memory?
12. Street cars are known as trams in England?
13. The giraffe's front legs are longer than its back legs?
14. Adam's ale is a kind of beer?
15. A necropolis is the same as a metropolis?
16. Gaul was the ancient name of France?
17. There are twenty-five sheets of paper in a quire?
18. A stallion is a small onion?
19. The metatarsal arch is in Italy?
20. The water in the bottom of a ship is called bilge?
21. The national salute is twenty-one guns?
22. A furlough is a measurement of length?
23. The Spanish Main was located off the coast of Spain?
24. There are 100 Senators in the U.S. Congress?
25. Norway offers the Nobel prize?

TRUE OR FALSE? NUMBER THREE.

Answers on page 273

Is it true or false that:
1. A plebe is a West Point freshman?
2. There are twelve stars in the big dipper?
3. The earth rotates on its axis from east to west?
4. A person normally has ten pairs of ribs?
5. In the comic strip Mutt is the tall one and Jeff the short one?
6. Cream is heavier than milk?
7. Moths eat holes in cloth?
8. There are 32 points to the compass?
9. There are 640 acres to the square mile?
10. Twenty-four years usually constitute a generation?
11. The Gobi is the world's largest desert?
12. A meter is longer than a yard?
13. Candytuft is a kind of hard candy?
14. Massachusetts means "place of the great hills"?
15. Zeta is the last letter of the Greek alphabet?
16. Cows are the only animals that chew their cuds?
17. Robin Hood's sweetheart's name was Maid Marian?

18. There are twelve years in a decade?
19. Jujitsu means literally "the gentle art"?
20. The three primary colors are red, orange, and green?
21. Bullion is a kind of soup?
22. A farthingale is a South American bird?
23. A hexagon has twelve sides?
24. There are twelve dozen in a gross?
25. There are 1000 watts in a kilowatt?

TRUE OR FALSE? NUMBER FOUR

Answers on page 273

Is it true or false that:
1. There are four leaves on a shamrock?
2. July second is the date of the middle day of the year?
3. Four score and seven years ago equals sixty-seven years?
4. A pedagogue is an instrument for recording distances in walking?
5. All pure gold is of the same grade?
6. London is farther North than Vancouver, B.C.?
7. Anne Hathaway was Shakespeare's mother's name?
8. It takes five inches of snow to equal an inch of rain?
9. Guam is nearer the United States than the Philippines?
10. Charles McCarthy is a noted ventriloquist?
11. A table fork usually has five prongs?
12. The Cape Cod Canal is 13 miles in length?
13. An oriel is a kind of bird?
14. A sheriff is a city officer?
15. Singular men are invariably bachelors?
16. Bronze consists of copper and tin?
17. The Nobel prize has never been awarded twice to the same person?
18. The extended right arm of the Statue of Liberty is forty-two feet long?
19. The crocus is the national flower of the United States?
20. Hiawatha was a girl?
21. Edward Everett Horton wrote "The Man Without a Country"?
22. Ceramics is the art of basket weaving?
23. The antonym of occidental is oriental?

24. The Lido is an Italian liquid measure?
25. The poet Longfellow is the only American to have his bust in Westminster Abbey?

MEN AND WOMEN QUIZ NUMBER I-A

Answers on page 274

1. What great man was born in Europe, died in Asia, and was buried in Africa?
2. What member of an 18th century royal family is reputed to have said: "Let 'em eat cake!"?
3. Who was the first Englishman to sail around the world?
4. What was the nationality of John Calvin?
5. Who was the first governor of the Massachusetts Bay Colony?
6. Who reigned over Scotland when John Knox achieved his first great fame?
7. Who invented the sliding doors used on our street cars, and when?
8. Was there ever a president elected who pledged to get us into war?
9. How was Napoleon III related to Napoleon I?
10. Alexander the Great founded what city in Egypt?
11. In what state is the home of Barbara Frietchie?
12. What king said: "After me, the deluge."?
13. What famous men had these nicknames: Light Horse Harry? Poor Richard? Mad Anthony?
14. What famous orator delivered an address two hours long at the Gettysburg dedication?
15. In which of the following activities was Molly Pitcher famous: medicine, war, fire, or flood?
16. At what battle did who say: "You may fire when ready, Gridley."?
17. What king was called the "Lion Hearted"?
18. What colony did Roger Williams found? What colony did William Penn found?
19. Who was Virginia Dare?
20. Who was the first Postmaster of the United States?
21. What king of France was called St. Louis?
22. Who was the wife of Hiawatha?

23. In what war did Lee and Grant fight on the same side?
24. Who was the commander of the ship Bounty?
25. With what enterprise do you connect Tom Thumb?

MEN AND WOMEN QUIZ NUMBER I-B
Answers on page 274

1. Name the opposing generals at the battle of Appomattox, Virginia, in 1865?
2. Who was the orator at the dedication of the Bunker Hill monument?
3. During whose reign was the Magna Charta signed in England?
4. At what American battle were Prescott and Warren leaders?
5. Who made George Washington's first set of false teeth?
6. What was the name of the other man who rode with Paul Revere?
7. Associate the following phrases with the correct sources:
   "Walk softly and carry a big stick."
   "My kingdom for a horse."
   "All for one, and one for all."
8. How did Mary Queen of Scots meet her death?
9. Who was president when the first bath tub was installed in the White House?
10. Complete the following pairs: Damon and ....? Anthony and ....? Gilbert and ....?
11. Who were Abigail and Rebecca Bates? What were they called, and why?
12. What queen reigned the longest in England?
13. What was Rembrandt's first name?
14. Marie Antoinette's nationality was Dutch, French, Austrian, or English?
15. Who painted the Mona Lisa?
16. Who was the mother of Romulus and Remus?
17. Who was America's first ambassador to England?
18. What have Morgenthau, Longfellow, and Ford in common?
19. For whom were the American continents named?
20. Who was the second husband of Napoleon's first wife?

21. Was Joan of Arc born at Rouen?
22. What relation was Louis XIV to Louis XV?
23. Who was Fletcher Christian?
24. Who was Richard Saunders?
25. What noted artist gave his name to a certain color of hair?

MEN AND WOMEN QUIZ NUMBER I-C

Answers on page 275

1. What was the present king of England's former title before he was proclaimed king?
2. Who cut the Gordian Knot?
3. What have the following in common: Long John Silver, Charlie McCarthy, and Peter Stuyvesant?
4. What philosopher was condemned to death by the drinking of hemlock?
5. Who said: "Why don't you speak for yourself, John?"?
6. What ancient Greek philosopher's real name was Aristocles?
7. Samuel F. B. Morse invented the magnetic telegraph. What do the two middle initials stand for?
8. What character famous in theatrical tradition is George Spelvin?
9. "Sic semper tyrannis!" was spoken by whom and under what circumstances?
10. What was the occupation of the man who told Julius Caesar to "beware the Ides of March."?
11. The Tiger was a familiar nickname of Al Smith, Fritz Kreisler, Kaiser Wilhelm, or Georges Clemenceau?
12. What name belongs opposite each of the following to make a pair of lovers famous in literature or history:
    Aucassin and ......?   Lady Hamilton and ......?
    Pelleas and ....?   Dante and ......?
13. Under what Prime Minister was the Suez Canal purchased by England?
14. What two things have the following in common: Orson Welles, Phyllis Brooks, and Arthur Lake?
15. Is it true that Socrates was a sculptor as well as a philosopher?
16. What American leader demanded the surrender of Fort

Ticonderoga "In the name of the great Jehovah and the Continental Congress."?

17. What man of ancient times was called the "Scourge of God"?

18. Who said: "What this country needs is a good five cent cigar."?

19. What have the following in common: Taft, Tilden, Shakespeare, and Powell?

20. Who sent Henry M. Stanley to Africa, and why?

21. Give the full names of the following: P. T. Barnum, Gene Tunney, Buffalo Bill.

22. What is the last name of these well known people: Dizzy and Daffy? Constance, Barbara, and Joan? Fred and Adele? Ethel, John, and Lionel?

23. John Cabot, an early explorer, was a native of what country?

24. Was Captain Kidd a real or a legendary character?

25. Fill in the following blanks:
Romeo died for love of ....
For Helen of Troy, ... plunged his country into war.
.... betrayed Caesar for Cleopatra.
Elaine waited at the window for Sir ....
To save ...., Pocahontas was willing to die.
Priscilla really loved ....

MEN AND WOMEN QUIZ NUMBER I-D

Answers on page 275

1. By what other name was Charles S. Stratton, born 101 years ago, known?

2. Where is George Washington buried? Where is Abraham Lincoln buried?

3. Who are the familiar partners of the following: Harlequin; Darby; David; Adam; Ruth?

4. Who made a famous march from Atlanta to the sea?

5. Who were the French and English generals who fought the battle of Quebec?

6. Who said: "We have met the enemy, and they are ours."?

7. With what country are the following associated: Frederick the Great? Peter the Great? George III?

8. Who painted the famous picture "The Blue Boy"?

9. With what important event do we associate the name of George W. Goethals?

10. What three women have their pictures on United States postage stamps?

11. For whose deaths are the following blamed: Aaron Burr, David, Othello?

12. What scientist do you associate with each of the following: kite, tea-kettle, apple?

13. Can you name four great men whose first name was Thomas?

14. Is Josephine Ford the name of a famous actress, an airplane, an authoress, or an artist?

15. Identify the following death-bed remark; by whom it was said, and of whom: "Don't let poor Nelly starve."?

16. "The Angelus" was painted by which of the following: Rubens, Millet, Gainsborough, or Whistler?

17. Who was the sculptor of the famous statue "The Thinker"?

18. Who was known as the "prince of shadows"?

19. The following are the real names of what famous people: Frederick Austerlitz; Asa Yoelson; William Claude Dukenfield; Spangler Arlington Brugh; Emmanuel Goldenburg?

20. Name five famous soldiers who fought in the Civil War, and tell which side each fought on?

21. Who were the assassins in the following cases: Lincoln, McKinley, and the attempted assassination of President Roosevelt in Miami?

22. What have the three following men in common: Hannibal Hamlin, Henry Wilson, and Garret Hobart?

23. Who was known as the Father of his Country?
Who was known as the Father of History?

24. Which name does not belong in this list: Twist, Pierce, Hardy, and Cromwell?

25. Give the middle names of the following people:

Alexander .... Bell.   Henry .... Lodge.
William .... Bryant.   William .... Bryan.

LAW AND ORDER QUIZ NUMBER ONE

Answers on page 276

1. What is the difference between a post card and a postal card?
2. How large an amount of money can be sent by one money order?
3. Why are letter carriers' uniforms the color they are?
4. What is unicameralism?
5. Of what crime are you guilty if you steal $25 from a person you are visiting at night?
6. If you were a Congressman arrested for speeding in Washington, D.C., would you identify yourself, ask the President to fix it, or pay the fine?
7. What does it mean to die intestate?
8. What term is applied to the giving of false testimony?
9. When a letter is mailed from a foreign country to the United States, which country gets the postage money?
10. Under what department of the federal government is the United States Weather Bureau?
11. How does murder differ from homicide?
12. What class mail is parcel post?
13. What is meant by the small letters *D* or *S* below the date on some pennies?
14. If you had a Caveat would you eat it, play on it, or read it?
15. What is meant by the word "cloture" as applied to legislative bodies?
16. What is the meaning of the phrase "Caveat Emptor"?
17. When a law case is *heard in camera* what does this mean?
18. In law, what is a legatee?
19. What is interest beyond the legal rate called?
20. What is the meaning of the words "bona fide"?
21. How far out is the high seas officially: 12 miles, the shore line, or 3 miles?
22. What is a mittimus?
23. Is there a law requiring Justices of the Supreme Court to be lawyers?
24. What are ad valorem duties?
25. By what process is an accused person surrendered to the justice of another government?

Answers on page 276

1. In parliamentary law, should a person who seconds a motion rise to his feet while doing so?
2. What is the meaning of the words "oyer" and "oyez"?
3. If a court is adjourned "sine die," in what manner is it adjourned?
4. Can you name the departments in the United States government under which the following are located: Supervision of National Parks; Supervision of Forests; Supervision of Forest Products?
5. If left wing members of the legislature are liberal or radical, what are right wing members?
6. What is the only state in the United States whose laws are not based on the English common law?
7. Can a dead person legally vote in an election?
8. What is manslaughter in the second degree?
9. What is sometimes referred to as being "nine points of the law"?
10. What is a subpoena?
11. What does the postal term "nixie" mean?
12. The longest term of office in the U.S. Government is: Attorney General, Comptroller General, Postmaster General?
13. What government department issues passports?
14. Name the three departments of the Federal government, and tell who or what represents each?
15. Who can send letters through the mail by simply writing their name in the corner of the envelope?
16. Of whom is the following said: "Neither snow nor rain nor heat nor night stays these couriers from the swift completion of their appointed rounds."?
17. What is the difference between libel and slander?
18. What is the cost to send an air mail letter anywhere in the United States?
19. Are signatures in lead pencil on legal documents valid?
20. There are five penitentiaries in the United States; where are they?
21. By what general name are coins and metallic money known?
22. One who has committed regicide has done what?
23. What is the feminine form of administrator?

24. What is a holographic will?
25. Which has the right of way when all are approaching an intersection at the same time: a fire truck, a funeral procession, a parade, police answering a burglar alarm, mail truck, an ambulance racing to a hospital with a dying man?

LAW AND ORDER QUIZ NUMBER THREE
Answers on page 277

1. In legal terms, what is the difference between John Doe and Richard Roe?
2. Why are the letters *UX* sometimes used under a name in printed legal notices?
3. How many United States stamps in a set up to and including the ten cent stamp?
4. Why do silver and gold coins have a rough or milled edge?
5. What is the difference between an administrator and an executor of a will?
6. Does it say "Post Card" or "Postal Card" on the back of a penny postcard?
7. What is the meaning of usury?
8. Can you repeat the first seven words of the Constitution of the United States?
9. According to law, what is the minimum number of persons that can create a riot?
10. Of what is one guilty when one plagiarizes?
11. What is a codicil?
12. For what do the initials "J.C.D." stand?
13. Under what department of the United States government is the Coast Guard?
14. What is the only crime defined in the Constitution of the United States?
15. What are the first ten amendments to the Constitution called?
16. What is the official name for the White House?
17. How is the Panama Canal Zone governed?
18. From what language are most legal terms derived?
19. What is a Gerrymander?
20. What is the meaning of the phrase "verbatim ac litteratim"?

21. Whose signatures appear on our paper money?
22. What is the Nineteenth Amendment?
23. What does the Baumes Law provide?
24. What is meant by "eminent domain"?
25. What does the Grand Jury consist of?

LAW AND ORDER QUIZ NUMBER FOUR

Answers on page 278

1. What is a quorum?
2. Of what does the national salute consist?
3. How many silver buttons on the front of a policeman's coat?
4. What state in the Union has the most United States senators?
5. Who is the chief executive of all federal prisons?
6. In law, what is meant by "double jeopardy"?
7. What does the legal term "Act of God" mean?
8. What is the literal meaning of the phrase "habeas corpus" as used in a law court?
9. What is equity?
10. The United States Secret Service is under what federal department?
11. From what document is the following quoted: ". . . to determine whether that nation, or any nation so conceived and so dedicated, can long endure."?
12. What word means both daily fare and a legislative assembly?
13. What was the name of the mail established April 3, 1860, between San Francisco and St. Joseph, Missouri?
14. Who appoints the Treasurer of the United States, and how long is his term of office?
15. On what meridian is the city of Greenwich, England?
16. Does the United States print money for any other country?
17. If you were 'sui juris', would you see your doctor, dentist, lawyer, minister, or do nothing?
18. If a man committed a lapsus linguae, what would he be guilty of?
19. Is a naturalized citizen of the United States entitled to all the privileges of a native citizen?
20. What is a government called that is run by women?

21. In weather signals, what color is used to indicate rain or snow?
22. What is the literal meaning of the word 'veto'?
23. From what observatory is Standard Time reckoned?
24. What are the four highest ranks in the United States Navy?
25. What have the following in common: Dannemora, Atlanta, Leavenworth?

SUPER QUIZ NUMBER I-A

Answers on page 278

1. What is meant by an amnesty?
2. How many inches are there in one meter?
3. Can you name four of the five fields of achievement in which Nobel prizes are awarded?
4. Who were Peasblossom, Mustardseed, Cobweb, and Moth?
5. What was the original purpose of the pyramids of Egypt?
6. What is the last number printed on a six foot rule?
7. What are the four highest ranks in the United States Army?
8. What is the center stone in an arch called?
9. You have often heard the expression, "make the welkin ring"; what is a welkin?
10. How many kinds of twins are there?
11. What determines the width and height of ships in the United States?
12. What is the official slogan of the Royal Canadian Mounted Police?
13. What is a sycophant?
14. Name a battle of the American Revolution which involved two kinds of liquor.
15. How many edges has a cube?
16. 62 degrees, 37 minutes, 4 seconds is: a measurement of temperature, time, or of an angle?
17. One state in the United States is divided into something other than counties. What state is it and into what is it divided?
18. What does the word jettison mean?
19. Under what circumstances would a person become an ascian?
20. What is a tierce?

21. What policy is followed by the navy department in naming the following types of war vessels: battleships, destroyers, submarines, cruisers?
22. How many shocks are there in a thrave of grain?
23. What is the scientific study of birds called?
24. What are the names of the three thermometric scales?
25. In the following problems the first two words bear to each other the same relationship that the third and the missing fourth words bear to each other. Can you supply the missing words?
    New York is to Albany as New Mexico is to . . . . ?
    Ophelia is to Hamlet as Olivia is to . . . . ?
    Lost Horizon is to James Hilton as *Rob Roy* is to . . . . ?
    Pikes Peak is to the United States as Mauna Loa is to . . . . ?

SUPER QUIZ NUMBER I-B

Answers on page 279

1. A chain is a unit of measure. How many links are there in one chain?
2. What is the difference East or West of the Prime Meridian called?
3. What is the difference between an armada and an escadrille?
4. What is a pictograph?
5. Male and female rabbits are called what?
6. Where would you look for a lactometer?
7. Taurus, one of the twelve signs of the Zodiac, is represented by what animal?
8. In Uncle Tom's Cabin Eliza crossed the river on the ice. What was the name of the river?
9. The United States Secret Service has two statutory duties. What are they?
10. What three phrases, in common use, mean the whole length or entire distance?
11. If your church organist played a threnody would the music be most suited to a wedding, a funeral, or a festival?
12. What caused the death of darling Clementine?
13. What is a wallaby?

14. What have the following in common: sabots, espadrilles, and huraches?
15. What four words follow "Alas, poor Yorick . . . ."?
16. A saturnine person can spoil the party by falling asleep too early in the evening, by telling old jokes, by insisting on kissing the ladies, or by being sullen or dull?
17. If you were having a house built and the architect asked you what fenestration you wanted, what would he mean?
18. What is the difference between a somnambulist and a funambulist?
19. What is the difference between the eyes of a tiger and those of a lion?
20. A man born in the year 59 B.C. died in the year 18 A.D. How old was he when he died?
21. What is the literal meaning of the word "dirigible"?
22. How long would it take a train one mile long to pass through a tunnel one mile long at the rate of one mile a minute?
23. What is a quintal?
24. If this and that, and one half of this and that, amounts to seven, how much is this and that?
25. What is a better known name for the Collegiate Church of St. Peter in London?

SUPER QUIZ NUMBER I-C

Answers on page 280

1. What play was being presented at Ford's theater when Lincoln was assassinated?
2. In what region are penguins found?
3. What is the Ides?
4. What is a pirogue?
5. What was the legendary name for the chalice from which Christ drank at the Last Supper?
6. If a man is sent to the well with a five-gallon and a three-gallon can, how can he get an accurately measured seven gallons?
7. What is a gandy dancer?
8. What two citizens of the United States possess, as official legal titles, "Excellency", by Legislative act?

9. In what direction is the force of dynamite propelled when exploded?
10. There is a rope ladder hanging over the side of a boat two feet from the water. The tide is rising one foot each hour. How many hours will it be before the water will reach the ladder?
11. What is the Bourse?
12. What is the name given to underground passages used as meeting places and tombs by the ancient Christians?
13. What is a puncheon?
14. By whom were the following loved: Queen of Sheba, Eurydice, Evangeline?
15. Who is Peter Funk?
16. Which is wider and deeper, the Suez Canal or the Panama Canal?
17. Since what tragic incident has the United States Secret Service been charged with guarding the President?
18. Did a woman ever run for President of the United States?
19. What is pogonology?
20. What is a syllabub?
21. In the way that John Bull represents England, and Uncle Sam the United States, who represents France?
22. How many letters are used in the Roman system of numerals?
23. What was the name given to the three great wars fought between the Romans and the Carthaginians?
24. Where would you find the International Date Line?
25. What is a penumbra?

SUPER QUIZ NUMBER I-D

Answers on page 280

1. The emblem that physicians' cars display is called what?
2. What does the term "Pan-American" mean?
3. The Parliament of what European country is called a Storthing?
4. When and by whom was the present calendar brought into use?
5. What is a thole-pin?

6. If the Northern Lights are called the Aurora Borealis, what is the similar phenomenon in the South called?
7. The character Caliban is in what play by Shakespeare?
8. A persec is an astronomical unit of measure. How long is it?
9. What is the latitude and longitude of the North Pole?
10. Do the United States Marines come under the jurisdiction of the Army or Navy?
11. What is the fruit of the blackthorn tree?
12. What is the difference between a majority and a plurality?
13. What hobby puts a premium on poor printing?
14. What is a digamist?
15. What is meant by the phrase "halcyon days"?
16. What is the name given to the fireman who steers the rear end of a hook and ladder truck?
17. What is the nautical name for the period a seaman spends at the wheel?
18. If glass is smoother than ice, why can't you skate on it?
19. What is a monochrome?
20. What is the literal meaning of the word "myriad"?
21. What statesman referred to a political opponent as "a sophisticated rhetorician, inebriated with the exuberance of his own verbosity"?
22. For what do the letters B.T.U. stand?
23. Where does one find these words: "Quiet is requested for the benefit of those who have retired"?
24. When it's springtime in the Rockies what season is it in the Andes?
25. In America, what corresponds to the "hire purchase" system of England?

ENGLISH QUIZ NUMBER II-A

Answers on page 281

1. Give five meanings for the word "bar".
2. When a person is garrulous, is he talkative, quarrelsome, or quick to anger?
3. What is the difference between encyclical and encyclopedia?

4. What is meant by the following colloquialisms: sinker, staff of life, stove pipe, uncle?
5. Give three definitions for the word "sack".
6. What is a spoonerism?
7. What two words, spelt differently, pronounced the same, denote a color?
8. What is the difference between combustible and comestible?
9. What is it that can refer to a disease, a part of a house, something hung out, or something done to a woman's hair?
10. What is the difference between a dialogue and a monologue?
11. Give four meanings of the word board.
12. What is used as a piece in a game and as a disguise?
13. If you are dying of ennui what's wrong with you?
14. How many uses do you know for the word plug?
15. What is the difference between a talesman and a talisman?
16. What do these colloquial phrases mean: on the cuff, on the up and up, on the house?
17. Give three definitions for the word magazine.
18. In words which begin with "auto-", such as autobiographic and automatic, what does the prefix auto mean?
19. Give two meanings for the word diligence.
20. What is the meaning of the expression "he can't stand the gaff"?
21. What is a plagiarist?
22. Give three definitions for the word file.
23. What is a person who models new styles called?
24. Name three different kinds of breeches.
25. Does the word subsequent mean prior or after?

ENGLISH II-B

Answers on page 282

1. What is the German phrase for " 'Til we meet again"?
2. If someone told you that you were being followed by a deficiency of light, caused by the interception of light waves by an opaque body in an illuminated arc, would you be worried?
3. Spell "rays" three different ways, and give a different meaning for each.

4. Is milk transparent, translucent, or opaque?
5. What word possesses more S's than the word possesses possesses?
6. What is a person called who can speak several languages?
7. "Tele" means distance; name three words that come from it.
8. What is the meaning of the word "eureka"?
9. Which one of these words defines the word "bucolic": drunk, rustic, enthusiastic?
10. What is the literal meaning of the word sympathy?
11. Give four uses of the word turkey.
12. Give the antonyms of the following words: straight, collect, accept, pain, credit, descend, deep, scatter, innocent.
13. If you were listening to a piscatorial tale, which of these three would it be: a fairy tale, a fish story, or a ghost story?
14. The name of what small pointed nail also means to change the course?
15. How many meanings are there for the word galley?
16. What is the difference between biennial and biannual?
17. What is meant by the word pedant?
18. If I promulgate a book, do I read it, write it, or publish it?
19. What word of six letters meaning joined, can be made into a word having exactly the opposite meaning by changing the two middle letters around?
20. Give four meanings of the word die.
21. The term good bye is a contraction of what?
22. If oversee is to fail to notice, what does overseer mean?
23. Give two meanings for the word frog, besides the usual one of amphibious animal.
24. What is a laconic note?
25. What is the difference between anonymous and pseudonymous?

ENGLISH II-C

Answers on page 282

1. If the words associate and assemble mean to join or combine, and dissociate is to separate, what is the meaning of dissemble?
2. Is the point in the heavens directly above the head of a

spectator called the zither, the zenith, the zephyr, or the zircon?

3. Give the opposites of these words: accept, accelerate, addition, accumulate.
4. What is the difference between a cat-tail and a cat-o'-nine-tails?
5. What does the word ignoramus mean?
6. An epoch and an era have what connection?
7. Give four meanings of the word scale.
8. Do perspire and transpire mean the same thing?
9. If you were considered pugnacious you would be: calm, thrifty, quarrelsome, or brilliant?
10. Is writing paper called stationery or stationary?
11. Three words beginning with the letter R are all pronounced the same, but with different meanings and spelling. What are the three words?
12. Is it true that scan means to skim over lightly or glance at hurriedly?
13. If the word back means rear, or towards the rear, what is a fullback, a razor back, and a drawback?
14. Which of these words means lazy: indigent, indigenous, indignant, indolent?
15. If your sweetheart is a termagant is she kind, abusive, or understanding?
16. What is the meaning of the phrase "nip and tuck"?
17. If you had a mule would you walk on it, ride it, or work on it?
18. If a poppy is a flower, and a cock is a stack of hay, what is poppy-cock?
19. What is a cliché?
20. What is the meaning of the word lachrymose?
21. What is the opposite of each of the following: abettor, remote, and wearisome?
22. What is the difference between candid and candied?
23. What do Englishmen call the hood of an automobile?
24. What are the common names for the following professions: thespian, terpsichorean, theurgist?
25. Would you consider a lethargic person one who was keen, sportive, drowsy, or a garden lover?

ENGLISH II-D

Answers on page 283

1. What word does not belong in the following group: avert, oblige, obstruct, counteract?
2. What words are the opposites of: alkali, light, noxious, obese, cursory?
3. Give four sets of homonyms.
4. Give four definitions for the word pound.
5. What word means both a style of hair dress and loud noises?
6. What is the scientific definition of the word work?
7. Do impish and impious mean the same thing?
8. Give four different words meaning employment.
9. Give three meanings for the word cricket.
10. What is euphonious cacophony?
11. If one were in a state of celibacy would he be: a famous person, a person in hiding, an unmarried person, or an insane person?
12. What is a common term for a "ruddy cylinder utilized for labiate enchantment and commonly manipulated with the diminutive dactyl"?
13. Give five meanings of the word pat.
14. How do you pronounce the word frequent, when it's used as a verb?
15. Give three meanings for the word fast.
16. What one word describes a spasmodic inspiration suddenly arrested by a closing of the glottis?
17. Which word in each of the following lists has no relation to the other three: division, segment, entirety, section? pistol, carbine, saber, revolver?
18. Give three meanings for the word squash.
19. What is the plural of the word kilt, the Scottish garb?
20. Give four words beginning with "sec".
21. Give three meanings of the word digit.
22. Name five words ending in "phone".
23. Name three kinds of knots.
24. Give five meanings for the word club.
25. When you say that something is salubrious, do you mean that it is healthy, intoxicating, or saddening?

GENERAL QUIZ NUMBER X-A

Answers on page 284

1. Where does mocha coffee come from?
2. What great baseball team became known as the "Gashouse Gang"?
3. The following are the first names of three vice-presidents of the United States; can you give the correct last names of each: Hannibal; Schuyler; Levi?
4. If someone gave you a brioche would you eat it, ride in it, wear it, or plant it?
5. How many presidents were born in Massachusetts?
6. What does the 'C' stand for in Herbert C. Hoover's name?
7. What are dehydrated foods, and desiccated eggs?
8. What is a rutabaga?
9. A ride on what winged steed is supposed to give inspiration to poets?
10. Name six sports in which a ball is used?
11. Orange juice is valued for what vitamin?
12. What are gregarious animals?
13. Do peanuts ripen above or below ground?
14. Give three sayings or proverbs in which the word 'horse' is used.
15. Your avuncular relation is your brother, uncle, or father?
16. If you had an aspic would you tie it around your neck, eat it, hang it on the Christmas tree, or dig a hole with it?
17. When a man becomes a physician what oath does he take?
18. Which of the following is used in architecture as a symbol of prosperity: corolla, eagle, cornucopia, or money bag?
19. If you were given a dinner of haberdine what would you have?
20. What have the following cities in common besides being state capitals: Boston, Annapolis, Lansing, St. Paul, Helena?
21. Other than July and August, what two consecutive months have 31 days?
22. Name four symbols of good luck.
23. What is a mousse?
24. What are the fine arts?
25. What is a jess?

GENERAL QUIZ NUMBER X-B

Answers on page 284

1. Why doesn't the name of Calvin Coolidge appear in Who's Who?
2. Which one of the following does not belong in the group: Northern Spy; Nodhead; Astrachan; Sheldon?
3. Who was the bald-headed president?
4. What color, common to all, would you associate with these words: fever, sea, stone, bird, jacket, and spot?
5. What animal produces the hudson seal?
6. What is a Grecian nose?
7. If you were studying oölogy, what would you be studying?
8. What is a male goose called? a male duck? a male turkey?
9. Who was "born on Monday, christened on Tuesday, married on Wednesday, got sick on Thursday, worse on Friday, died on Saturday, buried on Sunday, and that was the end of . . . ."?
10. To what family does the peanut plant belong?
11. Name three presidents whose first and last names begin with the same letter?
12. What have these names in common: mustang, percheron, bronco, Hambletonian?
13. Mohair is the fleece of what animal?
14. What fruit is named after a reptile?
15. Is rhubarb a fruit or a vegetable?
16. Which three of the following have one thing in common: amethyst, pearl, agate, clarendon?
17. In what sport do the players compete for the Ryder cup?
18. In what place are two heads better than one?
19. Where does the month of September get its name?
20. What is the origin of the slang word 'gat' meaning gun?
21. The height of a horse is measured in 'hands'. How much is a hand?
22. In golf, what is an eagle?
23. What is meant by a scratched horse?
24. Is Jersey lightning visible in a thunderstorm?
25. How is salt obtained?

GENERAL QUIZ NUMBER X-C

Answers on page 285

1. African golf is a game of golf played only in Africa over a 46 hole course, a dice game, or a black ball game played on a snow covered course?
2. A hooped back chair with numerous spindles is one of our best known early American types. What is its name?
3. In what sports are the following terms used: Christy, spare, deuce, riding off?
4. Are the following made with batter or with dough: Hot Cross buns, chocolate cake, waffles, muffins, crullers?
5. Give four slang expressions with the word 'dog' in them?
6. Which two of the following refer to the same animal: mink, woodchuck, muskrat, polecat, bobcat, groundhog, weasel?
7. Which of the following sports is ruled by the Marquis of Queensberry rules: baseball, boxing, tennis, football?
8. What would you do with lacrosse, ride it, play it, sleep on it, or eat it?
9. Is negus a dress material, a South American potentate, or a hot drink?
10. What is the difference between a novice and an amateur?
11. How did the Marathon race get its name and distance?
12. How many feet from home plate to first base?
13. Name four items of food used in terms of derision.
14. If you received a haymaker, would you immediately go to the barn, to the meadow, or to sleep?
15. With which of the following activities was Izaak Walton associated: golf, politics, religion, or fishing?
16. Of what games do these figures remind you: 3 (of a kind); 13; 7-11; 4 (fore).
17. What is a flying mare?
18. For what does the abbreviation T.N.T. stand?
19. What is a mongoose valuable for?
20. Who succeeded Abraham Lincoln as President of the United States?
21. In baseball, what is a goose egg?
22. What is a tittle?
23. Is this true or false: Newfoundland is controlled by Canada?

24. Where were the Olympic games held in 1916?
25. What is the plural of the word sheep?

GENERAL QUIZ NUMBER X-D

Answers on page 285

1. A savoy is which of the following: a cucumber, a sweet potato, a species of cabbage, a small vegetable marrow?
2. What sounds do the following animals make: Horse, donkey, pig, elephant, snake, hen?
3. If you were described as having a retroussé nose, would it mean that you had a long thin nose, a large one of the Jimmy Durante type, a turned up nose, or one of those bulbous W. C. Field specimens?
4. In the sports world, who was Joe the Beaut? The Barbados Demon? The $11,000 Demon?
5. Do the arteries carry blood to the heart, from the heart, or both?
6. What is the difference between a millet and a mullet?
7. What body of water usually surrounded a medieval castle?
8. What is a Quaker gun?
9. What is meant by the word "verboten"?
10. What is an amateur radio operator called?
11. What is a philatelist?
12. What is a seraglio?
13. What kind of medicine do we obtain from a cinchona tree?
14. What peculiarity of the eyes do the sea horse and the chameleon have in common?
15. Does the name peacock denote the male or female of the species?
16. Is it true or false that Mount Everest has ever been climbed?
17. When you go into a cafe and are served café noir, what do you get?
18. Riposté is a term used in music, bridge, or fencing?
19. What is the name of the largest of the Egyptian pyramids?
20. Is a palfrey a ruffled skirt, a saddle horse, or a valance?
21. Is a whelk an animal, a fish, or a part of speech?
22. What does a barber call a man who shaves himself?
23. What is the meaning of the 'gin' in cotton gin?

24. What is referred to as 'white coal'?
25. What are pyrotechnics?

OFF THE RECORD—BUT YOU SEE THEM EVERY DAY!

Answers on page 286

1. How many matches are there in a booklet of paper matches?
2. How many red and white bars are there on the United States flag?
3. How many cigarettes are there in the average pack?
4. On which side is a cow milked?
5. On the buffalo nickel does the buffalo face right or left?
6. How much water is used for the average bath?
7. On the Lincoln penny is Abraham Lincoln wearing a tie?
8. Is the coin return on a pay telephone on the right or left side?
9. How wide is a penny?
10. How many squares are there on a checkerboard?
11. What three colors are used in printing a U.S. one dollar bill?
12. How many feathers are shown on the head of the Indian on a nickel?
13. Which way does Washington face on the one, two, and three cent stamps?
14. What four words appear on every piece of U.S. coin?
15. Whose picture is on the internal revenue stamp on a package of cigarettes?
16. How many face cards are there in a pack of cards?
17. Whose portrait is on the penny postal card?
18. What is the eagle on a fifty cent piece carrying?
19. How many white and how many black keys are there on a standard piano keyboard?
20. What is on the other side of the buffalo on a buffalo nickel?
21. How many three cent stamps are there in a dozen?
22. How many columns are there in a standard newspaper?
23. What is the average life of a dollar bill in circulation?
24. Whose portraits are on the half and the one and a half cent stamps?
25. There are how many keys on the standard typewriter keyboard?

OFF THE RECORD—QUIZ NUMBER TWO

Answers on page 286

1. Estimate within a quarter of an inch the distance around a silver quarter.
2. What are the dimensions of a standard size newspaper page?
3. What colors are the following stamps: one cent, two cent, three cent?
4. How many dimes placed side by side would it take to make twelve inches?
5. How many one-eyed Jacks are there in a pack of cards?
6. What is the standard gauge of a railroad track?
7. How many times does the serial number appear on a dollar bill?
8. How wide is a newspaper column?
9. How long is a typewriter ribbon?
10. In standard playing cards one king has no moustache. Which is it?
11. Whose portrait is on the one cent stamp?
12. On a reply postcard whose face is pictured on the stamp?
13. How long is an ordinary cigarette?
14. What month of the year has the most letters in it?
15. How many feathers are there on the head of the Indian on the Indian head penny?
16. How many stars are there on a United States quarter?
17. What is the length and width of a one dollar bill?
18. What two units of three letters each appear in alphabetical order on a typewriter keyboard?
19. Why does a star precede the number on some United States currency?
20. How is the *four* made on a clock marked in Roman numerals?
21. Does the great seal of the United States appear on the one, ten, twenty, or one hundred dollar bills?
22. What is the largest denomination of paper money in the United States?
23. Is there a man or a woman's head on the fifty cent piece, the dime, the nickel, and the penny?
24. Whose pictures are on the following denominations of United States bills: one, two, five, ten?

25.   Give within ten the average number of times the milkman can use the bottle he leaves at your door mornings.

OFF THE RECORD QUIZ NUMBER THREE
Answers on page 287

1.   How many thousand dollar bills would there be in a million dollars?
2.   If you worked at a job for one cent the first day and had your salary doubled every day what would you receive at the end of thirty days?
3.   If you went to bed at eight o'clock at night and set the alarm clock to get up at nine the next morning, how long would you sleep?
4.   If it takes an hour to cook one duck, how long would it take to cook two ducks?
5.   Mongol, Mikado, and General are all names of what commonly used articles?
6.   On which side would you mount a horse?
7.   Do they have a Fourth of July in Canada?
8.   What is the world's greatest bargain?
9.   If you bought a stick of timber six inches square and twelve feet long, and had to pay five cents a board foot for it, how much would it cost?
10.   In filling a bathtub the hot water faucet is flowing twice as fast as the cold water faucet. Does the water in the tub get hotter?
11.   How many buttons are there on a bluejacket's trousers, and for what do they stand?
12.   To open a door which way do you turn the knob?
13.   What structure, commonly associated with Egypt is on the U.S. one dollar bill?
14.   How many birthdays does the average man have?
15.   How many leap years are there in a century?
16.   If the number four is on the top of a die what number is on the bottom?
17.   Can you change a dollar bill into fifty coins?
18.   When you open a window do you raise the sash or the frame?

19. What word appears above the head of Washington on the quarter?
20. If you had only one match and entered a room where there was a lamp, an oil heater, and a cigarette, which would you light first?
21. When the light is out how many times would you have to pull the chain before the light goes on five times?
22. How many months have twenty-eight days?
23. Answer the following in two letters of the alphabet: the name of a girl; what all earthly things come to.
24. What symbol commonly associated with a dictatorship appears on the U.S. dime?
25. How far can a dog run into the woods?

OFF THE RECORD QUIZ NUMBER FOUR
Answers on page 287

1. How many pockets are there in an average man's suit?
2. A man has one dollar and fifteen cents in change in his pocket. He can't change a dollar, a half dollar, a quarter, a dime, or a nickel. What change has he in his pocket?
3. Two trains are side by side, on parallel tracks, they leave the station at the same time, travel at the same rate of speed and arrive at the same destination. It took the first train eighty minutes and the second one hour and twenty minutes. How do you account for the difference?
4. A man spent two thirds of what money he had. He then had eight dollars left. How much did he have in the beginning?
5. A boat takes exactly twenty days to travel from San Francisco to Yokohama. If it starts March third, at noon, what date will it arrive in Yokohama?
6. Two books have one-eighth inch covers and all the pages in each volume are one and one-half inches thick. How far does a book-worm travel if he starts on page one of volume one and travels to the last page of volume two, assuming that he travels in a straight line?
7. If the doctor gave you three pills and told you to take one every half hour, how long would they last you?
8. Counting the strikes of a clock starting at one and going

up to and including twelve, how many times does the clock strike in that time interval?

9. A frog is at the bottom of a well twelve feet deep. Every day he jumps up four feet and every night he falls back three feet. How many days does it take the frog to jump out of the well?

10. If a person reading a book stopped on page fourteen, and wanted to mark his place would he put the book mark between pages thirteen and fourteen or between fourteen and fifteen? Why?

11. Would it take more pickets to build a fence over a hill than on level ground?

12. If you were on page seven hundred and fifty of a one thousand page book, and you picked up the book upside down, would the fewer pages be on your left or your right?

13. If I took your first name and you took my last name, would we both have the same name?

14. Can anything be wider than it is long?

15. If a picture is painted on the ceiling, will the bottom be at the nearer or farther end of the room as you enter?

16. Seven men dine at the same restaurant at the same time each day. But the first dines there every day, the second every other day, the third every third day, and so on, the seventh man dining there every seventh day. After how many days would all of them dine at the restaurant on the same day?

17. Where would you build a house so that all of the windows would have a southern exposure?

18. A is twenty-four years old, and twice as old as B was when A was as old as B is now. How old is B?

19. Which direction does the glass fly when you break an electric light bulb?

20. A train starts daily from San Francisco to New York, and one daily from New York to San Francisco, the journey lasting seven days. How many trains will a traveler meet in journeying from New York to San Francisco?

21. During any complete twenty-four hour period how many times does the minute hand pass the hour hand?

22. If a length of rope was stretched across a railroad track and a train passed over it, into how many pieces would the rope be cut?

23. Which letter of the alphabet is a measure? Which an industrious insect? a drink? a vegetable? a bird?

24. If you arrive at the railway station thinking that your train leaves at 3:30, but the porter tells you that it doesn't go until the next time the hands of the clock are together, what time does your train leave?

25. If a clock strikes hours only, how many times will it strike in a day?

FAMOUS ORIGINS NUMBER ONE

Answers on page 288

1. What is the origin of the word "NEWS"?
2. Where did the words "Johnny Cake" come from?
3. How did the month of June get its name?
4. With what French King did the style of high heels originate?
5. From Alpha to Omega means what? Why?
6. "Good-bye," a farewell greeting, is a contraction of what?
7. Why was Wall Street, in New York city, so named?
8. Explain the superstition attached to lighting three cigarettes with one match.
9. What is the origin of the word "Thursday?"
10. What is meant by the phrase "Beware the Ides of March"?
11. Why is court plaster so called?
12. Where did the puppets Punch and Judy get their names?
13. What is the origin of the word fido as applied to a dog?
14. Why are most all advertising clocks and watches set at eight seventeen?
15. Who first used the phrase "flaming youth"?
16. Why is our familiar sandwich so called?
17. How did the "baker's dozen" originate?
18. What is the source of the word Benedict, as applied to a newly married man?
19. What famous explorer is credited with having introduced tobacco into Europe?
20. What is the common origin of the words Czar and Kaiser?
21. Where did the nickname of "spud" for potatoes originate?
22. Why are country roads almost always sixty-six feet wide?

23. What is the origin of the custom of placing the engagement or wedding ring on the third finger?
24. Who coined the phrase "the almighty dollar"?
25. Who are the four Kings represented in a pack of playing cards?

FAMOUS ORIGINS NUMBER TWO

Answers on page 289

1. Where does the expression to "kowtow to someone" come from?
2. For whom was the month of August named?
3. From what is the word salary derived?
4. Who are the four Queens in a pack of cards supposed to represent?
5. Why is a person holding a position of no responsibility or authority called a figurehead?
6. What is the origin of our word cereal?
7. Why is the right hand always used for shaking hands?
8. Where did the following words come from: calico, damask, muslin, khaki?
9. Why is hamburg so called, when there is no ham in it?
10. What is the significance of the three golden balls over a pawnbroker's shop?
11. How did our sirloin steak get its name?
12. What do we mean when we say that a game is played "according to Hoyle"?
13. From what was the dollar mark on United States currency derived?
14. Why is a post road so called?
15. Members of the Toxophilite Society are interested in what and why?
16. Why is a certain type of china known as Wedgwood?
17. Who originated the expression "Knock, knock, who's there?"
18. What persons are privileged to drink the King of England's health sitting down?
19. Where is El Dorado, and what is the legend connected with it?
20. Where and what are the "roaring forties"?

21. Who first said "England expects every man to do his duty"?
22. How did the daisy get its name?
23. These are all familiar quotations, but do you know who first said them? "Tell it to the Marines"; "A one horse town"; "Fingers were made before forks"; "There wasn't room to swing a cat there".
24. Who was Uncle Sam's predecessor?
25. To whom can we attribute the expression "Hey, nonny nonny"?

FAMOUS ORIGINS NUMBER THREE

Answers on page 290

1. How did rabbits and eggs become associated with Easter?
2. How did the pen name of Mark Twain originate?
3. What is the derivation of the word milliner?
4. Why is Connecticut sometimes called the Nutmeg State?
5. What do the letters T.D. on a clay pipe stand for?
6. Why does a dog turn around several times before he lies down?
7. Where did the phrase "peeping Tom" originate?
8. From where do we get the expression "crazy as a loon"?
9. What is the meaning of the expression "to cross the Rubicon"?
10. Why do you wear a band on your hat?
11. Who started the saying "the customer is always right"?
12. What is the origin of the word fan as used in the phrase "baseball fan"?
13. Why was the custom of shaving first adopted?
14. What is the origin of the honeymoon?
15. How did the term "Yankee" originate?
16. How did the expression a "white elephant" originate?
17. What is referred to by the word rap in the phrase "it isn't worth a rap"?
18. Why are there fifty-two cards in a deck of ordinary playing cards?
19. Why is the southern part of the United States called Dixie?
20. Why is the waiting room for the use of actors called the Green Room?
21. What is the origin of the word "tip"?

22. From what is the word alphabet derived?
23. How did Greenland get its name?
24. Why is a pea-soup fog so called?
25. How did the phrase to give a person the "cold shoulder" originate?

FAMOUS ORIGINS NUMBER FOUR
Answers on page 292

1. How did English soldiers get the nickname of limeys?
2. How did the thimble get its name?
3. Where did the ouija board get its name?
4. What is meant by the phrase "Hobson's choice"?
5. Why is hypocritical grief called crocodile tears?
6. Why is a capital R with a line drawn through the tail used on the top of doctors' prescription blanks?
7. Why were buttons first put on coat sleeves?
8. Why is the equator so called?
9. Why were drinking glasses called tumblers?
10. How did sailors come to be called gobs?
11. What is the origin of the term Uncle Sam?
12. Why were the American red men called Indians?
13. You've heard the saying "Steve Brody took a chance" but who was Steve Brody, and what did he do?
14. Where did the expression "let George do it" originate?
15. What are policemen called in England and in Ireland, and why?
16. What is a southpaw and how did the name derive?
17. Where did the expression to "be in the limelight" originate?
18. Why is a small pocket knife called a pen-knife?
19. What was the origin of the two buttons on the back of a morning coat?
20. What is the origin of the phrase "it's Greek to me"?
21. What is the origin and significance of the phrase "A 1"?
22. What is the origin and meaning of the phrase "mind your p's and q's"?
23. How did the dollar get its name?
24. How did the month of January get its name?
25. What is the meaning of the phrase "the lion's share"?

Answers on page 293

1. What are gregarious animals?
2. If a polygon is a figure of many sides, what are each of the following: octagon, pentagon, hexagon?
3. What is tandem bicycle?
4. Which has the most teeth, a dog, a man, or a cat?
5. If you met a lot of men wearing short pants, no coats, gloves, each man carrying a club, and one man wearing a mask, to what type of organization would you say they belonged?
6. What distinguishes a revolver from other types of pistols?
7. What is a Rhodes scholar?
8. In what country did the goldfish originate?
9. What is a grotto?
10. Where are the following located: Egg Island, Plum Pudding Island, Roast Beef Island, and Sandwich Bay?
11. Name five animals living in the sea.
12. If you saw a sign in a store that read: "Pedal teguments artistically illuminated," what would you expect to have done there?
13. What court in Great Britain compares with the Supreme Court in the United States?
14. What is the difference between a depot and a station?
15. What is meant by a "laced drink"?
16. Give five meanings of the word "stock".
17. What difference is there in the shape of an oval, an ovate, and an ovoid?
18. If cotton gathering is picking cotton what is wool gathering?
19. On the Fahrenheit thermometer what is the difference in degrees between the freezing and boiling point of water?
20. In aviation what are the two meanings of the word ceiling?
21. To what does the following phrase refer: "Threaten me and millions will spring to my defense"?
22. What is the difference between a sanatorium and a sanatarium?
23. What is an ohm?

24. What three English words of three letters each are spelled differently, pronounced the same, and refer respectively to a person, an animal, and a tree?

25. What is the name of a nine sided polygon?

GENERAL QUIZ NUMBER IX-B

Answers on page 294

1. Will whiskey "age" in a glass container?
2. How many great grandparents does one have?
3. Arrange in the order of their birth: Plato. Socrates, Aristotle.
4. Where is the island of Reil?
5. Towards what part of an apple do the seeds point?
6. What is a Bengal light?
7. What is a samovar?
8. What is the wake of a ship?
9. What is a piebald animal?
10. What is the common name for a member of the Society of Friends?
11. From where does chamois come?
12. Cleave has two contradictory meanings. What are they?
13. What is the name of an Eskimo's snow hut?
14. Which demands the greater expenditure of energy, a smile or a frown?
15. What is the color of each of the following horses: sorrel, roan, bay?
16. What American city is nearest Europe?
17. Of what two United States coins are the following slang terms: two bits, a thin 'un?
18. What is the difference between a thief and a robber?
19. If you froze a pound of water would you get a pound of ice?
20. Name four different types of facial hirsute adornment.
21. What is the derivation of the word varsity?
22. What is a corduroy road?
23. In banking, what is collateral?
24. Is an allergic person sympathetic, sensitive, or apathetic?
25. What common term used in stage direction has been accepted in modern slang to describe a person who is a snob?

GENERAL QUIZ NUMBER XI-C

Answers on page 294

1. What is a logograph?
2. What is the meaning of the phrase "apropos"?
3. Does sound travel faster through air or water?
4. What is called the "funny bone"?
5. What is meant by a common carrier?
6. What is the international distress signal at sea?
7. To what industry do these terms apply: waft, woof, weft?
8. For what were the pyramids of ancient Egypt used?
9. Are the buttonholes on a man's shirt cut vertical or horizontal?
10. There are six definitions for the word "cob." How many of them can you give?
11. What else, besides a human being, has an appendix?
12. Is a letter-carrier limited to any definite number of pounds of mail matter he carries on each trip?
13. What does an archeologist study?
14. Is the income tax a progressive or a proportionate tax?
15. What famous Greek orator practiced with pebbles in his mouth?
16. If you are risible, what's the matter with you?
17. What is a carillon?
18. Give six meanings for the word bay.
19. What is a maverick?
20. What is an epigram?
21. To what do the terms "pulp" and "slick" refer when they are used as opposites?
22. What is the difference between acrid and acid?
23. Distinguish between pigeon English, pigeon hearted, and pigeon-hole.
24. Each month has a birthstone. Name five of the twelve.
25. What is an ocular contusion?

GENERAL QUIZ NUMBER XI-D

Answers on page 295

1. What is the difference between a decade, a century, and a chiliad?

2. Give four colloquial terms for a dollar bill.
3. In a pack of playing cards what card is sometimes called the puppyfoot?
4. What do the letters F.F.V. stand for?
5. Give six proper names by which the devil is known.
6. Name the four horsemen of the Apocalypse.
7. How is the height and width of United States battleships determined?
8. Which part of a wheel moves the faster, the upper or the lower?
9. Soldiers from what country are nicknamed "the ladies from hell"?
10. What is Nirvana?
11. What is a troglodyte?
12. What tree is cut only by moonlight, and why?
13. In the following list of slang words, how many are in the dictionary: bean (meaning head or to hit on the head), booster, click, double-cross.
14. Which has the larger capacity, a liter or a quart?
15. Of what metal is the Victoria Cross made?
16. How many arrows has the eagle in his claws on the back of a dollar bill?
17. If a cattle boat carries cattle, what does a pig boat carry?
18. If you were buying stamps from a stamp vending machine, which denomination, ones, twos, or threes, would give you the most for your money?
19. A twenty inch cube may be divided into how many two inch cubes?
20. What is a ladrone?
21. The proprietor of a livery stable owned a brougham, a surrey, a hansom, a victoria, and a gig. He decided to put rubber tires on all the wheels. How many tires did he have to buy in all?
22. What was the method of transportation of each of the following: Cinderella, Paul Revere, The Daring Young Man.
23. What are H. G. Wells' first two names?
24. If you weighed yourself at a weighing machine in England, and the attendant told you that your weight was ten stone, how much would you weigh?
25. What mode of transportation do each of the following

phrases refer to: ride the rod, burn up the road, go on shank's mare?

GENERAL QUIZ NUMBER XII-A
Answers on page 296

1. The lightest weight classification in boxing is: flyweight, light weight, bantam weight, or feather weight?
2. If you were the victim of aleurophobia, what would you be suffering from?
3. What name should not be in this list: beagle, dachshund, shetland, pointer, retriever.
4. How many and which of the following are good to eat: strawberry, bayberry, mulberry, dewberry?
5. What is traditionally supposed to be at the end of a rainbow?
6. What does it mean when it is said of a pugilist that "he pulled his punches?"
7. Re-arrange these letters as follows: Change *plug* into a hasty swallow. Change *lamp* into a tropical tree. Change *plea* into a jump.
8. What is the highest point in North America?
9. In spelling the names of the United States it requires every letter of the alphabet except one. What is that one?
10. What vegetable contains the most iron?
11. In a sheep pen there are 30 sheep, a man, and his dog. How many feet are there in the pen?
12. Is an electric eel a type of generator, a fresh water fish, an automatic railroad switch, or a sea-going reptile?
13. What is a sierra?
14. Name five popular songs that have the name of a girl as the title.
15. What colored letters do we eat?
16. Is Europe in the eastern or western hemisphere?
17. What is guava?
18. Which locality takes the most baking powder to bake a cake?
19. Where do we get the spice mace?
20. What color is Titian, and why is it so named?
21. What kind of fish is scrod?

137

22. What was known as "Clinton's Ditch"?
23. Jacobean furniture was named in honor of what king?
24. What kind of animals are kept in a warren?
25. What state in America has the smallest coastline?

GENERAL QUIZ NUMBER XII-B

Answers on page 296

1. What are two important products of citriculture?
2. Is a leopard striped or spotted?
3. What entire continent belongs to a single nation?
4. A prickly pear, an eel, and a large fish share what name?
5. Name four kinds of cooking beginning with the letter 'B.'
6. Which one of the following species of live stock does not belong in this group: capon, poult, squab, shoat?
7. What and where is Gretna Green?
8. What is the English translation of the Spanish name "Sierra Nevada"?
9. What, on record, is the longest baseball game ever played?
10. How far is the English shore from Europe?
11. A casserole is ordinarily used for a short skirt for women, for baking food in an oven, or as a frame for needlework?
12. Name the country associated with the following words: (for example, Volga suggests Russia): scarab, boomerang, vodka, mandarin, Gobi, Limehouse, Algonquin.
13. What is Valhalla?
14. Where is a prophet without honor?
15. What city is called the "Mother of the World"?
16. For what is the island of Madeira noted?
17. If you bought a bushel of maize, what would you get?
18. If an aristocrat is a person high in the social scale, what is aristology?
19. In what sports are the following terms used: stymie, huddle system, footfault?
20. Are oranges and lemons fruits, vegetables, or berries?
21. Can you name four songs in which the four seasons are mentioned.
22. It was Piccadilly to the British soldiers, and Broadway to the Americans; what was it to the Germans?

23. What country in South America formerly belonged to Portugal?
24. Who is often called the "Father of Geography"?
25. Which is the largest of the Great Lakes?

GENERAL QUIZ NUMBER XII-C

Answers on page 297

1. Four runners were trotting over a course of 20 miles. One of them got only one quarter of the way, the second got one half of the way, the third got three quarters of the way, and the fourth completed the course. What was the total number of miles covered by the runners?
2. A Basque is a wicker container used in Europe, an inhabitant of the western Pyrenees, or a tropical fish?
3. Which Kansas City is larger, that in Kansas, or that in Missouri?
4. If it were June and you were going to Argentina, would you take your summer formal, golf clubs, red flannels, overcoat, or slacks?
5. What is the name of the peninsula comprising Spain and Portugal?
6. Can you name the eight weight classifications in boxing?
7. Name three cities in the United States where coinage mints are located?
8. What city in the United States was called Old Fort Dearborn?
9. Where do Monday and Tuesday occur on the same day?
10. Give the names of animals used as derisive epithets.
11. What is a herd or school of whales called?
12. What is the correct way to carry rabbits?
13. What is the difference between the eyes of the tiger and those of the lion?
14. A jade is which of the following: a worn out horse, a vicious woman, or a semi-precious stone?
15. Which day of the week has the most letters? Which month has the most letters?
16. Name four presidents of the United States whose last names begin with the letter 'H.'
17. Name three presidents who dropped their Christian names.

18. Is a parr an animal, a bird, a fish, or a golf expression?
19. Which of the following are nuts: walnuts, castinas, peanuts?
20. Is Minneapolis or St. Paul the capital of Minnesota?
21. Hannibal, Missouri, is the boyhood home of Al Capone, Edward Bok, Mark Twain, or Vice-President Garner?
22. Six states in the Union have capitals beginning with the letter 'S.' Can you name four of them with their capitals?
23. What misstatement of fact is made in the following sentence: The ancient southwestern Indians often held their most solemn religious ceremonies on Lake Mead?
24. What do the following animals or birds signify: ant; bat; cat; crocodile; dove; ox; swan?
25. What presidents did the following vice-presidents serve under: Hannibal Hamlin; Henry Wilson; Adlai Stevenson; Garret A. Hobart; Charles W. Fairbanks?

GENERAL QUIZ NUMBER XII-D

Answers on page 297

1. Which three nations are the largest source of crude oil today?
2. Name as many states as you can beginning with the letter 'A.'
3. If a tycoon came your way, would you run for cover, speak a cordial greeting, or call the police?
4. With which one of the following activities is the word "Gerrymander" associated: literature, fishing, politics, or farming?
5. How does the movement of a cat's jaw differ from that of a dog's?
6. Looking at a glass of vodka, would you be most likely to mistake it for tea, water, whiskey?
7. What is the significance of the three colors in the American flag?
8. In a surveyor's measuring standard how many square miles make a township?
9. What is a ranaculturist?
10. Who are the patron saints of England, Scotland, Ireland, and Wales respectively?

11. The Ibis was the sacred bird of what race?
12. You've heard of buying a pig in a poke. What is a poke?
13. What is the difference between a guppy and a duppie?
14. If you had a hypopyon what would you do with it?
15. What is naupathia?
16. What is a mitticus?
17. What part of a forest is the duff?
18. To the Roman numeral C add a baker's dozen and subtract the number of people on a jury. What number is left?
19. Give the correct equivalents of these nautical measurements: six feet, ten cable's length, three nautical miles, sixty nautical miles.
20. If you were found guilty of cachinnation, what would you have done?
21. What is legal tender?
22. What is a catamaran?
23. What does the term log rolling apply to?
24. The press is called the "fourth estate." What are the other three?
25. Yesterday I saw a mammal having a flexible proboscis serving as a prehensile organ, and a piscivorous natatorial bird with a distensible gular pouch. What did I see?

GENERAL QUIZ NUMBER XIII-A

Answers on page 298

1. Describe the national flag of Hawaii.
2. What is a lead line?
3. What is fallow land?
4. Is xylographer a surgeon's instrument, one who classifies insects, a wood carver, or one who plays a musical instrument?
5. What is a dock?
6. Is a poltroon a Dutch philosopher, a forger, or a coward?
7. Can you name three different occupations in which one starts at the top and works down?
8. Is an earthquake tremor recorded on a barograph, a seismograph, or a tremolo?
9. By what technical name is the muscle of the scalp known?
10. Which is larger, Texas or Alaska?

11. Did the 20th Century begin January 1, 1900, or January 1, 1901.
12. What is a sand hog?
13. Which is the highest title: earl, duke, count, or viscount?
14. In what trades are the following tools used: orange stick, night stick, pallet knife, and shuttle?
15. What country do you associate with the Black Forest?
16. When is a shadow the shortest?
17. If you had a calumet, would you eat it, smoke it, or ride it?
18. What is the difference between paper and parchment?
19. From what part of the rubber tree is rubber made?
20. What is the hardest stone, after the diamond?
21. Which word is out of place in this list: pine, holly, spruce, mistletoe, maple, elm, and cedar?
22. What was the date of the year following 1 B.C.?
23. In selling his merchandise, what weights do the following people use: the grocer, druggist, jeweler?
24. Who was the greatest comedian of silent pictures?
25. If you had a punkah, would you eat it, ride it, fan yourself with it, or inflict punishment with it?

GENERAL QUIZ NUMBER XIII-B

Answers on page 298

1. What does the word ballistics mean?
2. What name is given to puppets worked with strings?
3. What is meant by morganatic marriage?
4. What do the four H's of the 4-H club stand for?
5. Which of the following are imaginary beings: elves, gnomes, sylphs?
6. What was the old time New England "spring medicine"?
7. What is a shorter way of saying two thousand thousand?
8. How many points are there on a Maltese cross?
9. What metal is 3,000 times as valuable as gold?
10. What is the meaning of the word sobriquet?
11. What is nitrous oxide commonly called?
12. Is the head of the Sphinx that of a man or a woman?
13. What is a dowager?
14. What remained in Pandora's box after she had opened it?

15. What is the name of the side of a triangle which lies opposite the right angle?
16. What does simian mean?
17. Who was Ichabod Crane?
18. Give the Arabic equivalent of MDCCC.
19. Name the three states having the most electoral votes.
20. What is the unit of currency in Hawaii?
21. What is the meaning of the expression "getting your second wind"?
22. Who wrote the fable of the fox and the grapes?
23. A fiddle is a musical instrument, but it is also what?
24. What is the difference east and west of the prime meridian called?
25. Where is the Acropolis?

GENERAL QUIZ NUMBER XIII-C
Answers on page 299

1. What is a patronymic?
2. Can a woman ever become president of the United States?
3. Who is the patron saint of shoemakers?
4. What is a moot-hill?
5. What is the science of dactyloscopy?
6. Give the next line after "I shot an arrow into the air . . ."?
7. Give the earliest and the latest date on which Easter may occur. How is the date determined?
8. What is a donee?
9. What is a prestidigitator?
10. When filled with hot water which cracks quicker, a thick glass or a thin one?
11. What are the steps of a ship's rope ladder called?
12. What have the following in common: trefoil, papal, ansate, swastika?
13. Who were the Forty Niners?
14. What is wrong with this sentence: The boy is too small to manipulate the pedals on his bicycle?
15. What have the following words in common: Ingrain, Wilton, Velvet, Brussels, and Axminster?
16. What kind of an expression is a "Mona Lisa" smile?

17. One of the following people does not wear kilts: Greeks, Scots, Hottentots.
18. What is the difference between cardinal and ordinal numerals?
19. Does a person become snowblind from a snowstorm?
20. From what is the substance used as glue on the back of a postage stamp made?
21. What does the word prodigal mean?
22. The calendar that we now use is called the Gothic, Mayan, Gregorian or Confucian?
23. What art did Goethe describe as "frozen music"?
24. What have the following in common: Crown Derby, Spode, and Swansea?
25. When is a countess's husband not a count?

GENERAL QUIZ NUMBER XIII-D

Answers on page 299

1. What is a pannier?
2. What do the following abbreviations mean to you: bbl.; C.P.A.; cwt.; H.I.H.; C.O.D.?
3. Why are emergency fire pails filled with sand instead of water?
4. On which could a motorist travel the farther, a gallon of gasoline purchased in the United States, or one purchased in Canada?
5. Tell the meaning of four of the six following words: octavo, versus, incognito, Dei gratia, ad libitum, per centum, ad valorem?
6. Complete the following affinities: rod and ......? bread and ......? boots and ......? mortar and ......? Beauty and ......? lost and ......? pen and ......? bacon and ......?
7. If you had a log ten feet long and you sawed a foot off every time, how many cuts would it take to complete the job?
8. Does a growth of cane-brake indicate a poor or rich soil?
9. What does a cooper do for a living?
10. One of the following flags is not white, red, and blue: Eng-

lish, French, United States, Cuban, or Italian flag. Which is it?

11. In English peerage, what is the difference between being a Knight and a Baron?

12. Is a zephyr a musical instrument, a wind, or an animal?

13. In stairs, what is the horizontal and the vertical part called?

14. If a cadet studied at New London, Connecticut, he would very likely be appointed an officer in what branch of government service after graduation?

15. When can you see the greatest distance, at night or day?

16. What is the difference between fog and cloud?

17. Would you fry or broil food over a spitfire?

18. When a theatrical manager gives orders to 'dress the house', does he mean to decorate it with flags, bunting, or to have it repainted?

19. For which one of the following purposes would you use a Hyatt light: in lighting a cellar, a lighthouse, or in flood lighting a skating rink?

20. Who is the "old lady of Threadneedle Street"?

21. If you had a diurnal, would you eat it, read it, or take it out in the garden and plant it?

22. An auk is a Turkish official, a large bird, or a shoemaker's tool?

23. What agricultural product does the boll weevil attack?

24. Name three aquatic mammals.

25. Can you complete the following sentences:
    Sukiyaki is a ....?
    A Horse's Neck is a ....?
    An anemone is a ....?
    Jai alai is a ....?
    A benjamin is an ....?

PROVERBS AND MYTHS QUIZ NUMBER ONE

Answers on page 300

1. Complete these old sayings: A penny saved ....
   Time and tide .... A man of words and not of deeds
   ....

2. Untangle these two well known proverbs: The hand gathers no moss in the bush in rolling a stone a bird is worth two.

3. What words complete these trite figures of speech: As poor as .... As brown as .... As stiff as ....
4. Explain two of the following: Taking the bull by the horns. Lock, stock and barrel. Killing two birds with one stone.
5. Complete this line: "The hand that rocks the cradle . . ."
6. Who would ride if wishes were what?
7. What two proverbs contradict themselves?
8. Who said: "God helps those who help themselves."?
9. Can you give four proverbs or sayings about dogs?
10. What is this in plain English: "Do not be lachrymose over lactic fluid already wasted."?
11. What is said to be the "sincerest flattery"?
12. What happens to the man who hesitates?
13. Supply the missing word in the following: As honest as the day is .... Nip and .... He spends money like a drunken .... It's as old as the ....
14. Which of these statements means the same thing as the proverb: Time lost is never found again: Tomorrow is another day; Time respects no man; Haste makes waste; When time passes it is gone for good?
15. Finish the following: A miss is .... A stitch in time .... Two's company but .... Where there's a will ....
16. According to Benjamin Franklin, what effect will being "early to bed and early to rise" have on one's fortune?
17. Complete the following proverbs: Still water .... Honesty is .... Charity covers ....
18. Where is it supposed to be most difficult to find a needle?
19. Finish these expressions: Hale and .... White as .... Cold as .... It never rains but it .... Bold as ....
20. What proverb does this refer to: "One should put into execution that which one urgently recommends."?
21. What kind of a stone gathers no moss? What kind of stones might be said to walk? What stone stands for flattery and guile?
22. Can you finish these quotations: Handsome is .... A friend in need .... Better late ....
23. Who wrote: "Nothing is certain in this world but death and taxes."?

24. Complete the following: Necessity is the mother of ....
Enough is as good as .... Faint heart ne'er won
....

25. Fill in the missing words in the following familiar phrases:
Fair, fat, and .... High, ..., and handsome.

PROVERBS AND MYTHS QUIZ NUMBER TWO

Answers on page 301

1. Complete the following quotations: Laugh, and the world
laughs with you, ... To err is human, ...
Truth crushed to earth ....

2. What is it that never waits for any man?

3. Complete the following expressions: Brave as a ....
Smooth as .... Pure as ....

4. Finish the following: "Shoe the old horse, and shoe the old
mare, but ...."?

5. What well known proverb is expressed in the following:
"Who counts, ere fractured are the shells,
His bipeds gallinaceous,
Is apt to find his calculations
Utterly fallacious."?

6. Finish these familiar quotations: It is more blessed to give
.... All is not gold .... Love thy neighbor
....

7. Give three adages the central thought of which is water.

8. Can you finish the following quotations: Man works from
sun to sun .... Mend your clothes upon your back
....

9. Complete the following expressions: As light as ....
As pretty as .... As smart as ....

10. Finish the following proverbs: Penny wise .... A
burned child .... The longest way round ....

11. Translate this into a familiar saying: "Superfluity of
culinary artists renders worthless the consomme."

12. Finish these familiar sayings: Bag and .... Kith and
.... Safe and .... Sum and ....

13. Can you give a contradictory proverb for either of the following: Save for a rainy day. Great minds run in the same
channel.

147

14. Complete the following expressions: Slick as a ....
    Thin as a .... Neat as a ....
15. How strong is a chain?
16. Unscramble this: That gold is not all glitters.
17. Finish these sayings: Give me liberty or .... United
    we stand .... One for all ....
18. Who said "Wise bees save honey, wise folks save money."?
19. Finish the following: As busy as .... As blind as a
    .... As happy as ....
20. Finish these proverbs: He who fights and runs away ....
    You can't get blood .... You can't make a silk purse
    ....
21. What is worth a bird in the hand?
22. Complete the following phrases: As weak as ....
    As flat as .... As warm as ....
23. Finish the following sentences: Deaf as a .... Spry
    as .... Dumb as ....
24. Who was Thoth?
25. Who was Thor?

PROVERBS AND MYTHS QUIZ NUMBER THREE

Answers on page 301

1. In ancient mythology, who was Minerva?
2. What are the Muses?
3. In Roman mythology, who was the wife of Jupiter?
4. Who is the god of Sleep?
5. What is the food of the gods? The home of the gods? The
    drink of the gods?
6. What part of Achilles was vulnerable, his forehead, his left
    leg, or his right heel?
7. How did Janus differ from the other gods?
8. What are the names of the three Fates?
9. Who is said to have stolen fire from Heaven and given it to
    man?
10. What, in mythology, was known as the "Pillars of Her-
    cules"?
11. Who was the fleet-footed god of the Greeks who wore
    winged sandals?
12. In classical mythology, who was the goddess of Health?

148

13. What is a satyr?
14. What giant, in Greek mythology, supported the world?
15. The famous hair of Medusa's head is represented by which of the following: doves, laurel leaves, cupids, snakes, or flowers?
16. Where is the River Styx?
17. What golden fruit was cast among the gods, inscribed "For the Fairest"?
18. Who were the following characters in mythology: Neptune, Nemesis, Diana?
19. Who was the Roman god of war?
20. What feature was peculiar to Argus and Cyclops?
21. In mythology, who supported the universe while Atlas plucked three golden apples from the garden of the Hesperides?
22. In mythology, what did Narcissus do?
23. What did the Gorgon's head do?
24. Who were Ceres, Flora, and Pomona?
25. Aphrodite was the Greek goddess of war, love, revenge, or harvest?

PROVERBS AND MYTHS QUIZ NUMBER FOUR
Answers on page 302

1. The Achilles tendon refers to what part of the human body?
2. Judging from the statue of Venus, which one of the following subjects would she be most likely not to study: seismology, paidology, dactylology, or ornithology?
3. What was the name of the queen of the Amazons?
4. Who was Lorelei?
5. What sculptor fell in love with a statue he had made, and which came to life through the favor of Venus?
6. In mythology, of what was Vesta the goddess?
7. From what two Roman poets were most of the myths derived?
8. What was the Elysian Plain?
9. Who was the sun god in Greek mythology?
10. Who was the god of fire?
11. What goddess appeared each night in the silvery moon?
12. Who played the pipes?

13. Who was Pegasus?
14. What famous city was captured by soldiers hidden in a wooden horse?
15. What shrine did sailors seek in Greek mythology?
16. Who was the daughter of Jupiter and Juno?
17. In times of sickness, to which of the gods did the Greeks pray?
18. Which of the continents is named for a goddess?
19. What author is best known for his collection of myths?
20. King Midas had the ears of what animal?
21. What Greek goddess sprang from the sea?
22. Who dragged Hector's body three times around the walls of Troy?
23. Who was the patron of thieves and other rascals, as well as the guardian of travelers?
24. What does the name of Mars, the god of war, mean?
25. Who was Asclepius?

FROM FLORA TO REPTILIA NUMBER ONE

Answers on page 302

1. What flower is the symbol of Mother's Day?
2. Which flower is said to be arrayed even better than Solomon in all his glory?
3. Can a whale drown?
4. What is the meaning of the word "hippopotamus"?
5. Can you name five birds that cry or speak their own name?
6. Each of the following calls is peculiar to a particular type of bird. Identify the bird by the call: caw, scream, hoot.
7. A butterfly was used as the signature of what famous painter?
8. Why were ants' eggs engraved on the silver cup that was presented to Jenny Lind when she visited the United States?
9. What three things connected with baseball remind you of something with wings?
10. Name the three classifications of bees.
11. Of what state is the mistletoe the official flower?
12. What is a set of spiders?
13. What is the diet of the silkworm?
14. What grasses grow to a height of fifty or sixty feet?

15. What United States government ships are named for flowers?
16. Give four flowers which contain the names of animals.
17. How many toes has an ostrich?
18. Name two birds with the name of a city, state, or country included as a part of their names.
19. Which do you think quacks the louder: a duck or a drake?
20. In the canary family who does the singing, the male or the female?
21. Do bats lay eggs?
22. Which has the greater number of vertebrae in its neck, a sparrow or a giraffe?
23. What are motmots?
24. Could you take a bath with a zoophyte?
25. If a swan belongs to the duck family, to what family does the turkey belong?

FROM FLORA TO REPTILIA NUMBER TWO
Answers on page 303

1. What is a brood of pheasants called?
2. If you were out hunting for birds, would you shoot a jackal, a jackanapes, a jackboot, a jackdaw, or a jackpot?
3. Is ichthyology the study of plants, fishes, birds, trees, or minerals?
4. Is a macaw a bird that is allied to the owl, the parrot, crow, or sparrow?
5. Where are a crab's teeth?
6. If a person "ate like a bird" approximately how much would he eat?
7. What bird is: a church dignitary; frolicsome; a household pet; melancholy; crazy?
8. What is a caterpillar?
9. How are honey bees sold?
10. What is the figure on the weather vane on historic Faneuil Hall, in Boston?
11. What male insect lives on flowers, while the female lives on animals?
12. What nation do you associate with each of these flowers:

edelweiss, thistle, fleur-de-lis, shamrock, lotus, cornflower, rose, lily?

13. How many legs has a spider?
14. What are the four stages in the life of a moth?
15. What does the word porifera mean?
16. What is a bittern?
17. What bird uses its wings for swimming?
18. If you had flea power, how high could you jump?
19. Give the following "antsers." "Antsers" must be one word and contain the last three letters ant. Example: a prompt ant is instant. The others are: a garden ant, a far away ant, a left over ant, a trading ant, and inclined ant.
20. If you had an adder tongue, a jack in the pulpit, and a dutchman's breeches, what would you have?
21. Lame duck describes what?
22. What vertebrate animal lives the longest?
23. What is the difference between a crocodile and an alligator?
24. What is a chuckwalla?
25. What is an egret?

FROM FLORA TO REPTILIA NUMBER THREE

Answers on page 303

1. How many legs does a lobster have?
2. If an octopus has eight arms, how many does a cuttlefish have?
3. If a married man brought an alewife home could he be arrested for bigamy?
4. What is a canvas back?
5. Why is the mocking bird so called?
6. How many legs have three titmice?
7. If curfew is the ringing of a bell, what is curlew?
8. Give three common expressions using the name of a bird.
9. When you say that salmon and herring are anadromous, what do you mean?
10. What is the state flower of Florida?
11. What animal is the chief lumberman, engineer, and builder of the animal kingdom?
12. When you puff like a grampus you are imitating the sound of what animal?

13. What is a skink?
14. Name five water birds whose habitat is New England.
15. Is an earwig a bird, an insect, or a fish?
16. What two varieties of snakes grow to the largest size?
17. Why do fish swim upstream?
18. What is a cayman?
19. Can alligators eat on land?
20. The skin of only one bird has been successfully tanned. What is the bird?
21. Which of these is the national flower of Alaska: rose, daisy, forget-me-not, or dandelion?
22. What is a baby frog called?
23. The Walrus and the Carpenter had a big feed on what edible bivalve?
24. What have the following in common: dragonhead, lamb's ears, crane's bill?
25. What bird can kick hard enough to kill a man?

FROM FLORA TO REPTILIA NUMBER FOUR
Answers on page 304

1. What have the following in common: pewee, grackle, junco, dicksissel, and towhee?
2. Is a raddock a fish, a bird, or an insect?
3. What is the fat of the whale called?
4. What snake is the most poisonous?
5. Why does a snake sleep with its eyes open?
6. Why is the codfish used as the sacred emblem of Massachusetts?
7. What animal is grown commercially by sowing seed?
8. What is a grayling?
9. What amphibious animal has its tongue fastened at the front of its mouth, rather than at the back?
10. Is a sea lion really a seal?
11. Name four animals classified as reptiles.
12. Does a rattlesnake have to be coiled before it strikes?
13. What famous city was saved by the cackling of geese?
14. Geese migrate in what formation?
15. What plant is cultivated in nearly every civilized country

in the world, but is not used for either food, shelter, or clothing?

16. Name three drugs obtained from the poppy plant.
17. Mycology is the study of what?
18. Name three trees that have the name of a color in them.
19. What are flora and fauna?
20. It is easier for natives to climb up or down a pineapple tree?
21. What is the technical name for the green coloring matter in plants?
22. How can one tell a worker from a drone bee?
23. What is a brood of eagles or hawks called?
24. What bird of ancient times was trained by man to hunt?
25. "Say it with flowers": What did the bride call the bridegroom? What was his object in matrimony? How did he offer himself? What did the bride wear in her hair? What did the groom wear for the last time? What did he call her after ten years?

LITERARY QUIZ NUMBER II-A
Answers on page 304

1. In what play of Shakespeare's do we find the "Ides of March" mentioned?
2. Who wrote "Gulliver's Travels"?
3. Give the lines *preceding* the following:
   "Make me a child again just for tonight."
   "Whence all but him had fled."
   " 'Tis folly to be wise."
4. What was the name of the submarine in Jules Verne's "20,000 Leagues under the Sea"?
5. "Shoot if you must this old gray head,
   But spare your country's flag, she said."
   Who was *she?*
6. Who wrote both "Scaramouche" and "Captain Blood"?
7. From what poem does this line come: "And the children coming home from school look in at the open door"?
8. In what Shakespearean play is there a character named Caliban?
9. What well known character of fiction tilted at a windmill?

10. From what Shakespearean play is this quotation taken: "It is a wise father that knows his own child."?
11. Name four male characters from the Dickens's novel, David Copperfield.
12. Give the next line after: "Breathes there a man with soul so dead . . ."
13. In what famous novel does the character Hester Prynne appear?
14. Give the plays from which the following Shakespearean quotations are taken: "Uneasy lies the head that wears the crown." "A horse! A horse! My kingdom for a horse!" "Brevity is the soul of wit."
15. Who was the author of Don Quixote?
16. "Pilgrim's Progress" was written by which of the following: Mark Twain, John Eliot, John Bunyan, or John Keats?
17. Who was the slave who wrote a book of fables?
18. Who said "All Gaul is divided into three parts."?
19. Complete the following: "But there is no joy in Mudville . . ."?
20. Who killed what in Coleridge's "The Ancient Mariner."?
21. Does "Nicholas Nickleby" tell of life in a penitentiary, a boarding school, or a slave ship?
22. What was the last play completed by Shakespeare?
23. Who wrote "Little Men" and "Little Women"?
24. Whose daughter was Jessica, and in what famous play does she appear?
25. Who wrote "Moby Dick, or The White Whale"?

LITERARY QUIZ NUMBER II-B
Answers on page 305

1. Name three plays by George Bernard Shaw.
2. In what great novel does the character Fagin appear?
3. What was the name of Tom Sawyer's aunt?
4. "What is so rare as a day in June?" is from "Abou Ben Adhem", "The Daffodils", "The Pied Piper of Hamelin", "The Vision of Sir Launfal", or "The Barefoot Boy"?
5. Give the titles of three books which include a color.
6. In what book by a noted English author would you find the character Uriah Heep?

7. From what poem are the lines taken, and who wrote it?
   "Do you think, O blue-eyed banditti,
   Because you have scaled the wall,
   Such an old mustache as I am
   Is not a match for you all?"
8. "Robinson Crusoe" was written in which century: the 17th, 18th, 19th, or 20th?
9. Mrs. Deborah Primrose is a character in "Uncle Tom's Cabin," "Penrod," "The Vicar of Wakefield," or "Guy Mannering?"
10. Was Baron Munchausen, the writer of the ridiculously impossible adventure stories, a Russian?
11. What are the names of the Shakespearean plays in which these characters appear: Rosalind, Falstaff, Cassius, Banquo?
12. From what books do the following characters come: Scrooge, Sydney Carton, Simon Legree, Becky Sharp?
13. In the poem "Casey at the Bat," did Casey hit a home run or strike out?
14. Who wrote "The Legend of Sleepy Hollow"?
15. Who wrote the "Prince and the Pauper"?
16. What five words follow: "Water, water everywhere . . ."?
17. In what famous adventure story does the character of Long John Silver appear?
18. Give the titles of three books whose names consist of two words each beginning with the same letter.
19. Give the next line after: "Half a league, half a league, half a league onward . . ."
20. In Margaret Mitchell's "Gone with the Wind" who were the three husbands of Scarlett O'Hara?
21. What English writer is renowned for his stories of India?
22. What unsuccessful romance among the New England colonists did Longfellow write about?
23. What are the first two lines of Longfellow's poem "The Psalm of Life."?
24. What was the name of Dombey's son in Dickens's book?
25. To what historical events do the first lines of the following poems allude:
   "Listen, my children, and you shall hear . . ."?
   "The breaking waves dashed high on a stern and rock bound coast . . ."?

"By the rude bridge that arched the flood . . ."?
"Up from the south at break of day . . ."?

LITERARY QUIZ NUMBER II-C

Answers on page 306

1. From what poem are the following lines taken: "I pray thee, then, write me as one that loves his fellow men."?
2. What is a pseudonym?
3. Who said "If you have tears, prepare to shed them now."?
4. Who wrote "Of all sad words of tongue or pen, the saddest are these, it might have been."?
5. Give the next line after: "It was an ancient mariner . . ."
6. "Scintillate, scintillate, globule vivific,
   Wonderfully contemplated by men scientific,
   Elevated and poised in ether capacious,
   Resembling a coruscant gem carbonaceous."
   What poem does this parody?
7. Give the next line after: "Much have I travell'd in the realms of gold"?
8. What have the following in common: Prospero, Miranda, and Caliban?
9. These lines are from what poem: "The snow had begun in the gloaming, and busily all the night . . ."?
10. About whom was it said "Age cannot wither her nor custom stale her infinite variety."?
11. Name the book from which each of the following characters come: Portia, the March Hare, Bob Cratchit.
12. Give the real names of the persons using these literary pseudonyms: Boz, Lewis Carroll, Elia, O. Henry, Diedrich Knickerbocker, Mark Twain, Poor Richard, Uncle Remus.
13. Give the next line after: "All the world's a stage . . ."
14. What are the first two lines of Longfellow's poem "The Village Blacksmith"?
15. Who wrote "Les Miserables", and who is the principal character of the book?
16. What is the name of the little lame boy in Dickens's "The Christmas Carol"?
17. In what book do the most famous bloodhounds of literature appear?

18. Where was John Bunyan when he wrote "Pilgrim's Progress"?
19. Who was Micawber?
20. Name at least three characters from the "Last of the Mohicans."
21. Of what Shakespearean play is this the first line: "In sooth, I know not why I am so sad:"?
22. Who wrote the famous story "A Message to Garcia"?
23. In what famous book is Topsy a character?
24. "All for one, and one for all" was the motto of what group?
25. From what poem are these lines taken:
"The stag at eve had drunk his fill
Where danced the moon on Monan's rill."?

LITERARY QUIZ NUMBER II-D

Answers on page 306

1. What author used the expression "Though this be madness, yet there is method in't", and in what work?
2. In "Dr. Jekyll and Mr. Hyde", which personality was the evil one?
3. How much was one pound of flesh worth to Shylock?
4. In what book is Bill Sykes a character?
5. Who were Simon Legree, Little Nell, and Cordelia?
6. What have the following in common: Wickfield, Heep, Trotwood, and Micawber?
7. Give the next line and the title of the poem from which the following lines are taken:
"It was many and many a year ago . . ."
"Shoot if you must this old gray head . . ."
"For men may come and men may go . . ."
8. In what story by Dickens were the unknown children named in alphabetical order?
9. In what book is the "Valley of the Shadow of Death" mentioned?
10. John Watson, M.D., is a character in what book by what author?
11. Was Hiawatha, in Longfellow's poem of the same name, a boy or a girl?

12. Who first told the story of George Washington and his hatchet?
13. In what novel does the expression "Barkis is willin' " appear?
14. Who was known as the Quaker poet?
15. Give the name of the poem and the next line after: "One if by land and two if by sea . . .".
16. What great author died in Kensington, England, on July 20, 1896?
17. Who killed Macbeth?
18. Who is the best known Indiana poet?
19. What authors created the following characters: Shylock, The Headless Horseman, Rhett Butler, Sherlock Holmes?
20. Which of the following books are from the New Testament, and which from the Old Testament: Luke, Psalms, Daniel, Jonah, and Revelation?
21. Who wrote "The Strange Case of Dr. Jekyll and Mr. Hyde"?
22. Who wrote "My Battle"?
23. Dick Swiveller is a character in "Penrod," "Gulliver's Travels," "Bleak House," or "The Old Curiosity Shop"?
24. Complete the following quotation: "Won't you step into my parlor, said the . . . .".
25. Name four persons in fiction or folklore who were famous for their hair.

HOW'S YOUR HISTORY? QUIZ NUMBER I-A

Answers on page 307

1. What event in United States history was known as Seward's Folly?
2. In what century did Columbus discover America? In what century did the Pilgrims land in Plymouth?
3. Name one of the three states which has joined the Union since 1900.
4. During the Civil War what group was known as the Copperheads?
5. Give the years of the following great fires: Chicago, Boston, and San Francisco.

6. To which one of the French Kings was Marie Antoinette married?
7. What event of world wide interest occurred on December 11th, 1936?
8. By whom was the North pole discovered?
9. To what historical event do the following lines refer: "One if by land and two if by sea, and I on the opposite shore will be"?
10. What tragic event in American history occurred at the Pan American Exposition on September 6th, 1901?
11. Was New Hampshire one of the thirteen original states?
12. What famous king could not speak the language of his country?
13. What is or was a shin plaster?
14. Which was the first state to be admitted to the Union after the original thirteen?
15. The famous cry of the French Revolution was: "Give me liberty or give me death", "Down with Napoleon", "Liberty, equality, fraternity", or "Freedom and justice for all"?
16. What ancient ruler wept because he had no more worlds to conquer?
17. During what year did the United States have a war with Spain?
18. Who was the Generalissimo of the Allied Armies in France during the World War?
19. What were the names of the states in the Confederacy?
20. In what year did the Boston Tea Party take place?
21. In what year did the Boxer Rebellion occur in China?
22. When did the World War begin?
23. What did the famous Liberty Bell announce when it was first rung?
24. Queen Victoria celebrated two Jubilees. What were they?
25. What assassination in 1914 proved to be the concrete act which hastened the declaration of the World War?

HOW'S YOUR HISTORY? QUIZ NUMBER I-B

Answers on page 308

1. What modern country had three Kings in one year?
2. What was "the shot heard round the world"?

3. Identify these patriots by these quotations:
   "Give me liberty or give me death".
   "I regret that I have but one life to give for my country".
   "Stand your ground. Don't fire unless fired upon, but if they want war, let it begin here".?
4. Who were called the pen, the tongue, and the sword of the American Revolution?
5. Who was the Captain of the Mayflower?
6. The War of 1812 was fought between what two countries?
7. What American Generals were known as "the immortal three"?
8. At what city did Cornwallis surrender in the Revolution?
9. What famous family was enriched by the Battle of Waterloo?
10. How many amendments to the Constitution have been repealed?
11. What famous battle was fought after the War of 1812 had officially ended?
12. From what country did the United States purchase the Virgin Islands?
13. What country presented the Statue of Liberty to the United States?
14. Which country was the first to recognize the United States?
15. What is the name applied to a government, such as that of Great Britain, where there is a King but the actual power lies in the hands of a cabinet or Parliament?
16. With what countries was Holland allied during the World War?
17. Did the French and Indian War take place before or after the American Revolution?
18. Why is the month of April so fateful to the United States?
19. How many queens have ruled in France?
20. Did the United States flag ever have more than thirteen stripes?
21. What did General Grant do with the sword of General Lee after the latter's surrender at Appomattox?
22. For whom was the Liberty Bell tolling when it cracked?
23. What anachronism exists in the famous painting of Washington crossing the Delaware?
24. What was the name given to the earliest Egyptian writing?

25. Of what was Alfred Dreyfus, of the famous Dreyfus case, accused?

HOW'S YOUR HISTORY? QUIZ NUMBER I-C
Answers on page 308

1. What country was once ruled by the Emperor Maximilian?
2. What were the three chief countries that colonized America?
3. Name two of the three generals never defeated in battle.
4. Did Columbus make three or four voyages to America?
5. Who crowned Napoleon Emperor of France?
6. What Indian Chief was responsible for the Custer massacre?
7. What did it cost to send an ounce of mail by pony express?
8. Arrange the following characters in historical order: Abraham Lincoln, William Shakespeare, George Washington, Moses, and Julius Caesar.
9. Who commanded the English fleet at the battle of Trafalgar?
10. Connect each of the following poems with an historical event: "Barbara Frietchie", "Paul Revere's Ride", "In Flanders Field".
11. What was the popular war cry of the Americans during the Spanish American War?
12. What was Columbus seeking when he accidentally discovered America?
13. What was the name of the central governing body of the American colonies during the Revolutionary War?
14. What was the name of Admiral Dewey's flagship?
15. What did Marie Antoinette and Mary Queen of Scots have in common?
16. What war was won by a wooden horse?
17. What privilege has the state of Texas that no other state has?
18. What state has been under six flags, and what were they?
19. When will there be a new star added to the United States flag?
20. What did the Governor of North Carolina say to the Governor of South Carolina?

21. How many decisive naval battles were fought in the World War?
22. What two great English houses fought the War of the Roses?
23. Who were the King and Queen of Spain at the time Columbus left for America?
24. At what battle during the World War did the phrase "they shall not pass" originate?
25. What city of the United States was capital of the country for one day only?

HOW'S YOUR HISTORY? QUIZ NUMBER I-D

Answers on page 309

1. In what war was there a battle between the Monitor and the Merrimac?
2. What was the Diet of Worms?
3. What was the trade of Paul Revere?
4. From what town in England did the Pilgrims come to Plymouth, Massachusetts?
5. Might Napoleon and George Washington have visited each other?
6. What year is marked on Plymouth Rock?
7. Give the date of the landing at Jamestown.
8. What were the names of Columbus' three ships?
9. What British General of the Revolutionary War was nick-named "Gentleman Johnny"?
10. What are the first ten amendments to the United States Constitution called?
11. Give the last six words of Lincoln's Gettysburg address?
12. How many names were signed to the Declaration of Independence?
13. Where is England's Unknown Soldier buried?
14. Who were "Rogers' Rangers"?
15. What large country is ruled by a Shah?
16. Whom did Napoleon divorce to marry whom?
17. Name three wars which occurred during the 19th century.
18. What Emperor had a morbid fear of cats?
19. Who is the English prototype of Uncle Sam?

20. The twenty-fourth of May is observed as what legal holiday in Canada?
21. Who won the battle of Bunker Hill, the Americans or the British?
22. What were the names of the three ships involved in the Boston Tea Party?
23. Name the three largest cities of the Colonies at the outbreak of the American Revolution.
24. What countries are known as the A B C powers?
25. Who was the most famous son of Henry the Second of England?

GENERAL QUIZ NUMBER XIV-A
Answers on page 309

1. How many years does it require to produce a tree large enough for lumber?
2. If you had a funicular, would you ride on it, eat it, sell it to the junk man, or give it away?
3. Is puce a color, a disease, an animal, or a flower?
4. Name three Indians helpful to the early American colonists.
5. In "Uncle Tom's Cabin", Eliza crossed what river on the ice?
6. What is the Kohinoor?
7. Name four common words beginning with the letter "Z".
8. What is a pentagon?
9. How much larger is a circle four inches in diameter than a circle two inches in diameter?
10. Is a cataclysm an underground tomb, a set of questions and answers of a religious nature, or a catastrophe?
11. Give in order of size the five next units of military organization lower than a brigade.
12. What is a sad iron?
13. In what kind of advertisements do you find the word "kapok"? What is it, and what is it used for?
14. What word does not belong in the following group, and why: helium, hydrogen, copper, and nitrogen?
15. What is reveille?
16. What is a codger?

17. What is the only animal whose upper jaw is movable?
18. What is an amphibian?
19. Can you give two familiar quotations using the word "shoes"?
20. If three candles were burning side by side, one red, one white, and one green, what color would the light be?
21. Candle pin and duck pins refer to what sport?
22. If you had a piece of ambergris would you eat it, sell it, or throw it away?
23. How many hairs are there on your head?
24. Which is lighter in weight, a good egg or a bad egg?
25. Lucrative means most nearly which of the following: atrocious, fraudulent, wise, profitable, or abundant?

GENERAL QUIZ NUMBER XIV-B
Answers on page 310

1. Does the window sash hold the sills, the glass, or the jamb?
2. What is the average period of the moon's revolution around the earth?
3. Does the ocean contain more salt or chlorine?
4. What is a citadel?
5. Why are red and green used as colors in traffic lights?
6. What very beautiful flower grows from the smallest seed in the world?
7. What does an Englishman call a railway coach?
8. What have sheepshank, bowline, and sheet bend in common?
9. What do hunters mean when they say that an animal freezes?
10. If you haven't a thermometer, the best way to test the bath water for the baby is to put your finger in it, test it with your elbow, or put the baby in it and see if he turns red?
11. One of these is not a nationally known fraternal order: Elks, Moose, Giraffes, Lions, Eagles. Which is it?
12. If patricide is killing one's father, and suicide is killing oneself, what is lapicide?
13. Is the backbone of a camel curved upward in the middle?
14. Is a shekel a real coin?

15. What is the meaning of the philatelic expression "a first day cover"?
16. What is known as the universal solvent?
17. Who went "down to the bottom of the sea"? Who was shot? Who was hung? Who was killed by a fall? Who was killed in a railroad wreck?
18. Why do we have an extra day in leap year?
19. What does the word planet mean?
20. Who wrote the famous "Merry Widow" waltz?
21. How many different types of skis are there?
22. What caused the death of "darling Clementine"?
23. How much is 3 times 3, minus 3, divided by 3?
24. What is the great vein of the neck called?
25. Do you think that the average man could pick up and carry a cubic foot of gold?

GENERAL QUIZ NUMBER XIV-C

Answers on page 311

1. An army ten miles long marches ten miles a day. How long would it take a messenger leaving the rear of the column to reach the head of the column if he traveled twenty miles a day?
2. What does S O S mean?
3. Is belladonna a dancer, a plant, a painting, or an instrument?
4. A foible is a myth or legend, a peculiarity of character, or a clumsy movement?
5. In how many different positions could you seat five people at a table?
6. In sawing a piece of wood with the grain, would you use a rip-saw, a cut-off saw, or a hack saw?
7. Who said "Better to remain silent and be thought a fool, than to speak and remove all doubt."?
8. What is the difference between a perennial and an annual plant?
9. Supply the correct month in the following: What is so rare as a day in ....? It's June in ....? April showers bring .... flowers?
10. Name three flowers that mention time in their names.

11. What is a stiletto?
12. What is peculiar about the "Winged Victory"?
13. How many feet are there in a military pace?
14. Why can't a Rocky Mountain canary live in a cage?
15. What state has always been famous for its mint juleps?
16. How high do ocean waves go?
17. What does a red silk star on a postman's uniform mean?
18. What are the six greatest technical developments since 1900?
19. What per cent of the earth's surface is water?
20. What is a toby?
21. How many tropics are there?
22. Name the central star in the solar system.
23. Can you name five means of transportation beginning with the letter "T"?
24. What is a Martian?
25. Why was the name Great Britain adopted?

GENERAL QUIZ NUMBER XIV-D

Answers on page 311

1. What is the difference between glue and mucilage?
2. What is said to be the oldest cosmetic in history?
3. If meet means to join or intersect, and meat is what we eat, what does mete mean?
4. What is a solarium?
5. If you suffer from acute coryza, what is the matter with you?
6. The tall fur hat worn by a drum major is called what?
7. In Colonial days, what was an ordinary?
8. For what do the letters G.O.P. stand as applied to the Republican party?
9. What was the first talking picture, and who was the star?
10. What would you call a person who is very loquacious?
11. Has the United States government ever been out of debt?
12. Name three breeds of dogs beginning with the letter "S".
13. What is a newel post?
14. Who invented bi-focal glasses?
15. What farming implement looks like a question mark?
16. If you had the following four breeds of hens, what color

eggs would they lay: Brown Leghorn; White Wyandotte; Black Minorca; Barred Plymouth Rock?

17. If you had a million dollars and gave me ten cents, how much would you have left?
18. One of the following is included among the seven wonders of the ancient world: pyramids of Egypt, Cleopatra's Needle, Niagara Falls, or King Solomon's Temple?
19. If you had a tucket would you eat it, wear it, or play it?
20. What is a tuber? What is a tuba?
21. Distinguish between alto and contralto.
22. Where are the following mountains: Matterhorn, Fujiyama, Mt. McKinley?
23. Would you be going east or west if you were going from Reno to Los Angeles?
24. What lakes in Ireland are the subject of many songs?
25. What country besides the United States has the abbreviation U.S.A.?

GENERAL QUIZ NUMBER XV-A

Answers on page 312

1. If your firm sent you to Nicaragua, would you sail for Africa, West Indies, Central America, or South America?
2. Give the names of three flowers with the word "sweet" as part of the name.
3. What is the longest and shortest day of the year?
4. Why is a billion dollars in London worth a thousand times as much as a billion dollars in New York?
5. Is it true that the Liberty Bell cracked when ringing Independence on July 4, 1776?
6. If a clock is 5 hours and 40 minutes slow, how fast is it?
7. The Lexington and Saratoga are sea-going vessels named for land battles. For what are they used?
8. A bonanza is a Mexican general, a rich ore deposit, a tropical tree?
9. On which side of a printed page are the even numbers in a book?
10. What have the following in common: gingham, calico, and organdie?

11. Complete the following: He eats like a ......? He swims like a ....? She sings like a ....?
12. What number, when doubled, equals twice as much as when squared?
13. Name three plants the leaves of which are used for food?
14. What part of the egg becomes the chick?
15. Name four sports that begin with the letter "A".
16. Name three bivalves found in New England waters.
17. Who ranks first in the President's Cabinet?
18. Name three herbs used in cooking.
19. What was President Garfield's full name?
20. The names of the Three Wise Men were: Wynken, Blynken, and Nod; Athos, Porthos, and Aramis; Gaspar, Melchior, and Balthazar?
21. Black Maria is another name for typhoid fever, a police patrol wagon, Queen Marie IV of France, whiskey, or a famous cook?
22. A talisman is a native of what country?
23. When if ever, does February have five Sundays?
24. By what other name are the West Indies called?
25. Are there more states east or west of the Mississippi River?

GENERAL QUIZ NUMBER XV-B

Answers on page 312

1. If a man had a wolf, a goat, and a load of hay on one side of the river, and he wanted to get them to the other side in a boat that would hold just himself and one of the other three, how could he do it? If he left the two animals and carried the hay, the wolf would eat the goat. If he took the wolf, the goat would eat the hay.
2. Is a shallot a shoulder wrap, a sail boat, a fish, or a vegetable?
3. The capital cities of what states are names of former presidents?
4. Where is Miami University?
5. About how many acres did Washington have at Mt. Vernon?
6. What do the words Nova Scotia mean?
7. What is Irak?

8. Are there any volcanoes in Alaska?
9. Of what state is mistletoe the official flower?
10. What bank of a river is called the "right" bank?
11. What would you have if you had a member of the rodent family? The bovine family? The porcine family? The venison family?
12. If a room contained a heterogeneous collection, would the collection be unusual, sacred, miscellaneous, weird, or valuable?
13. Is a procrastinator a baby carriage, one whose motto is "Manana", or a person with a big family?
14. What is the masculine of the following: heifer, ewe, hind, witch, doe?
15. Why is Pennsylvania known as the Keystone State?
16. Where did the superstition originate that it is unlucky to spill salt?
17. For what is General Ambrose Burnsides remembered?
18. What do the abbreviations in the following names stand for: Cristobal, C.Z.; Hilo, T.H.; Mexico, D.F.?
19. If your business was manufacturing mohair fabrics, you would have a natural interest in the Angora goat market, the cotton industry, the camel industry, or the flax crop?
20. If Maine extends the farthest east, which of the following states extends the farthest west: California, Washington, Oregon?
21. What would you do with a nimrod: fish with it, hunt with it, mend a boat with it, or spank a naughty child with it?
22. "Oh, what a lovely compote!" said the Duchess of Umph, as she took out her false teeth, finished her stewed fruit, sipped her wine, or glanced covertly at the handsome butler?
23. Is a kumquat a South American preserve, a Latin novel of the 4th century, a species of Hawaiian pineapple, or a Chinese fruit?
24. An elm tree has forty branches; each branch has two twigs. If there are two acorns on each twig, how many acorns are there on the tree?
25. A man has four cans of paint: blue, red, yellow, and black. What would he use to paint a chair purple? To paint it brown? To paint it green? To paint it orange?

GENERAL QUIZ NUMBER XV-C

Answers on page 313

1. Exactly where is the oft-mentioned Mason-Dixon Line?
2. Is a gambit used in ice hockey, badminton, or chess?
3. What is the difference between an isotherm and an isobar?
4. What seas are referred to as the "Seven Seas"?
5. Where is Lake Lucerne?
6. Of what island is Port au Prince the capital?
7. What are the Doldrums?
8. Is the Rosetta Stone still existent?
9. If the Green Mountains are in Vermont, where is the Red River?
10. If two sides of a three sided figure are equal it is called a scalene triangle, an eternal triangle, or an isosceles triangle?
11. If you had a gherkin would you put it on, eat it, put it out to pasture, or decorate the house with it?
12. What one color would you associate with these words: skin, bird, cross, and tape?
13. Which end of a cucumber has no seeds?
14. What cards must you hold in your hand in order to have a royal flush in poker?
15. If you were a discobolus, would you be a politician, a doctor, an athlete, a lawyer, or a dentist?
16. What are adult male seals called?
17. If a camel is noted for its humps, and a leopard for its spots, for what is a camelopard noted?
18. To what do these names apply, besides cities: Hamburg, Concord, Tokay, and Malaga?
19. Can you eat a granadilla?
20. Is a crepe suzette a kind of cloth, something to eat, a flirt, or something to wear?
21. Is a loquat a fruit, a fish, a bird, or an animal?
22. Name the six men used in a game of chess.
23. What was the marvel of the Sixties: the Pony Express, the Wright Brothers' first flying machine, the initial publication of "Uncle Tom's Cabin"?
24. There are eight teams in the National Baseball League. What are their names and their nicknames?
25. Locate San Diego and Santiago.

GENERAL QUIZ NUMBER XV-D
Answers on page 313

1. What heavyweight boxer won the world's championship in Sydney, Australia, and lost it later in Havana, Cuba?
2. If you were playing poker and the dealer dealt you a royal flush, and himself four aces, what would you do?
3. Give the nicknames of three of these five colleges: Fordham, Holy Cross, Boston College, Duke, Southern California?
4. If you were goal tender on a hockey team, there would be how many of the following number of players on the ice with you: 6, 5, 11, 10, 9?
5. The inhabitants of Pitcairn Island are said to be descended from whom?
6. What state has only three counties?
7. Within what city is the famous Hollywood community located?
8. Name two great kingdoms that are not countries.
9. What state of the Union has the longest name?
10. Can you name three famous New England products?
11. If a stilt is a piece of wood used as a support, what is a Stilton?
12. The onion is a member of what family?
13. What have the following in common: cashew, filbert, pistachio?
14. Name three of the first six presidents.
15. What is the plural of young geese?
16. Name three forms of water.
17. If a baseball player hits for .333, how many times does he get a hit?
18. Make a word out of the first letters of each of the Great Lakes.
19. On which island of the Philippines is the city of Manila?
20. If you had a capon, would you wear it, kick it, or stuff it?
21. Is Honolulu on the island of Hawaii?
22. Give a sentence that contains all the letters of the alphabet.
23. What is halite?
24. To what family does the turkey belong?
25. A light comedy actress is sometimes called a soudanese, a soubrette, or a sobriquet?

GENERAL QUIZ NUMBER XVI-A

Answers on page 314

1. Which is the heavier, a quart of milk or a quart of cream?
2. What organ controls the sense of balance in the body?
3. To what does still life painting refer?
4. Is a courante a bird, a dance, or a messenger?
5. What do you associate with the names Currier and Ives?
6. When is twilight?
7. In what kind of advertisements do you find the word lapin?
8. In the fraction 3/4 which figure is the denominator and which the numerator?
9. At what age does a horse become an aged horse?
10. What makes a Mexican jumping bean jump?
11. How long is a generation?
12. What is barter?
13. At an airport, which has the right of way, an ascending or a descending plane?
14. What is a certified check?
15. In what free republic can no white man vote?
16. What is the distinction between lava and larva?
17. Identify the following gangsters to the extent of giving their names from these nicknames: Scarface, Baby Face, Legs.
18. Where in the human body are the three bones known as the hammer, anvil, and stirrup located?
19. What is a ferrule?
20. Who originated toboggans?
21. Under what department of the government is the patent office?
22. If you were told to tether a cow, what would you do to it?
23. Among the old gods of Greece and Rome who was known as the goddess of wisdom?
24. What is the primary use of cowhide?
25. If a mongoose is a small cat-like animal, what is a monsoon?

GENERAL QUIZ NUMBER XVI-B

Answers on page 314

1. What are Lucy Stoners?
2. If you had a soiree, would you eat it, go to it, ride it, or keep it?

3. What is dromomania?
4. By law a motorist must drive on which side of the road in Canada, England, and Sweden?
5. What is the lowest order of English knights?
6. How much would $1,000 in new one dollar bills weigh?
7. What is the difference between a dark horse and a charley horse?
8. Which is the only female deer that has antlers?
9. What is a dum-dum bullet?
10. With what art is Ruth St. Denis' name associated?
11. What did Ponce de Leon seek in Florida?
12. What is the green eyed monster?
13. If squatty means short, what does squatter mean?
14. What are the four phases of the moon?
15. Which sex is most afflicted with color blindness?
16. What name is applied to each of the two springs in a watch?
17. What does the word postillion mean?
18. The Morse code is composed of what characters and sounds?
19. Why does ice float?
20. What American port is entered through Ambrose Channel?
21. What have the following in common: brace and bit, hammer, miter box, square?
22. Does honey always have the same flavor?
23. Which one of the following is the head of the Church of England: the Pope, the King of England, or the Archbishop of Canterbury?
24. What is the date of Hallowe'en?
25. What birds are used to carry messages?

GENERAL QUIZ NUMBER XVI-C

Answers on page 315

1. What is the beam of a ship?
2. Name six breeds of cats.
3. What is the color of a silver fox?
4. In what part of the year is Indian summer?
5. Can objects be seen clearly through a translucent body?
6. What is a Swami?
7. By what other name is Memorial Day known?

8. Where is the famous "Flirtation Walk"?
9. What is a tine?
10. How many sails has a prairie schooner?
11. Where are most automobile plates made?
12. Whom do we call "buttons", and why?
13. Distinguish between catacomb, cataclysm, and catamount.
14. What is the difference between the ancient Roman circus and the present day circus?
15. What do each of the following refer to: canine, feline, equine, and bovine?
16. Differentiate between an atheist and an agnostic.
17. Would you lead an unbridled horse by the forelock or the fetlock?
18. Identify the following: yellow jacket, blue jacket, pea jacket.
19. What is a hob? What is a hobble-de-hoy?
20. If a sand bar is in a river, and a handle bar on a bicycle, where would you look for an isobar?
21. If Walla-Walla is a city what is a chuckwalla?
22. What is the difference between a typhoon, a buffoon, and a pontoon?
23. If a blacksmith is one who works in iron, what is a white-smith?
24. In the seal family, what is a male, a female, and a baby seal called?
25. What is the difference between a matador and a picador in a bull fight?

GENERAL QUIZ NUMBER XVI-D

Answers on page 316

1. If the husband of a duchess is a duke, what is a ship's husband?
2. If you had a zoril would you eat it, put it around your neck, bury it, or sing to it?
3. What is the difference between convex and concave?
4. If a censor is a critic, what is a censer?
5. If a person is afflicted with strabismus, what's the matter with him?
6. What is a wallaby?

7. What is a protocol?
8. What is the distinction between an eruption and an irruption?
9. A gemsbok is a kind of bird, fish, flower, or animal?
10. What is a Duroc-Jersey?
11. If you had a flapjack, a bootjack, and a wagon jack, what would you do with them?
12. What is the Hegira?
13. Define cruise, crews, and cruse.
14. What is the difference between a latitudinarian, a valetudinarian, and a valedictorian?
15. What is a colander?
16. Is a sciurus carolinensis a plant, a fish, or a rodent?
17. What is the difference between a billy goat and a billet doux?
18. When does an aviator become an Ace?
19. What are each of the following colors: chartreuse, vermilion, indigo, carmine?
20. Why is the court of Great Britain named the Court of St. James?
21. When you aim a rifle at a target at any range is the barrel above, in line with, or below the target?
22. Why are white clothes preferred to black in the tropics?
23. Of what people is Romany the language?
24. If a lentil is a bean or a pea, what is a lintel?
25. In what city is Johns Hopkins University?

HOMO SAPIENS MALE AND FEMALE II-A
Answers on page 316

1. Who was William Frederick Cody?
2. What English author is frequently referred to as "G.B.S."?
3. Who discovered the South Pole?
4. Who were known by the following names: Father of Anglers, Father of Jests, Old Hickory, The Rail Splitter, The Scourge of God, the Swedish Nightingale?
5. Who said "I came, I saw, I conquered"?
6. Who was the first secretary of the treasury?
7. During the Crimean War what English woman became famous as a nurse?

8. What are the professional names of the following women: Mrs. Guthrie McClintock, Mrs. Paul C. Wilson, Mrs. Charles MacArthur, Mrs. Sinclair Lewis?
9. What Scandinavian is famous for his books of fairy tales?
10. Who cut the Gordian knot?
11. Who is credited with having written the Declaration of Independence?
12. What Scotch Queen was beheaded by Queen Elizabeth?
13. Who is the best known Indiana poet?
14. What celebrated woman author lived at Orchard House, in Concord, Massachusetts?
15. Who was Calamity Jane?
16. What man first talked about the "power of the press"?
17. For whom did who spread out his cloak over a mud puddle?
18. Which John did Pocahontas marry: John Rolfe, John Smith, John Cabot, or John Alden?
19. Lord Beaconsfield is better known by what name?
20. Who is the present poet laureate of England?
21. Who was known as the Man of Destiny?
22. What man is referred to as "The Empire Builder"?
23. Who said: "There never was a good war or a bad peace"?
24. Can a porcupine throw his quills?
25. What was the name of the boy who stood on the burning deck?

HOMO SAPIENS MALE AND FEMALE II-B

Answers on page 317

1. Name five famous bachelors of history.
2. Who was Philip Nolan?
3. What do the names George Sand, Michael Strange and George Eliot have in common?
4. With what sports do you associate the following: Glenn Cunningham, Eddie Shore, Lawson Little, Don Budge, Dizzy Dean, and Gene Tunney?
5. Who wrote under the nom de plume of Poor Richard?
6. Give the first names of these famous composers: Mendelssohn, Beethoven, and Brahms.
7. Who said the classic lines "Why don't you speak for yourself, John"?

8. Name three presidents that have the double "o" in their last names.
9. Who wrote the following books: "Northwest Passage", "An American Doctor's Odyssey" and "How To Win Friends and Influence People"?
10. Who composed the opera Faust?
11. Name the six wives of Henry the Eighth.
12. De Soto discovered what?
13. Name a set of brothers in each of the following sports: baseball, hockey, and track.
14. What have Handel, Mozart, and Gounod in common?
15. What are the last names of these writers: James Fenimore ...., Robert Louis ...., Hans Christian ......, Elizabeth Barrett ....?
16. What president wrote a history of the United States in five hundred words?
17. Who was known as the "March King"?
18. Who was Nokomis?
19. What famous dramatist was married to Anne Hathaway?
20. What president's daughter had a color named for her?
21. George Washington and Thomas Jefferson had wives whose first name was the same. What was it?
22. Who was the wife of King Arthur?
23. What was the pen name of Samuel Clemens?
24. Who wrote "Anna Christie"?
25. Whom did Robin Hood love?

HOMO SAPIENS MALE AND FEMALE II-C

Answers on page 318

1. What civil war general wrote a best selling novel?
2. What were the names of the three musketeers?
3. Who wrote "The Man Without a Country"?
4. What famous composer wrote some of his greatest works after becoming deaf?
5. With what sports do you associate the following people: Patty Berg, Tommy Hitchcock, "Pie" Traynor?
6. Who was known as "the autocrat of the breakfast table"?
7. Who was the first Englishman to travel around the world?

8. What was the real name of the detective story writer S. S. Van Dine?

9. What English poet laureate is buried in an upright position in Westminster Abbey?

10. Who is the author of "She Stoops to Conquer"?

11. Who discovered the St. Lawrence River?

12. What famous poet swam the Hellespont?

13. To which Jackson in history was the name "Stonewall" given and to which the name "Old Hickory"?

14. Who said that the farmer at Concord "fired the shot heard round the world"?

15. One of America's best known playwrights wrote "Elizabeth the Queen". What is his name?

16. With what sports do you associate the following: Jimmie Foxx, Jim Londos, Gene Sarazen, and Ellsworth Vines?

17. What have the following in common: Booth, Guiteau, and Czolgosz?

18. Who wrote "A Doll's House"?

19. What author created the character Captain Blood?

20. Who was the bravest of King Arthur's Knights?

21. Give the last names of the following: James Montgomery ......, Howard Chandler ......, Charles Dana ....

22. Balboa discovered what?

23. Who was called the Quaker poet?

24. Who were Boz and Phiz?

25. The rescue of what woman caused a ten year war?

HOMO SAPIENS MALE AND FEMALE II-D

Answers on page 318

1. What have the following in common: Gilbert Stuart, John Singleton Copley, and Benjamin West?

2. What have John Calvin, John Huss, and John Knox in common?

3. What are the last names of: Harriet Beecher ......, Edgar Allan ......, Ralph Waldo ......?

4. Who was the first poet laureate of England?

5. William Sidney Porter is better known by what other name?

6. Who wrote "Alice In Wonderland"?

7. What are the last names of these "Sir Isaac's": Sir Isaac (shorthand); Sir Isaac (gravity); Sir Isaac (angler)?
8. Was Omar Khayyam a real or legendary figure?
9. Who was Edmond Dantes?
10. What American playwright received the Pulitzer prize three times?
11. Who was Mary Todd?
12. Who was the "henpecked philosopher"?
13. What man bought Manhattan from the Indians?
14. What American Admiral was called the "hero of Manila"?
15. Who was Virginia Dare?
16. What writer used the pen name of "Uncle Remus"?
17. What American author is generally regarded as the originator of the modern detective story?
18. Who wrote Westward Ho?
19. What discovery is credited to William Harvey, English physician?
20. Whose sweetheart was named Minnehaha?
21. What Austrian composer's three sons were also composers?
22. What famous artist invented the wheelbarrow?
23. Who wrote "Bleak House"?
24. In mythology, who adjudged Venus the fairest of the goddesses?
25. Who was the most envied woman in December of 1936?

HERE ARE THE ANSWERS....YOU ASK THE QUESTIONS. ....II-A

Answers on page 319

1. The population must be at least 12,000 to receive this name.
2. The first is a liquid measure of four quarts; the second a tape or binding.
3. Both Eddie Cantor and Papa Dionne have this distinction.
4. This is the seaman's term for the hemp used in calking boats.
5. This word means a coarse linen cloth which has been stiffened. It was a common in the early days of our country.
6. This famous phrase of self-improvement was originated by Emile Coué.

7. These two words which sound similar refer to a famous painter and a breed of cattle respectively.
8. This man was noted for both his tea and his sailing of yachts.
9. Here is the significance of these three dates: the first marked the beginning of the First World War; the second the date of United States entry; the third the signing of the Armistice.
10. Here are their nicknames: Evergreen; Lone Star; Green Mountain; Blue Grass; Granite; Nutmeg.
11. It is a small island in the Bermuda group, and is noted for having the largest floating drydock in the world.
12. There is 240 pounds difference; the first is 2,240 pounds, the second 2,000 pounds.
13. It's divided into six periods of four hours each.
14. You see it first because light travels so much faster than sound.
15. Sirius, the Dog Star, the Vega have this distinction.
16. He was the first great United States naval hero.
17. This term is applied to a drug that produces deep sleep.
18. This term is applied to a ship's jailhouse.
19. It's a statue in Egypt which gave out musical notes when the sun rose and again when it set.
20. It's just a four syllable word for homesickness.
21. This is a bag-like device raised on a pole to determine the direction of the wind.
22. Water in the cells freezes and bursts them.
23. This famous surrender of history occurred at Appomattox.
24. This is the measurement of one half mile in feet.
25. It's the scientific study of languages and their structure.

HERE ARE THE ANSWERS....YOU ASK THE QUESTIONS. . . . II-B

Answers on page 319

1. The first means a copy of the original by the originator, while the second means a copy made by someone else.
2. Airplane, radium, antiseptics and antitoxins, X-ray, radio, and telephone.
3. This fruit was frequently used on the designs of Colonial furniture because it was considered a symbol of hospitality.

4. When the highest section of steel is placed, steel workers display it to indicate the fact.

5. This refers to an official document or letter issued by the Pope and is so called because the parchment is sealed with a leaden seal, or bulla.

6. This famous battle, for which a London square was named, was fought between France and Spain on the one side, and England on the other.

7. It is the name used to describe a young salmon.

8. His name was Casabianca.

9. This term describes places on the earth's surface which are diametrically opposite to each other.

10. These three letters stand for a term which is applied to a telephone switchboard and means "Private branch exchange".

11. This is a New Yorker's term for that part of the city around Times Square. It also applies nautically to that part of the seas between 40 and 50 degrees north and south of the equator.

12. This stands for nitre in the chemical alphabet.

13. The Strait of Gibraltar and the Suez Canal are the two outlets.

14. The first means to scatter, the second to dip in.

15. Each one of them represents approximately 280,674 people.

16. This word means both an apartment and level.

17. The first is a foreigner, the second a specialist in mental diseases.

18. This word is used to describe what is left in a pipe after smoking.

19. You would look for this famous island in the pancreas of the stomach.

20. This race is a mixture of French and Spanish.

21. It can't jump unless the temperature is at least 62 degrees Fahrenheit.

22. Dwt. is the abbreviation.

23. This strange paradox occurs on the 180th meridian.

24. The word describes a self-evident truth.

25. It's the furry pouch worn with kilts.

Answers on page 320

1. The first is a wig, and the second that sounds similar, means a dark colored tobacco grown in Louisiana.
2. This word describes a three legged stand or support.
3. This botanical term describes the stem of a flower.
4. According to Einstein time is the answer.
5. This title was accorded to the King of Siam.
6. This is the name of a large diamond which became part of the English Crown Jewels in 1849.
7. This word describes a bell tower, especially one built separately from a church.
8. This describes a moon that is more than half full, yet not quite full, as the word itself means protuberant or convex.
9. The only one still in existence is the Pyramids of Egypt.
10. The first is a fur bearing animal, and the second, although pronounced the same, means a bird of the swallow family.
11. There were one hundred and two passengers in this famous boat.
12. The discovery of dynamite enabled him to endow this famous prize.
13. This stands for eighty-four in Roman numerals.
14. It is called the nadir.
15. It's a baker's long flat wooden shovel for reaching into the oven.
16. This refers to a water wheel which gets its water from the top.
17. Geological survey places this in Pierce County, a few miles west of Devil's Lake, North Dakota.
18. This is another name for Joan of Arc, who led the French against the English at the siege of Orleans.
19. The word refers to a row of hay racked together.
20. One means the external ear, and the other a deity supposed to foretell the future.
21. The first is the foot of an animal, the second, which is twice the first, refers to a banana-like fruit.
22. This famous pass connects India and Afghanistan.
23. It's the old bridge that connected the Doge's palace with the prison in Venice.

24. This phrase originated from the old custom of breaking a craftsman's stone when he failed to pay his debts.
25. The first is a small firearm, the second an old gold coin of Spain and France worth about $3.92.

HERE ARE THE ANSWERS....YOU ASK THE QUESTIONS. . . . II-D

Answers on page 320

1. It's called a paddy field.
2. It's the motto of the Boy Scouts of America.
3. He was born in 1564 and died in 1616.
4. It means a candlenut tree and also a receptacle for wine.
5. This word describes a person who classifies diseases.
6. Bear, beaver, buffalo, and baboon answer this question.
7. It's the medical term for baldness.
8. Translated it means "One out of many".
9. The Yellowstone National Park has this distinction.
10. This is the term for the mineral sought by the alchemists which would, by mere contact, transmute baser metals into gold.
11. The S.S. Savannah, which left Savannah May 22 and arrived in Liverpool, England, June 20, 1819, has this distinction.
12. This word refers to the troops of the Australian and New Zealand Army Corps.
13. It was named the Victory, and is now a training ship at Southampton, England.
14. He was the student in the story of the same name, who made the monster.
15. It means a dog house, a pack of hounds, the gutter of a street, and a puddle or channel.
16. Its name means "river horse".
17. This is a region of the North Atlantic whose surface is covered with floating Gulf weed.
18. Ense petit placidum sub libertate quietem, which reads translated: "By the sword she seeks settled peace with liberty."
19. This word describes a person who is seventy years old.
20. This small fish is known as the sea-horse.

21. Spruce, pine, fir, hemlock, tamarack, and poplar are all extensively used in this process.
22. It's the sixth star in the first row.
23. It is about one and one-sixth land miles.
24. Harvard University, founded in 1636.
25. This famous English bank is privately owned.

CONUNDRUM QUIZ NUMBER ONE
Answers on page 321

1. What was the biggest surgical operation ever performed?
2. What is the temperature under the blankets of the quintuplets?
3. Why are soldiers always tired on the first of April?
4. How many wives does the Bible allow a man?
5. Which side of a boy's pants is the West side?
6. When is a boy ready for the barber?
7. If the devil lost his tail, where would he go to get a new one?
8. Why was Goliath surprised when David hit him with a stone?
9. Why is a fish dealer never generous?
10. Why is the man in the moon always in poverty?
11. What skins make the best slippers?
12. Why are little birds usually melancholy in the morning?
13. At what time of day was Adam created?
14. Why is an apple like a pair of skates?
15. Some say pigs are the wisest animals on earth. Why?
16. Why can't a deaf man be convicted?
17. What is the "Chop Suey Scissors"?
18. If all of the letters of the alphabet were asked to go out to dinner, why couldn't they all go together?
19. If you came home and found a horse in your bathtub, what would you do?
20. When was money first mentioned in the Bible?
21. How far is it from March to June?
22. What birds cannot fly?
23. Which reserved seat in a theatre would be most appropriate for a dog?
24. How does the word love mean everything in one sense and nothing in another?
25. Why is there water in a watermelon?

CONUNDRUM QUIZ NUMBER TWO

Answers on page 321

1. When is a member of a baseball team first mentioned in the Bible?
2. If a man gave one son fifteen cents and another son ten cents, what time would it be?
3. What two things does a ball do when it stops rolling?
4. Why is a ship always called a "she"?
5. If a man carrying five lamps should drop one, what would he become?
6. What is meant by "beastly weather"?
7. Why is a bald head like heaven?
8. Which type of person marries earliest, the light haired or the dark?
9. Why is a hill like a lazy dog?
10. Why should Ireland be the richest country in the world?
11. How would you know if your dog had been eating axle grease?
12. What is the difference between a glutton and a hungry man?
13. What is the name of the only state mentioned in the Bible?
14. Why shouldn't ladies learn to speak French?
15. When is the best time to pay a doctor?
16. What is the difference between Noah's Ark and Joan of Arc?
17. What fish travels the farthest?
18. Both books and hotels have what?
19. Why didn't Jonah take any cheese on the Ark for the mice?
20. How does a sailor know that there is a man in the moon?
21. Why is coal the most contradictory article known to commerce?
22. Why are tall people the laziest?
23. What chins are never shaved?
24. Why is a man's face, shaved in January, like a celebrated fur?
25. What is the difference between one yard and two yards?

CONUNDRUM QUIZ NUMBER THREE

Answers on page 322

1. What was the name of Washington's valet?
2. Why is an umbrella like an Easter egg?

3. When is a doctor most annoyed?
4. There were three men on a raft, each with a cigarette. They had no lighter, no rocks, no matches, nothing to light the cigarettes with, yet they did get them lighted. How?
5. What is put on the table frequently, cut several times, but never eaten?
6. If a man is locked in a room which contains only a bed, a piano, and a calendar, how can he eat, drink, and get out of the room?
7. If Ireland sank, what would float?
8. What two animals had the least luggage in the Ark?
9. Why should a greedy man wear a plaid vest?
10. What kind of a ship has two mates and no captain?
11. Which is the swifter, heat or cold?
12. What book has the most stirring chapters?
13. When was the price of beef at its highest?
14. Why is a clay pipe the best kind to smoke?
15. When will there be only twenty-five letters in the alphabet?
16. In what respects do tennis players resemble criminals?
17. What trade would you mention to a short boy?
18. What business man always finds things dull?
19. When is a cigar like dried beef?
20. Why is the Statue of Liberty's hand only eleven inches long?
21. What would you call the middle of the hour glass?
22. When did Washington first take a carriage?
23. When is a gate like a bell?
24. Is it true that in England they can't hang a man with a wooden leg?
25. What is the penalty for flirtation in most states?

CONUNDRUM QUIZ NUMBER FOUR
Answers on page 322

1. What increases its value when turned upside down?
2. Is there anything you can't preserve in alcohol?
3. When I went to work I got it; if I had found it I would have thrown it away; I couldn't find it, so I took it home with me. What was it?

187

4. What is it that George Washington seldom saw, God never saw, and we see every day?
5. What hand do you use to stir your coffee?
6. What makes an empty match box superior to any other?
7. What is the most difficult train to catch?
8. What is wasted energy?
9. If you saw a man walking on a slippery road, what musical warning should you give him?
10. Why is St. Paul's Cathedral like a bird's nest?
11. Why is your nose in the middle of your face?
12. What is worse than raining cats and dogs?
13. Why are fowls the most profitable things a farmer can raise?
14. Why couldn't they play cards in the Ark?
15. Why couldn't a man starve on the Sahara Desert?
16. What animal has more lives than a cat?
17. Answer the following "nation" questions with the appropriate words: What nation has produced the most Kings? Is immune from disease? Is most murderous? Is noted for its dullness? Is the slowest? Exercises the greatest authority? Is famous for its lighting system?
18. Why are a man's trousers always too short for him?
19. When it's born it flies, when it's alive it lies, and when it's dead it runs. What is it?
20. What is the difference between a jailor and a jeweler?
21. Which is the more valuable, a dollar bill or a dollar in change?
22. If the peacock which belongs to your neighbor should lay an egg on your property, to whom would the egg belong?
23. Can you spell "blind pig" with only two letters?
24. When is a horse not a horse?
25. What runs and never stops, has a bed but never sleeps, a bank but no money, and branches but no leaves?

HISTORY QUIZ NUMBER II-A

Answers on page 323

1. What is the significance of Appomattox courthouse in American history?
2. In what war was the American Flag first used?

3. When was the battle of Lexington fought?
4. What famous document was signed in the meadow of Runnymede in the year 1215?
5. What was the reigning house of England after the Tudors?
6. What is the Bill of Rights?
7. The victory of the Monitor over the Merrimac was important to the North because: the Merrimac was ramming and sinking the North's biggest ships; because the Monitor was the first ship with torpedoes; because the Merrimac was to lead an attack on New York City?
8. What historic river did Caesar cross?
9. What was the first state to ratify the Constitution?
10. What was Libby Prison?
11. When was the frigate "Constitution" launched?
12. How can the Constitution be amended?
13. Where does "When in the course of human events, etc." come from?
14. Give the dates of the six wars starting with the Revolutionary War.
15. What city was the first capital of the United States?
16. In French history, what was a dauphin?
17. In American history, what was known as the Underground Railroad?
18. How many amendments are there to the United States Constitution?
19. What memorable events took place in the years 1492 and 1620?
20. Who is the patron saint of England?
21. In what war was "Remember the Maine!" a slogan?
22. Which was the last state admitted to the Union?
23. What two countries fought in the Punic Wars?
24. The English crown jewels are kept in Buckingham Palace, the House of Parliament, or the Tower of London?
25. What was the Heptarchy?

HISTORY QUIZ NUMBER II-B

Answers on page 324

1. Where was the first capital of the Southern Confederacy?
2. Iceland is ruled by a president, a fiscal representative, or by the King of Denmark?

3. What does the date May 4, 1607 mean to you?
4. What treaty terminated the War of 1812?
5. In what war did Ethan Allen fight?
6. What American colony was called the "Old Dominion"?
7. In what wars were the following battles fought: the battle of Bennington, the battle of the Wilderness, the battle of Belleau Wood?
8. What were the inhabitants of ancient France called?
9. Where did Washington first take command of the American Army?
10. Name the six wars in which the United States has participated.
11. The city of Paris, France, was in the hands of what nation from 1430 to 1436?
12. In what war did the Rough Riders participate?
13. What city did Oglethorpe found?
14. Which state in the Union is still governed under its original constitution?
15. Which of these nations has a president: Finland, Norway, or Sweden?
16. When the British crossed from Boston to fight at Bunker Hill they landed at Moulton's Point; what is located there now?
17. Name the three islands closely associated with the life of Napoleon.
18. In what Federal department is the United States Children's Bureau?
19. What English king thought he could make the tides obey him, and was drowned while trying to do it?
20. When and where was the battleship Maine blown up?
21. Who won the following battles: Saratoga, 1777? Second Bull Run, 1862? Manila Bay, 1898?
22. Where was the first shot of the Civil War fired?
23. What was the first flag to fly over Texas?
24. Where is Christopher Columbus buried?
25. When was the Great Wall of China built?

HISTORY QUIZ NUMBER II-C
Answers on page 324

1. In American politics, what does the term "lame duck" mean?

2. What flag was called the "Stars and Bars"?
3. Who was the Polish general who fought for the colonists in the American War of Independence, and was killed?
4. Over what country did Richard the Lion Hearted rule?
5. In what state is Yorktown, where Cornwallis surrendered to the American and French troops, thus ending the war?
6. What was the fate of the assassin who is credited with starting the World War?
7. What famous document begins with the words: "We, the people . . ."?
8. How many stripes did the flag of the United States have during the War of 1812?
9. Name three foreign soldiers who came over to help Washington in the Revolution?
10. Is there any of the tea from the Boston Tea Party now in Boston?
11. In what state was Daniel Boone born?
12. Where was this phrase used: "Don't shoot till you see the whites of their eyes."?
13. In what year did Washington, D.C. become the capital of the United States?
14. Give the year in which each of the following wars ended: Revolutionary War, War of 1812, Civil War, World War?
15. Who was the first person to be called "Father of his country"?
16. What nationality was Napoleon?
17. In French history, what was the "Hundred Days"?
18. Who was the president of the Southern Confederacy?
19. Are Indians citizens of the United States?
20. Of what department is the Attorney General the head?
21. What is the term of office of a United States senator?
22. What is the twenty-first amendment to the Constitution?
23. What was the name of the ruling family in Russia for the three hundred years from 1613-1917?
24. During the Civil War, where was the famous "battle above the clouds" fought?
25. Gettysburg, scene of the famous Civil War battle, is in which of the following states: Virginia, Pennsylvania, New York or Maryland?

HISTORY QUIZ NUMBER II-D

Answers on page 325

1. Name the winning and losing forces in the following battles: Waterloo, Santiago, Sedan.
2. Was Peru once ruled by the Aztecs, Mayans, or Incas?
3. What war in which the United States did not take part ended with the signing of a treaty in the United States, and where was it signed?
4. What country first began work on the Panama Canal?
5. Who was the famous "Little Corporal"?
6. From what tribe of Indians did the Dutch purchase the site of New York?
7. With what wars were the following boats connected: Maine, Monitor, Old Ironsides?
8. Is Bunker Hill monument on Bunker Hill?
9. What is the nature of the Brazilian government?
10. What was the favorite song of the troops in the Spanish War?
11. What three great generals were never defeated?
12. What did Caesar say when crossing the Rubicon?
13. How many chests of tea were cut open and their contents emptied into Boston Harbor in the Boston Tea Party?
14. Which of these two men was born first: Benjamin Franklin or William Penn?
15. Which ancient city was destroyed when Vesuvius erupted in 79 A.D.?
16. Who were the Green Mountain Boys?
17. By whom was the cornerstone of the national capitol at Washington laid?
18. Can you give the titles of the seven officers of the Cabinet in Washington?
19. How many attended the Boston Tea Party?
20. What is the meaning of the letters R.I. after the name of the King of England?
21. What was Black Friday?
22. How many nations besides the United States have red, white, and blue flags?
23. Give the first three and last three words of the pledge of Allegiance to the flag.

24. The state of Texas has existed under six flags; what are they?
25. How many were killed in the Boston Massacre?

GENERAL QUIZ NUMBER XVII-A

Answers on page 326

1. Who was the vice-president under each of the following: Harding, Coolidge, Hoover?
2. What are the two extreme points of Great Britain?
3. Who was Bob Cratchit?
4. Where is the San Francisco River?
5. What is the southernmost capital of the world?
6. What city in the United States has the largest drydock?
7. What is the capital of Nevada?
8. What is meant by Lilliputian?
9. What state's boundaries touch only one other state?
10. What is the name of Santa Claus in Scandinavian countries?
11. If you had a chanticleer would you take it for a walk, put it in the barnyard, or use it for a light?
12. The Ohio river forms the entire northern boundary of what state?
13. The Ganges river flows into what body of water?
14. Next to Massachusetts, what state grows the most cranberries?
15. What Italian city was called the Bride of the Adriatic?
16. Rounding the Horn was a familiar expression when sailing craft were important. What is meant by the expression?
17. What two rivers unite at Pittsburgh, Pennsylvania, to form the Ohio river?
18. Give within 2,000 miles the circumference of the globe.
19. What have the following in common: Uhlan, Zouave, Sepoy?
20. What men of science were the following electrical terms named after: volt, ampere, watt?
21. What is a drachma?
22. To what animals do the following terms refer: Reynard, Bruin, Leo, Dobbin?
23. Before blotting paper, what was used to take up excess ink?

24. What is the capital of Missouri?
25. What does the A. in James A. Farley's name stand for?

GENERAL QUIZ NUMBER XVII-B

Answers on page 326

1. What are the Antilles?
2. Is Timbuctoo an Indian chief, the name of a city, the title of a book, or a musical instrument?
3. What is the largest state east of the Mississippi river?
4. From where does the custom of Christmas trees derive?
5. If, on arriving at your home, you saw a sign which read: "Mephitis Mephitis inside", would you call the police, the board of health, your lawyer, or a doctor?
6. There are four states whose capitals end in "city". What are they?
7. In the poem "The Night Before Christmas", what did Santa Claus do just before going up the chimney?
8. For whom was Louisiana named?
9. Which is the longest distance of these three: two furlongs, one quarter of a mile, or eighty rods?
10. Supply the missing names of the following present day authors: ...... Tarkington, ... Ludwig, ... Sabatini, Sir Philip ......, Wilhelm ....
11. Is Deadwood Dick related to Deadeye Dick?
12. Why is June the traditional month for marriages?
13. Name the six Time Belts of North America.
14. What is the most densely populated state in the world?
15. What is a brood of pheasants called?
16. What river do you associate with each of the following: Mark Twain, Stephen Foster, Cleopatra, When a laddie meets a lassie?
17. Is Texas about twice the size of Alaska, or vice versa?
18. Name two of the three states which have only four letters in their name.
19. What work of art made the number thirteen unpopular?
20. What is the second smallest state in the Union?
21. What does the phrase "in mufti" mean?
22. Who was Marley's ghost?
23. Which has the larger area, Brazil or the United States?

24. Which of the following republics are in Central America?
25. During the administration of what president was the slogan "fifty-four forty, or fight" used?

GENERAL QUIZ NUMBER XVII-C

Answers on page 327

1. Who is the author of the expression "caviar to the general"?
2. Those who visit Regent's Park, London, enjoy what?
3. Where is the city of elms?
4. When was the celebration of Christmas forbidden by law in this country?
5. Lake Champlain lies between what two states?
6. For what product are each of the following cities known: Minneapolis, Milwaukee, Brockton, New Orleans?
7. Where is the Erie Canal?
8. Is "noël" an English, French, or Latin word?
9. Who comprises the President's official family?
10. Name three presidents whose last names began with the letter T.
11. Where is the Isle of Capri located?
12. Name three motion pictures whose titles contain the name of a color.
13. In what state could you find the following places within a radius of twenty miles: Denmark, Mexico, Norway, Poland, Sweden?
14. When were Christmas cards first used in the United States?
15. What is the Golden Gate?
16. Complete these unfinished affinities: Adam and ......, Army and ......, fine and ......, Cain and ......, soap and ......, touch and ......, hit and ......, butter and ......, stars and ......, pen and ......, moonlight and ......, cash and ......, ball and ......, nut and ....
17. Beyond whose deep and dreamless sleep did the silent stars go by?
18. What did these men have in common: Daniel Thomkins, George Dallas, Henry Wilson, William Wheeler, and William King?
19. Name six evergreens used in Christmas decorations.
20. A state of the United States west of the Mississippi river is:

Tennessee, Mississippi, Arkansas, Ohio, Michigan, or Kentucky?
21. The offspring of what four animals are called calves?
22. How did the dahlia get its name?
23. What is meant by saying that a horse is in the race "just for the breeze"?
24. Where is the buffalo used to cultivate rice?
25. What is man's principal source of ivory?

GENERAL QUIZ NUMBER XVII-D
Answers on page 327

1. What is a shavetail?
2. Give within two the number of quarts of water that pass through an oyster in the course of an hour.
3. What is a rotunda?
4. In deep sea diving, what is known as the bends?
5. What is the English equivalent of the American word gasoline?
6. Of what great inventor has it been said "he needs no memorial"?
7. The abbreviations of what states are: a metal, sick, a note of the scale, a boat in the Bible, a Church service?
8. What is meant by the letters F.O.B.?
9. Is there the rank of Commodore in the United States Navy?
10. What is meant by piping an officer over the side of a ship?
11. If you took up xylography as your vocation, what would you do?
12. What would you regard as the distinction between a rebellion and a revolution?
13. Where was daylight saving time originated?
14. If a Marquis is a nobleman, what is marquisette?
15. List three fish which mention a tool as part of their name.
16. Which of these beams contain the most metal: sun beam, moon beam, or I beam?
17. How high in the air is a plane when the pilot resorts to taxiing?
18. In how many different directions could one travel at the North Pole?
19. Does a bee really hum?

20. Distinguish between a solar year and a calendar year.
21. What dog is noted for a sour mug, an iron jaw, bowlegs, and a seagoing gate?
22. Who was St. Valentine?
23. What is a clavichord?
24. What is a "link-boy"?
25. What character did Maude Adams make famous on the stage?

GENERAL QUIZ NUMBER XVIII-A

Answers on page 328

1. What is a taxidermist?
2. What does osculation mean?
3. A cummerbund is worn by a man with: overalls, bathing suit, riding habit, or tuxedo?
4. Who sponsored Jenny Lind, the Swedish Nightingale, in her American debut?
5. What is the longest street in the world?
6. What famous book did Fannie Merritt Farmer write?
7. These famous colleges were named for their founders. Here are their last names, you supply their first: Harvard, Yale, Stanford.
8. What is the difference between an automobile accessory and an automobile part?
9. About how much does it cost Uncle Sam to make a dollar bill?
10. What historic English building did P. T. Barnum try to buy in order to bring it to America?
11. If a palette is a thin board on which a painter mixes his pigments, what is a pallet?
12. What is the proper way to display the American flag on Memorial Day?
13. Is there any difference in the way in which a man's and woman's coat folds in front?
14. What is the name of the beetle held sacred in Egypt?
15. In this list of animals is one which always washes its food before eating it; which one is it? Cat, beaver, antelope, lion, raccoon, buzzard?
16. The lemon tree is native to what country?

197

17. What three animals besides the elephant provide ivory?
18. Where is the Blarney Stone, and what is the superstition connected with it?
19. Paul Bunyan was an English author, a legendary figure, or an American soldier?
20. Is the sap of the ebony tree black or white?
21. For how many years is a copyright good?
22. For what is Delft, Holland, famous?
23. What were the last words of Julius Caesar?
24. What is the lowest tide called?
25. What countries have awarded these forms of distinction: Iron Cross, D.S.O., Victoria Cross, Croix de Guerre?

GENERAL QUIZ NUMBER XVIII-B

Answers on page 329

1. Does gold or silver braid show the highest rank in the United States army?
2. To what does the term "onion skin" apply, besides onions?
3. Why do long distance swimmers smear their bodies with grease?
4. Who were the traditional enemies of ancient Greece? Of modern Greece?
5. What is the Flying Dutchman?
6. Which is the colder, the North or South pole?
7. If you inspire when you breathe, what do you do when you don't breathe?
8. What industry uses the most silver?
9. What well known and famous painting has a wheel-barrow pictured in it?
10. Is dry ice warmer or colder than liquid air?
11. On what date was prohibition fully repealed?
12. Which is the higher rank, a Captain in the United States Army or Navy?
13. Why do we galvanize iron?
14. Which is the higher, the Rock of Gibraltar or the Empire State Building?
15. If you were piloting a ship into an American port, on which side of the channel would you find the red buoys?
16. What is the difference between peeling and paring fruit?

17. If a robin is a bird, what is a round-robin?
18. What is meant by the shroud of a ship?
19. What is the difference between ruminant and ruminate?
20. What is a chanty?
21. What is the difference between bigamy and digamy?
22. Name three nursery rhymes which mention animals?
23. What is the distinction between a prevaricator and a prestidigitator?
24. What is meant by the Open Door policy in China?
25. Distinguish between velvet and velveteen.

GENERAL QUIZ NUMBER XVIII-C

Answers on page 329

1. What is a filigree?
2. Who was Sinbad the sailor?
3. What is meant by the expression "buying a pig in a poke"?
4. What are the pictures on the twenty-five, thirty, and fifty cent United States postage stamps?
5. What is choreography?
6. What is the fastest thing that you can do?
7. What do the following abbreviations mean in a newspaper: U.P.; A.P.; I.N.S.?
8. In the United States navy, what is a flag Lieutenant?
9. What two bodies of water are connected by the Cape Cod Canal?
10. What is horse billiards?
11. What is meant by a blue-stocking?
12. Why is it unlikely that George Washington ever threw a dollar across the Rappahannock River?
13. What is an apothecary?
14. If a pentagon is a five sided geometric figure, what is a paragon?
15. The word pogrom means which of the following: an arranged plan of action, an organized massacre of a group or class, or the bloodless invasion of a country?
16. Name three of the twelve signs of the Zodiac.
17. The word bus is a contraction of what word?
18. Name five colorless liquids.
19. What is the difference between an agnostic and an atheist?

20. Who or what is the main guy around a circus lot?
21. If you had the Beale Street Blues, what city would you be homesick for?
22. When you speak of a surname you are referring to: the first name, last name, middle name, or nickname?
23. What is the difference, if any, between five square miles and a five mile square?
24. Is there any difference between commute and compute?
25. Define the words squib, squid, and squill.

GENERAL QUIZ NUMBER XVIII-D

Answers on page 330

1. What is the difference between an esophagus and a sarcophagus?
2. If the aristocrats of ancient Rome were called patricians, what were the common people called?
3. Distinguish between etymology and entomology.
4. What is a tramp steamer?
5. Do almonds grow in California?
6. If a seer is one who tells of the future, and a sucker is a kind of fish, what is a seersucker?
7. The word dog appears in the familiar answer to each of these questions: When a man has quarreled with his wife he's in the ......? When a person is high-stepping we call him ......? When one is all dressed up we say he's ......? When we're weary we're ......?
8. If an incubator is an apparatus for hatching eggs, what is an incubus?
9. What is an abacus?
10. If you drive a car thirty miles an hour, how many feet do you travel per second?
11. Which of these parts of the camera determines how much light will strike the film: lens, shutter, bellows?
12. What have the following in common: Talisman, American Beauty, Sweetheart?
13. What is a turncoat?
14. What was so unique about King Arthur's sword, Excalibur?
15. A mule and a horse are turned loose in a well filled oat bin, and proceed to eat. How much will each animal eat?

16. Why does a Russian soldier wear brass buttons on his coat and a German soldier steel ones?
17. Could a champion swimmer cover a mile more quickly than a champion walker?
18. Distinguish between a fiesta, a fiasco, and a fiacre?
19. We know the words limp and pet, but what is a limpet?
20. What is the next line after this in the Christmas song: "Oh, Little town of Bethlehem, how still we see thee lie"?
21. What is Scotland Yard?
22. What is the chain from which the missing link is missing?
23. If milk contains 12% solids and 4% butter fat, of what does the remaining 84% consist?
24. What section of New York city corresponds roughly with the Latin Quarter of Paris?
25. Say "good bye" in four different languages.

GENERAL QUIZ NUMBER XIX-A

Answers on page 331

1. What is a blunderbuss?
2. What is the only living thing that can be turned inside out and still live?
3. What is a friar?
4. What is an arbiter?
5. What is America's most important industry?
6. If someone told you that you were refulgent, would you feel hurt or flattered?
7. If you were told to "pull the rip cord", you'd know that you were in: a theater back stage, a stocking factory, a parachute, an upper berth?
8. Are a cat's whiskers necessary to the animal or merely ornamental?
9. What have these three in common: kerosene, gasoline, and naphtha?
10. What is a pontoon bridge?
11. Give within one hundred pounds the average weight of a bale of cotton.
12. Name five methods of transportation beginning with the letter T.

13. List the following in the order of their rank: boatswain, ablebodied seaman, skipper, chief mate.
14. What does a barometer register?
15. What is a wildcat scheme?
16. Why are pine trees less likely to be struck by lightning than other trees?
17. What is a Dutch Treat?
18. What are pillar posts?
19. Name three citrus fruits.
20. What are rookies?
21. What is an igloo?
22. How many states are there in the United States beginning with the letter B?
23. What kind of a rock can be cut with a knife?
24. What is a greenback?
25. What language was spoken in ancient Rome?

GENERAL QUIZ NUMBER XIX-B

Answers on page 331

1. From what race of people did France derive its name?
2. Name five types of sailing vessels.
3. What is the natural color of teakwood?
4. What is a dragoman?
5. Why is it warmer to wear two thin garments rather than one thicker one?
6. If Miss-issippi wore Miss-ouri's New Jersey, what would Dela-ware?
7. What is the difference between a finger wave and a marcel?
8. When the joker is used as a wild card in a poker game, what is the highest hand you could hold?
9. A quire of paper is how many sheets? A ream?
10. Which food gives the greatest amount of calcium in an average serving?
11. What is a millennium?
12. Name the three states which have the most electoral votes.
13. Why is a traveling salesman sometimes called a drummer?
14. What does it mean to antedate?
15. When you have a proxy, what have you got?

16. What three things do the most to help a man get up in the world?
17. What metal will flow without heating?
18. If a flatfoot is a policeman, what is a footpad?
19. What is a water mark?
20. Of what material are parachutes made?
21. What is a trundle bed?
22. What is meant by the term "mother Carey's chickens"?
23. Why is there always a red and white pole outside of a barber's shop?
24. Is a hair's breadth a unit of measure, or merely a figure of speech?
25. What is weight?

GENERAL QUIZ NUMBER XIX-C

Answers on page 332

1. Was the Grand Canyon made by man, swiftly flowing water, or earthquakes?
2. What are the four different names for the American flag as used in the military service?
3. Where and when did Columbus die?
4. Is paper organic or inorganic matter?
5. What automobile license number is always reserved for the president's car?
6. How old was Alexander Graham Bell the year the telephone was patented?
7. In telephoning in England what phrase is substituted for "hello"?
8. What does the abbreviation "Bart." after an Englishman's name stand for?
9. Why did China adopt extensive tea drinking?
10. If you employ duress, of what are you making use?
11. What is the difference between rochet and rocket?
12. What is a whatnot?
13. What is a prawn?
14. If your skin became etiolated, would it be blue, yellow, white, red, or tan?
15. About how many drops of water are there in a teaspoon?
16. What animal possesses the heaviest fur?

17. Of all metals which one has the highest melting point?
18. Can the American flag ever be flown upside down?
19. If you had a piece of potsherd what would you do with it?
20. Which of the two entrances to the Panama Canal, the Atlantic or the Pacific, is farther east?
21. If you took out citizenship papers in Madagascar, what country would you owe allegiance to?
22. Are there any birds that have teeth?
23. Ides and nones were dates used by what people? ·
24. What is the correct pronunciation of the word data?
25. The name of what great battle has become a household word for defeat?

GENERAL QUIZ NUMBER XIX-D

Answers on page 332

1. In three yards and three quarters, how many quarters are there?
2. How many edges has a triangular pyramid?
3. What principle of science enables a thermos bottle to keep liquid either hot or cold?
4. Is a benison a cut of meat, a benediction, or a salutation?
5. What is meant by adiaphorism?
6. What are the conventional figures or spots on playing cards and dominoes called?
7. A cube has: how many flat surfaces? how many corners? how many edges?
8. What is the name of Great Britain's equivalent to our West Point?
9. When someone says "It might as well be in Timbuktu", just where does he mean?
10. If you were to participate in a cotillion would you play at an organ recital, dance a lively quadrille, or help build a bird sanctuary?
11. What is the source of rosin?
12. What is shoddy?
13. What is a colporteur?
14. Klieg is a name for a type of furnace, light, match, or furniture?
15. Is an eel an animal, a fish, or a serpent?

16. What vice-president and statesman fought a duel in 1804 in which one of them was killed?
17. What is the smallest country in North America?
18. Identify the blondes, red heads, and brunettes in the following: Betty co-ed, Tillie the Toiler, Little Orphan Annie, Betty Boop.
19. What is the difference between species and specie?
20. If your boss firmly refused to give you a raise would you call him adhesive, addled, adamant, or adroit?
21. Name four birds or fishes which have been domesticated solely for ornamental purposes.
22. A ewe being a sheep, what is a ewer?
23. What bird exceeds all others in the variety and quality of its song?
24. In the poem "On the Road to Mandalay", there is mention of what animal being engaged in what occupation and where?
25. How often should one wind a barometer?

DON'T CONFUSE 'EM! II-A

Answers on page 333

1. What is the difference between a tarantella and a tarantula?
2. What is the difference between a gossoon and a bassoon?
3. Distinguish between a gourmand and a gourmet.
4. If a dog is one of our domestic animals what is doggerel?
5. Differentiate between an autocracy, a democracy and a plutocracy.
6. Define bi-weekly, bi-monthly and bi-annually.
7. If an icicle is a pendant of ice what is an ossicle?
8. If an alien is a foreigner what is an alienist?
9. What is the difference between epistles and apostles?
10. What are each of the following: yellow jacket, blue jacket, eton jacket, strait jacket?
11. What is the difference between antimony and antinomy?
12. Do the words stationary and stationery mean the same thing?
13. Explain the difference between voracity and veracity.
14. Compare ingenious and ingenuous.
15. A scimitar is a small curved sword; what is a simitaur?

16. Discriminate between a watch dog and a dog watch.
17. What is the distinction between a zither and a zephyr?
18. Contrast a hurricane, a tornado and a cyclone.
19. What are the meanings of the following words: statue, stature, and statute?
20. What is an ordnance and what is an ordinance?
21. Distinguish between a pinnacle and a pinnace?
22. What is the meaning of lea and lee?
23. What is the difference between resin and rosin?
24. Are collusion and collision synonymous?
25. What is the difference, if any, between condemnation and commendation?

DON'T CONFUSE 'EM! SET NUMBER II-B

Answers on page 334

1. What are the differences in meaning of the words: emanate, emulate and emigrate?
2. Distinguish between genealogy and geology.
3. Identify dory, lory, and Tory.
4. If cabbage is a vegetable what is cribbage?
5. What is the difference between an armadillo and a peccadillo?
6. Contrast raising and razing.
7. Identify any two of the following: Hetty Green, Paris Green, Bowling Green.
8. Define four of the following: red cap, madcap, foolscap, percussion cap, and cap and bells.
9. Compare pathos and bathos.
10. Distinguish between an oculist and an optician.
11. Caret and carat have two different meanings. What are they?
12. Are prodigy and protegee the same thing? If not, what's the difference?
13. Define husband and husbandman.
14. What's the difference between a ewe and a ewer?
15. Identify jurist and juror.
16. Explain the difference between an asteroid and an asterisk.
17. Define stereoscope, stethoscope, and periscope.

18. Can you explain the difference between a metropolis, a necropolis, and an acropolis?
19. Distinguish between mantel and mantle.
20. Compare auger with augur.
21. If humorous means amusing, what does humerus mean?
22. If a racketeer is a gangster what is a raconteur?
23. A pentagon is a figure with five sides and an octagon is one with eight sides. What is a paragon?
24. Compare a somnambulist with a somniloquist.
25. Distinguish between an anecdote and an antidote.

DON'T CONFUSE 'EM! SET NUMBER II-C

Answers on page 335

1. What is the difference between a talisman and a talesman?
2. Distinguish between a carton and a cartoon.
3. If there is a difference between adobe and abode, what is it?
4. What is the difference between celestial and celesta?
5. Distinguish between emigrant and immigrant.
6. Compare avenge and revenge.
7. You know what a breast pin and a hair pin are, but what is a cotter pin?
8. Distinguish between a rip and riprap.
9. Contrast a fiesta and a siesta.
10. Identify each of the following: antiseptic, germicide, and anaesthetic.
11. If nostrum and rostrum are not synonymous explain the difference.
12. If rusty means to be covered with rust what does rusticate mean?
13. Distinguish between a stork and a stoic.
14. If a man is a human being and a drill is a pointed tool, what is a mandrill?
15. If ossification is a hardening into stone what is osculation?
16. What is the meaning of hobnob, kowtow, and pow wow?
17. With what do you associate the following points: needlepoint, pencil point, counterpoint, and West Point?
18. If a navy is a fleet of ships, what is a navvy?
19. What's the difference between a barnacle and a binnacle?
20. If a mouse is a small rodent what is a titmouse?

21. Matrimony is marriage and alimony is a mistake in marriage; what is antimony?
22. Explain the difference between a chateau and a plateau?
23. If a burrow is a hole in the ground and a borough is a corporate town, what is a burro?
24. Distinguish between French doors, stevedores, and humidors.
25. Identify ballad, ballet, and ballot.

DON'T CONFUSE 'EM QUIZ NUMBER II-D

Answers on page 336

1. What is the opposite of philanthropy?
2. What is the difference in meaning of the two words canon and cannon?
3. Contrast ante and anti.
4. Compare in shape an oval, an ovate, and an ovoid.
5. If entomology is the study of insects what is etymology?
6. What is the difference between infectious and contagious?
7. Identify a coiffeur and a coiffure.
8. What is the distinction between chiropody and chirography?
9. Identify a faker and a fakir.
10. What is the difference between a lama and a llama?
11. Distinguish between flotsam and jetsam.
12. The words indite and indict are pronounced alike. What does each mean?
13. To what kingdom do each of the following belong: celanese, pekinese, and manganese?
14. What is the difference between a caddie and a caddy?
15. Compare conscription with description.
16. Identify: monogamy, polyandry, and polygamy.
17. What is the difference between a waif, wafer, and a waiver?
18. Identify ham and hamlet.
19. If a benediction is a blessing what is a benedict?
20. Distinguish between bisect and dissect.
21. What is the difference between a shaker and a shako?
22. Identify whetstone, grindstone, lodestone, and rhinestone.
23. What are each of the following: a travelogue, a decalogue, an analogue, and a catalogue?

24. What is a trundle bed?
25. Is there any difference between an aviator and a sky pilot?

TRAVEL QUIZ NUMBER II-A

Answers on page 337

1. In what state is Pikes Peak?
2. Name three important rivers of Canada.
3. What state is bounded by the largest number of states?
4. Does the name Hongkong suggest to you a city, an island, or a country?
5. What state has no seacoast yet boasts of a navy yard?
6. What city in California was formerly called Sutter's Fort?
7. The ancient great city once known as Byzantium is now Rome, Athens, Cairo, or Constantinople?
8. Is India north or south of the Equator?
9. Name the capitals of the following: Samoa; Philippine Islands; Puerto Rico; Alaska.
10. On what continent was ancient Babylon?
11. Is the capital of Arizona Yuma, Tucson, or Phoenix?
12. Corsica belongs to what country?
13. Where are the Sierra Nevadas?
14. What city is considered the oldest in the world? What city is considered the oldest in the United States?
15. In what country is the Don River?
16. Name the states whose capitals are personal names.
17. Which one of the Great Lakes is entirely within the boundary of the United States?
18. What body of water lies between Ireland and Scotland?
19. What river forms the southern boundary of the United States?
20. Is Andalusia in Spain or South America?
21. What city is called "Washington of South America"?
22. What New England state has more water than what New England state has land?
23. Where are the Thousand Islands located?
24. Which of the thirteen original states was named for Queen Elizabeth?
25. For what is the River Rhone in France noted?

TRAVEL QUIZ NUMBER II-B

Answers on page 338

1. What body of water lies between Great Britain and France?
2. Where is the Republic of Andorra?
3. Can you locate the following: the White Sea; the Yellow River; the Blue Ridge Mountains; the Orange Free State?
4. What two cities are known as the "twin cities"?
5. What is the capital of Norway?
6. Is Portland the capital of Oregon?
7. What states in the United States have two words in their names?
8. Which is England's second largest city?
9. What body of water is associated with each of the following: Bering, Hudson, Red, Indian, Caribbean, Puget, Yellow, North?
10. Which continent lies entirely south of the Equator?
11. Name three of the six famous notches in the White Mountains, New Hampshire.
12. If Walla Walla is in Washington, where is Wagga Wagga?
13. What two seaports on the opposite sides of the United States have the same name?
14. Venice is located in the Aegean Sea, the Red Sea, the Mediterranean Sea, or the Adriatic Sea?
15. Name the countries in which the following cities are located: Hamm, Bologna, Frankfurt.
16. What is the capital of Canada?
17. What country was once known as Iberia?
18. What is the name of the leading seaport of France?
19. Did Byrd discover the South Pole?
20. Where are St. John and St. Johns located?
21. Name the five boroughs of New York City.
22. What is the principal river of Palestine?
23. In what ocean is the Island of Guam?
24. What river is called the American Rhine?
25. Name five of the nine Canadian provinces.

TRAVEL QUIZ NUMBER II-C

Answers on page 338

1. How high is the Tower of Pisa? How much inclination has it?

2.   Where would you be if you were on the road to Mandalay?
3.   In what states are the following cities or towns located: Maine, New Hampshire, Vermont?
4.   If you sail due east out of Boston Harbor, what country will you reach first?
5.   In what state is the Yellowstone National Park?
6.   For what is Myra famous?
7.   Is the Tropic of Cancer north or south of the Equator?
8.   Name five of the eleven countries of South America.
9.   By what name is the bridge connecting St. Stephen, New Brunswick, and Calais, Maine, known?
10. Where is what is known as Evangeline's Land?
11. What four states join at one point?
12. Brooklyn Bridge in New York is over what river?
13. What four states pronounce their first syllables as girls' names?
14. Where is the Isle of Man?
15. What island in the western hemisphere is touched by an ocean, a gulf, and a sea?
16. To what country would you go to see Fujiyama?
17. Where is the Portsmouth Navy Yard?
18. Where is Trinidad?
19. What is the capital of Bulgaria?
20. How many states in the Union begin with the letter 'I'?
21. Where is El Dorado located?
22. What state in the United States is surrounded by the most water?
23. What is the largest state east of the Mississippi?
24. Where is New South Wales?
25. There are five states' capitals which begin with the letter "A"; how many can you name?

TRAVEL QUIZ NUMBER II-D

Answers on page 339

1.   With what cities or countries are the following associated: Taj Mahal; the Latin Quarter; the Kremlin; the Blarney Stone?
2.   What is the capital of Argentina?

3. What two cities of the same name meet at the border line of two different states?
4. By what name was Ireland known to the ancient Romans?
5. Where is the only active volcano in the United States?
6. What is the largest capital city in the United States?
7. In what states are the following forts: Fort Sumter; Fort Warren; Fort Niagara; Fort Ethan Allen?
8. Where are the following mountains located: the Alps; Mount Everest; Mount Mansfield; the Andes?
9. What three states in the United States have five letters in their names?
10. Which of the New England states is minus a seaport?
11. Name four of the ten states that are touched by the Mississippi River?
12. What is the highest peak of the Alps?
13. Is Washington the only city in the District of Columbia?
14. Which is the largest in area: the United States, Australia, or Brazil?
15. Into what body of water does the Congo River empty?
16. Where is Cathay?
17. On which river is the United States Naval Academy located?
18. What is the highest mountain in Europe?
19. What is the "Pearl of the Antilles"?
20. What is the Great Divide?
21. What sea lies between Italy and Jugoslavia?
22. Where are the White Mountains, the Green Mountains, the Blue Mountains?
23. In what city or town on the Atlantic coast can one see the sun set in the Atlantic Ocean?
24. Did Shakespeare gather his world-wide experience from actual travel?
25. Where is the only walled city of North America?

MUSIC QUIZ NUMBER II-A

Answers on page 339

1. The "musical sweet potato" is another name for which of the following: accordion, harmonica, ocarina or saxophone?

2. Give the next line after: "On the shore dimly seen through the mists of the deep" . . .?
3. For what is the D'Oyly Carte opera company famous?
4. In the song "Sweet and Low", what is it that is "sweet and low"?
5. Where is the original "Old Oaken Bucket" located?
6. In music, what is meant by pianissimo?
7. To what is it "a long, long trail a-winding"?
8. What is the last work of a composer called?
9. How many times does the word "America" appear in the hymn "My country 'tis of thee"?
10. From what song are the following lines taken: "And there was Captain Washington upon a slapping stallion, a-giving orders to his men, I guess there was a million."?
11. Can you give the names of some songs using the following colors in their titles: blue, yellow, red, green, rose?
12. Richard Wagner was married to the daughter of what famous pianist?
13. What is the difference between "swing", "jam" and "scat" music?
14. In what opera is "La donna e mobile" an aria?
15. What is a chromatic scale?
16. What is the difference between an orchestra and a band?
17. How many verses are there to "Yankee Doodle"? What is the chorus?
18. What is a celesta?
19. Who wrote the libretti of Wagner's operas?
20. What is the difference between tempo and time?
21. Was Stephen Foster a Northerner or a Southerner?
22. What words follow these: "You'll look sweet . . . ."?
23. At which of the following operas would you hear a reckless, self-confident baritone bellow the "Toreador" song? "Rigoletto", "Carmen", "Madame Butterfly"?
24. Is "Thais" a novel or an opera?
25. Name four musical instruments requiring both hands and feet to play.

MUSIC QUIZ NUMBER II-B
Answers on page 340

1. What instrument in an orchestra is named after a kitchen utensil?

213

2. What is the meaning of the following musical terms: fortissimo, presto, cantare?

3. In what opera is the character who "polished up the handle of the big front door"?

4. How many strings has a jewsharp?

5. What was the war song of the Confederate States of America?

6. Name three songs with the name "Alice" in the title.

7. What was the name of Annie Rooney's "steady"?

8. Who composed the opera "Faust"?

9. The song "Old Man River" was first sung in what musical comedy?

10. Who was the Scotch girl for whom a renowned love song was written by William Douglas?

11. What famous Scotch comedian popularized the song that asserts that it's nice to get up in the morning, but it's nicer to lie in bed?

12. Who composed "Kiss me again"?

13. If you had a rebec, would you eat it, cook it, write with it, or play it?

14. Name three song titles that have reference to the farm or things on the farm.

15. What is tintinnabulation?

16. In the song "Yankee Doodle", what does the word "macaroni" mean?

17. Name four songs containing the name of a musical instrument.

18. Is a spinet most like: a piano, a harp, a harpsichord?

19. Who composed "Alexander's Ragtime Band"?

20. Is it true that Nero fiddled while Rome burned?

21. Name four musical instruments that begin with the letter "C".

22. Name five Strauss waltzes.

23. Who "floats through the air with the greatest of ease."?

24. Who composed "The Chocolate Soldier"?

25. The impresario of an opera company is the: star singer, male lead, manager, female lead, or best all around substitute?

MUSIC QUIZ NUMBER II-C

Answers on page 340

1. With a keyless instrument like the bugle, the various notes are played by sounding the undertones, overtones, half-tones, or keytones?
2. In the song "America", we find the words: "I love thy rocks and rills." What are rills?
3. Who is the "she" referred to in the song "She'll be coming round the mountain when she comes."?
4. Where have you heard these names: Yum Yum, Pitti Sing, and Peep Bo?
5. What is the color of the hair and eyes of the "Sweetheart of Sigma Chi"?
6. A balalaika is a folk dance, a vehicle, or a musical instrument?
7. Who wrote "La Marseillaise", the national anthem of France?
8. Is a barcarolle a melody sung by Venetian gondoliers, a red fleshed fish, or a child's sled used in Russia?
9. If an octet is a musical composition for eight parts, what is an octave?
10. What stringed instrument is played by the wind?
11. Who composed the "Moonlight Sonata"?
12. What river gave its name to a famous waltz?
13. What musical instrument "skirls"?
14. Name four musical instruments beginning with the letter "T".
15. What is the first line of "The Old Oaken Bucket"?
16. Name two grand operas introducing a boat scene.
17. Who "wept with delight when you gave her a smile"?
18. Name three song titles with the word "blue" in them.
19. The defense of what fort inspired the writing of the "Star-Spangled Banner"?
20. In the song "Listen to the mocking bird", what is the girl's name?
21. If you had a vina, would you eat it, play it, or drive it?
22. A marimba is a song, a dance, a musical instrument?
23. Name two songs including the name of the country they sing of?
24. Who wrote "The Old Oaken Bucket"?

25. For what musical instrument did Chopin write most of his work?

MUSIC QUIZ NUMBER II-D

Answers on page 341

1. Name four songs with the names of flowers in their titles.
2. According to the old ballad, Frankie found Johnny making love to: a girl from Cheyenne, Annie Oakley, Nelly Bly, or a grass widow?
3. Give the next line after "I love thy rocks and rills"?
4. The name of what musical instrument begins with the letter "X"?
5. Give three songs whose titles mention food.
6. Which of these is correct: a dulcimer is one of the intricate steps of the tango, seaweed found on the beach or a musical instrument?
7. From what musical productions do the following come: "This is it"; "Sing a song of Sunbeams"; "Franklin D. Roosevelt Jones"; "Sing for your Supper".
8. Give five song titles using the word "home" in them.
9. What opera reminds one of Spain, who wrote it, and in what language is it written?
10. Give the titles of three songs containing the names of states.
11. Name three songs with the word "kiss" in the title.
12. Is a bandore a string or wind instrument?
13. The tympani player in an orchestra is the one who plays out of tune quite frequently, the one who plays a muted trumpet, the kettledrums, or a cymbal crash?
14. Name three songs that include names of wearing apparel in their titles.
15. What is the title of the song from which these lines are taken: "When true hearts lie withered and fond ones are flown, Oh, who would inhabit this bleak world alone?"?
16. Give the names of three songs which mention "Annie" in their titles.
17. Does the word "allegro" in music mean: a pause, play softly, play briskly, or slow and sad?
18. Name three orchestras which are named after a state or a dominion.

19. Where was Francis Scott Key when he wrote the "Star-Spangled Banner"?
20. Name three songs which include in the title the word "Heaven".
21. In what poem or song can these words be found: "And this be our motto, in God is our trust."?
22. Name five songs with the names of rivers in their titles.
23. In what year was the Star-Spangled Banner written?
24. If symphonic means harmony, what does cacophonic mean?
25. What name does not belong in the following group: Paderewski, Rachmaninoff, Grainger, Toscanini?

SUPER QUIZ II-A

Answers on page 342

1. Does the word echidna describe a salad, a death dealing insect, or an egg laying mammal?
2. What is the swiftest played game in the world of sport?
3. What part of a circus is the tan bark?
4. What is the difference between ophiology and ophthalmology?
5. What is a gambeson?
6. You would be doing what to have need for a plectrum?
7. If a footcandle is not a foot warmer or a hot foot, what is it?
8. What kind of a line is a plimsoll line?
9. What is the name of the *groove* between your nose and your lips?
10. Does a bean vine climb around a pole the way the sun travels around it or opposite?
11. What is a pulkha?
12. If ric-rac is an edging or trimming on a dress, what is rip-rap?
13. If the cutting edge of an ax is called the blade, what is the handle called?
14. What is the difference between stockinet and stockade?
15. Does air have any weight?
16. Is a mandrake the same as a mandrill?
17. In the expression "beer and skittles", what are skittles?
18. What is the difference between centrifugal force and centripetal force?

19. What is a squeegee?
20. What is a mullion?
21. Describe a molecule.
22. Identify British Consols.
23. What is the building over a coal mine shaft called?
24. What is another word meaning the facet or side of a jewel?
25. What is a kiosk?

SUPER QUIZ II-B
Answers on page 342

1. What is a colliery?
2. What is a decibel?
3. What is a tonsure?
4. Distinguish between extinct and instinct.
5. What is meant by squaring the circle?
6. Describe a bireme.
7. Is there any difference between a stock and a bond?
8. What article is familiarly known as a hempen collar?
9. How long would it take an aeroplane to travel from the earth to the sun if it traveled at the rate of 200 miles per hour?
10. What proportion of the world's population lives south of the equator?
11. What would be the trouble with you if you were suffering from septicemia?
12. What is Big Ben?
13. Distinguish between an hygrometer and an hydrometer.
14. If a goblin is a spirit what is a gobelin?
15. What is the name given to the hats worn by the King's guards?
16. Define one horsepower.
17. The wood of what tree is most commonly used in making lead pencils?
18. Why is the Statue of Liberty placed with her back towards the United States?
19. What is the name of the mineral called fool's gold?
20. The unit of electricity, volt, was named in honor of an Italian, an Englishman, or a Frenchman?
21. Who was the inventor of printing presses?

22. "Eric the Red" was which of the following: Russian, German, English, or Scandinavian?
23. What is a Dutch concert?
24. What is the purpose of the Binet-Simon test?
25. What is an eleemosynary institution?

SUPER QUIZ II-C

Answers on page 343

1. What is a calabash?
2. How far can a penguin fly?
3. If a bandmaster is a man who directs a band, a postmaster one who directs a post office, what is a bushmaster?
4. What is a savanna?
5. Describe a serape.
6. If you were invited to go "barn-door-skating", what would you expect to do?
7. What is the official name of the World Court?
8. What use would you make of an actinometer?
9. In America what corresponds to the hire-purchase system of England?
10. What commodity is put into its container after the container is sealed?
11. In the measurement of liquids, what is the difference between the standard and the Imperial gallon?
12. What is a cosmopolite?
13. What is an axiom?
14. To what use would you put a collimator?
15. What bird has no wishbone?
16. Who was Duncan Phyfe?
17. Who invented the flashlight?
18. How many accompanied Columbus when he discovered America?
19. If equal volumes of hot and cold water are poured together simultaneously into a third vessel at room temperature what happens to the temperature of the resulting mixture?
20. What is a phantasmagoria?
21. Does a ship weigh less when it is going east or west?
22. What is meant by the galaxy?
23. To what does this line refer: "I count no hours but unclouded ones"?

24. What are sagas?
25. What is a foot pound?

SUPER QUIZ II-D
Answers on page 344

1. What is the difference between a treasury note and a bank note?
2. What is the Prater?
3. What would you do if you went on a Nantucket sleigh ride?
4. What is known as "the art of pothooks"?
5. What is the difference between a bull and a bear in the stock market?
6. The head of a whale is six feet long; his tail is as long as his head and half his body, and his body is half of his whole length. How long is the whale?
7. What is rackarock?
8. How many cubic feet are there in a cord of wood?
9. What is the chief source of iodine?
10. What is a night-walker?
11. What is meant by pasteurization?
12. Who or what is a paranoiac?
13. What mineral is most nearly transparent?
14. Where and when did King John of England sign the Magna Charta?
15. London's Wall Street is called what?
16. What is a copper's nark?
17. What is a sugar bush?
18. How many vibrations per second are made by the wings of a fly and of a bee? Give each within twenty.
19. What is a yarborough?
20. What was the Anabasis, and who wrote it?
21. What two women of noble birth are reputed to have poisoned a number of people?
22. Who, besides Samuel Clemens, signed his name "Mark Twain"?
23. The electric phenomenon Northern Lights is called Aurora Borealis in northern latitudes; what is it called in southern latitudes?
24. What are naval stores?
25. What is a verger?

ANSWERS

ANSWERS TO DON'T CONFUSE 'EM QUIZ NUMBER I-A

1. Gross weight is the whole weight, including the goods and package; tare weight is the weight of the package alone; net weight is the weight of the goods only.

2. The introduction to a dramatic work or performance.

3. On the Fahrenheit thermometer, water freezes at 32 degrees and boils at 212 degrees. On the Centigrade thermometer, it freezes at zero and boils at 100 degrees.

4. A tabor is a small drum; a tabard is a mantle worn by knights.

5. A sailor. A form of drinking cup with a stem.

6. Eminent means high in office or rank. Imminent means threatening, said of peril.

7. A stamp collector; a sleep walker; one who has more than one wife at the same time.

8. Amnesia is loss of memory; asthenia is loss of strength.

9. Related by blood.

10. Stalactites are ice-like formations which hang from the ceiling of a cave. Stalagmites are ice-like formations which grow up from the floor of a cave.

11. Introspection is a looking-inward, an examination of one's thoughts or motives. Retrospection is the faculty or act of looking back on the past.

12. Rhodium is a bright rustless metal. Radium is an element possessing the property of giving off heat-giving luminous rays, and it is used medicinally.

13. It is the upright piece that casts the shadow on a sun-dial.

14. An alembic is an apparatus used in distillation; ceramics is the art of making things of baked clay, such as pottery, tile, etc.; polemics is the practice of disputation or controversy.

15. A howdah is a seat or pavilion, usually covered, on the back of an elephant. A hookah is a tobacco pipe in which the smoke is cooled by passing through water.

16. It means to embezzle, to pilfer, or to defraud the public.

17. Maternity means motherhood; husbandry pertains to the farm, agriculture.

18. A skipper is the master of the ship; the scupper is a hole at the side of the vessel to permit water to run off the decks.

19. A translucent substance permits the passage of light through it, but objects cannot be seen distinctly. Objects can be seen clearly through a transparent substance; and an opaque object does not permit the passage of rays of light.

20. A small hotel or tavern. An entrance, particularly to a small harbor or sheltering cove.

21. Plurality is the excess of votes cast for any one candidate who receives the next largest number of votes at an election where there are three or more candidates for the same office. Majority is the greater of two numbers, looked

upon as a part of the whole.
22. Bingo is a game; dingo is an Australian wild dog; and lingo is a colloquial language.
23. Convey means to carry; convoy means to attend for defence.

24. A gourmet is one who is selective in his choice of food; a gourmand is one who overeats.
25. A relic is remains, a souvenir, memento or memorial.

ANSWERS TO DON'T CONFUSE 'EM QUIZ NUMBER I-B

1. A bridge is a way over water; a viaduct is a way over land; an aqueduct is a conduit for carrying water.
2. One who shoes horses.
3. A misogamist is a hater of marriage, and a misogynist is a hater of women.
4. A wealthy person; an insect nest; a storm.
5. Convex curves out and concave curves in.
6. A priestess of Apollo at Delphi.
7. Selvage is the edge of cloth, woven to prevent raveling; a woven border. Salvage is goods or vessels saved from the dangers of the sea, or a wreck.
8. Open or public.
9. A replica is a copy by the same hand that executed the original; a reproduction is a copy by some one else.
10. An English gold coin, commonly called a sovereign.
11. An izard is a wild goat of the Pyrenees, and izzard is an old name for the letter Z.
12. Auger is a tool for boring holes; augur means to prophecy or foretell future events.

13. A tax collector, a much despised man in Biblical times.
14. A shallow lake or creek connected with the sea or river.
15. A polygon is a figure having many angles; polypod is having many feet.
16. A musical instrument; fiber used in twine; an American Indian.
17. There is no difference, they both mean to eat away.
18. The art of writing in cipher or secret characters.
19. A cornucopia is a horn of plenty; a cornopean is an organ stop of the reed family.
20. It is a projecting water spout of stone, usually carved in some fantastic shape.
21. Interstate means between two different states; intrastate means within one state.
22. A shell fish belonging to the scallop species.
23. Terra cotta is a brick; terra firma is dry land; terrapin is a species of turtle.
24. Shameless.
25. A disinfectant kills bacteria, while an antiseptic only inhibits the growth of bacteria without necessarily killing them.

ANSWERS TO DON'T CONFUSE 'EM QUIZ NUMBER I-C

1. Terminal is the station, the yard of the railroad in a city; terminus is the city at the end of a railroad.

2. A short rest or nap.
3. A polygon is a geometric figure having an indefinite number of sides; a hexagon is a six-sided figure; and a lexicon is a dictionary or a vocabulary.
4. Timber is the natural tree. Lumber is the wood cut from trees, although the words are now loosely used as synonyms.
5. Amnesia is loss of memory; aphasia is inability to control one's speech, one thinks, but one can't say it.
6. A word, sentence, or verse that is the same when read backward or forward. Ex: madam.
7. Indict is to charge formally with crime; indite is to write or compose.
8. A wooden measure, one fourth of a barrel; a small pickle; a waistcoat.
9. A lama is a priest or monk of Tibet. A llama is a beast of burden resembling the camel used in the Andes.
10. A very fleet animal of the cat family.
11. A picaroon is a pirate; a picador is a horseman in a bull fight; a piccolo is a small flute.
12. A chateau is a castle; a bando is a hat band; a plateau is a high plain.
13. Caddie is a boy who carries golf clubs; caddy is a small box for keeping tea; cadi is a Mohammedan judge.

14. A hall mark is a mark or proof of genuineness. A water mark is a device or mark made in the substance of paper during manufacturing. A land mark is a mark to designate the boundary of land.
15. An audience listens, a spectator watches.
16. Parsimonious means miserly, and persimmons are American plumlike fruits.
17. A scapegoat is one who bears the blame for others; a scapegrace is an irresponsible person; a scapula is a shoulder blade.
18. Grief or remorse.
19. An aviary is a place to keep birds and an apiary is a place to keep bees.
20. Adhesion is the joining together of atoms of different natures. Cohesion is the joining of atoms of a like nature.
21. Martial law means that troops are being used to maintain peace, not wage war. Military law implies a state of siege.
22. A papoose is an Indian baby; a porpoise is a sea animal.
23. Surplus means an excess of that which is required. Surplice means vestments with wide sleeves worn by the clergy.
24. Carat is a unit of measure for precious stones and metals. Caret is a mark used to indicate an omission. Carrot is a vegetable.
25. A kitchen.

ANSWERS TO DON'T CONFUSE 'EM QUIZ NUMBER I-D

1. An esophagus is a tube in the throat leading to the stomach. A sarcophagus is a tomb or stone coffin.

2. Specie is coined money, especially gold or silver; species means a particular sort or kind of thing, as species of plant, etc.
3. They both mean the same thing.
4. A subterranean burial place with niches hollowed out for the dead.
5. A tomb bearing the name of a person buried elsewhere.
6. A valedictorian is the person giving the parting address at a graduation, the first in honor at the graduation exercises. A valetudinarian is a chronic invalid.
7. A broad leather belt worn over the shoulder and across the breast for carrying ammunition.
8. A bell buoy is a channel marking at sea. A highboy is an article of furniture. A breeches buoy is a life-saving device used to rescue from boats.
9. A derelict is one unfaithful to duty, or a vessel abandoned at sea. A dialect is a form of speech marked by local peculiarities.
10. A room in a theatre where the actors and the audience may meet.
11. A patricide is the killing of a father, and a parasite is an organism that lives on some other organism from which it derives its nourishment.
12. The owner of a wharf.
13. Counterfoil is that part of a document (as a cheque) which is retained by the drawer. Counterpoint is the science of harmony, the art of composite melody.
14. A bar of metal.
15. Explode means to burst outward; implode means to burst inward as a light bulb does when broken.
16. A stretch of 8 notes. The 8th of a circle. An animal with eight feet.
17. One that is generally greatly exaggerated or highly imaginative.
18. Liniment is a medicated liquid for rubbing; lineament is a feature or an outline.
19. A shoestring.
20. The tuft of hair growing on a horse's ankle just above the hoof.
21. The first was an English poet of the 19th century; the second was a 19th century composer.
22. A panoramic picture taken from an airplane.
23. A sailor, as a crow's nest is a lookout or watch tower on the mainmast of a ship. A mare's nest is a hoax or a figment of the imagination.
24. They are all tractless plains, but the tundra is in the Arctic, the savanna in Florida, and the pampas in the Argentine.
25. Dido was Queen of Carthage; dado is the flat surface at the base of a wall; the dodo is an extinct bird.

ANSWERS TO MUSIC QUIZ NUMBER I-A

1. Most musical terms come from the Italian.
2. Annie Laurie—"her brow is like the snowdrift".
Clementine—"And her shoes were number nine".
Juanita—"In thy dark eyes splendor".

Alice—"Sweet Alice with hair so brown."

3. Both songs were written by Sir Thomas Moore.

4. A cantata is a musical work of a dramatic nature sung without costumes, scenery, or action. An opera is a dramatic musical work sung with costumes, scenery, and action.

5. It commemorates Sherman's famous march to the sea during the Civil War.

6. Strangely enough it doesn't appear once in all the stanzas.

7. John Henry, Cardinal Newman.

8. Francis Scott Key wrote these words to the "Star-Spangled Banner".

9. The Lorelei.

10. A violin has four strings; G-D-A-E.

11. Bach, Beethoven, and Brahms.

12. Eighty-five years old. "She's three times six, four times seven, twenty-eight and eleven. She's a young thing and cannot leave her mother."

13. The opera "Clairi" in London in 1823.

14. "Little Brown Jug".

15. "Arms and the Man".

16. Intermezzo—meaning a song or chorus dance between the acts of an opera.

17. A derby hat.

18. No. "The Star-Spangled Banner" is our national anthem. The song "America" has the same tune as "God Save the King", the British national anthem.

19. Tin Pan Alley is a section of New York from which emanate many of our popular tunes.

20. Prince Albert.

21. A lyre in this sense is a small harp.

22. "The Maple Leaf Forever," with words and music by Alexander Muir.

23. Rio Grande, Colorado, Swanee, Ohio, Wabash, Red River.

24. Use the hands and feet as it is a small organ.

25. It is an instrument of the oboe and bassoon family.

ANSWERS TO MUSIC QUIZ NUMBER I-B

1. Sweet music.

2. "Swanee River" doesn't belong in the list. It was written by Stephen Foster. The others were written by Irving Berlin.

3. "Pale Moon", "Wabash Moon", "Harvest Moon", "Carolina Moon", and "Blue Moon".

4. "Sweet Sue", "Margie", "Diane", "Rosalie", "Mary Lou", "Louise" and "Marie".

5. A bass drum is the larger.

6. Because it was written by Franz Peter Schubert.

7. A type of music combining two or more melodies simultaneously.

8. Peep-Bo was one of the "three little maids from school" in Gilbert and Sullivan's operetta "The Mikado".

9. "School Days".

10. By an act of Congress on March third, 1931.

11. From the "Pirates of Penzance" by Gilbert and Sullivan.

12. "Il Trovatore" by Verdi.

13. It describes the loudest noise a pipe organ can make.

14. According to the song: "With your lassie by your side".
15. It refers to the river Rye, in Scotland.
16. The opera "Carmen" by Georges Bizet.
17. It's in Minnesota. Its name is made up of two Sioux Indian words meaning "sky colored water".
18. "Waltz Me Around Again, Willie", "Blue Danube Waltz", "Skater's Waltz", "Save the Last Waltz For Me" or "The Flirtation Waltz".
19. "And twas from Aunt Dinah's quilting party I was seeing Nellie Home".
20. Ethelbert Nevin, Franz Liszt, Claude Debussy, Franz Liszt, and Franz Lehar in that order.
21. "Lo Hear the Gentle Lark", "When the Red Red Robin Comes Bob, Bob, etc. etc." "When the "Swallows Homeward Fly", "Last Night the Nightingale Woke Me", and "When the Whippoorwill Sings Marguerite".
22. Wagner and Mendelssohn.
23. Strings, wood winds, brasses, and percussion instruments.
24. John Philip Sousa.
25. The harmonica.

ANSWERS TO MUSIC QUIZ NUMBER I-C

1. The short pipes.
2. There are eight notes in one octave, fifteen in two octaves.
3. Saturday and Monday. From "Sally in our Alley".
4. "Jingle Bells".
5. "The Battle Hymn of the Republic".
6. Organ, piano, traps, harp.
7. Banjo—six strings; guitar—five strings.
8. On the Bowery according to the song.
9. "Just a Song at Twilight".
10. Literally in church or chapel style; also refers to a chorus of voices unaccompanied by music.
11. Glen Gray, Ben Bernie, Kay Kyser, Cab Calloway, Horace Heidt, Tommy Tucker.
12. "Button Up Your Overcoat", "Alice Blue Gown", "Where Did You Get that Hat?", "Breaking in a New Pair of Shoes".
13. "Home Sweet Home".
14. The Sweetheart of Sigma Chi.
15. "Deep Purple", "Wearing of the Green", "Little Gray Home in the West", "Red Sails in the Sunset".
16. "Aida", "Il Trovatore", "La Traviata", "Rigoletto".
17. Robert Burns.
18. Ben Jonson, an Elizabethan poet.
19. "Let a smile be your umbrella".
20. A funeral song, refrain or dirge.
21. "Old Kentucky Home", "Old Black Joe", "Old Folks at Home", "Swanee River", "Oh! Susanna", "Massa's in De Cold Cold Ground.
22. Fidelio.
23. Violoncello.
24. A violin maker.
25. They are all types of horns.

1. The negro poet James Bland.
2. It's a western movie.
3. There is no difference, the word pianoforte has been shortened by popular usage.
4. It is neither of English origin nor is it a horn. It's a woodwind instrument of French origin and is really an alto oboe.
5. She was an Ethiopian.
6. They are both musical scales.
7. The harp on the flag of Ireland.
8. An instrument marking time by means of a pendulum.
9. Schubert, Schumann, Sullivan.
10. Calliope.
11. Duke Ellington, Earle Hines, Count Bassi, Henry King.
12. In music it's a sixty-fourth note.
13. From "Robin Hood" by Reginald de Koven.
14. It's an old Russian stringed instrument.
15. A musical term for songs sung by the Venetian gondolier.
16. Melodies are produced by notes in succession; harmonies are produced by notes in combination.
17. "The Barber of Seville".
18. Richard Wagner was married to Cosima, the daughter of Franz Liszt.
19. The harmonica.
20. According to the old song "in the land of my dreams".
21. "The Peer Gynt Suite" of Edvard Grieg.
22. Ludwig van Beethoven.
23. Susanna in Stephen Foster's song "Oh! Susanna".
24. Music written for a small string orchestra, usually a trio or quartet.
25. "Samson and Delilah".

ANSWERS TO BIBLE QUIZ NUMBER ONE.

1. An eye for an eye, and a tooth for a tooth.
2. Adam.
3. Ananias.
4. Methuselah; 969 years old.
5. 150.
6. Job.
7. Solomon.
8. "Proclaim liberty throughout the land unto all the inhabitants".
9. The love of money.
10. The third day.
11. A raven and a dove.
12. The twenty-third.
13. Mount Ararat, in Armenia.
14. The ten commandments.
15. Yes; the first five books.
16. Sandals.
17. Samson.
18. Joseph.
19. Luke.
20. 39 in the Old Testament; 27 in the New.
21. Because they thought it was a good opening for a young man.
22. It was three hundred feet in height.
23. David.
24. Tax collector.
25. The jaw-bone of an ass.

ANSWERS TO BIBLE QUIZ NUMBER TWO.

1. Nebuchadnezzar.
2. The feast of Belshazzar.
3. The Torah.
4. Solomon.
5. Esau.
6. Isaac and Rebecca were their parents; Abraham and Sara their grand-parents.
7. The Red Sea.
8. The Queen of Sheba.
9. Aramaic, a dialect of Northern Syria.
10. The Apocrypha.
11. After the army had marched around the city for seven days, the high priests blew upon trumpets, the people shouted, and the walls crumpled.
12. Cain; he killed Abel, leaving only Adam, Eve, and himself.
13. Ecclesiastes, Esther, Exodus, Ezekiel, Ezra.
14. "Good news".
15. Jesus wept. John 11:35.
16. At that time, around 1700 B.C., only three dyes were known: blue, purple, and scarlet.
17. Do not cast pearls before swine. Train a child in the way he should go. Spare the rod and spoil the child.
18. John Elliot of Natick, Massachusetts.
19. In the one hundred and seventh Psalm, twenty-third verse.
20. An ancient measure of length determined by the distance between the elbow and the tip of the middle finger, thus making it about seventeen or eighteen inches.
21. Daniel.
22. Cain.
23. Matthew, Mark, Luke, and John.
24. Joshua.
25. The fatted calf.

ANSWERS TO BIBLE QUIZ NUMBER THREE.

1. He stuttered badly.
2. The first five books of the Old Testament.
3. Lot's wife, who met her death by being turned into a pillar of salt.
4. The tradition is that Solomon invited them to wash their hands after their long journey. The boys washed only their hands, but the girls rolled up their sleeves and washed their arms as well.
5. Noah, because he floated a limited company when all the rest of the world was in liquidation.
6. In his hair.
7. Revelation; 16:16.
8. Lot's wife who was turned to a pillar of salt; Jonah, who was swallowed by the whale and then spewed out.
9. Exodus.
10. Ezra, Joel, Jude, Luke, John, Mark, Ruth, Amos.
11. Only boys were killed by Herod.
12. Yes, twice.
13. Yes; the Vulgate is a Latin version of the Bible prepared by St. Jerome late in the fourth century.
14. Thomas the apostle.
15. Adam and Eve were husband and wife; Cain and Abel were brothers; Ruth was Naomi's daughter-in-law; Solomon was David's son; Saul of Tarsus and Paul were the same person.

16. Job; 19:20.
17. A Hebrew youth who came out of the fiery furnace unharmed.
18. Toga.
19. The Jordan river which flows in a southerly direction.
20. Simon Peter, Paul, Andrew, Simon, James, John, Philip, Thomas, Matthew, Thaddeus, James the son of Alpheus, and Judas Iscariot.
21. Egypt.
22. Some magi from the East who studied the stars and their effect on human affairs.
23. As "a Saviour" and "Christ the Lord".
24. Judea of Galilee.
25. In Armenia. The Ark landed there when the waters subsided.

ANSWERS TO BIBLE QUIZ NUMBER FOUR.

1. A star.
2. They had gone there to be enrolled in accordance with a decree of Augustus Caesar.
3. Gold, frankincense, myrrh.
4. Peace, towards men of good will.
5. Bethlehem.
6. "All things whatsoever ye would that men should do to you, do ye even so to them".
7. John the Baptist, John the Apostle, and John Mark, usually called Mark.
8. Jephthah; Judges 11:31-40.
9. "A glad father".
10. Jonathan.
11. Saul.
12. The word means "six books" and refers to the first six books of the Bible.
13. Exodus.
14. Athaliah.
15. Herod the Great.
16. It means "God".
17. John the Baptist.
18. Moses.
19. Second John.
20. It has been given two meanings; one that it calls for an outburst of music, the second a rest or pause.
21. They were unchanging and unchangeable.
22. Psalms, with one hundred and fifty.
23. His wife and his three sons and their wives, and one each of every living creature, a male and a female. Genesis; 6:18-20.
24. Forty days.
25. The dove, bearing an olive leaf.

ANSWERS TO LITERARY QUIZ NUMBER I-A.

1. *Romeo and Juliet, A Midsummer Night's Dream, Twelfth Night,* and *The Merchant of Venice.*
2. *The Iliad* and *The Odyssey.*
3. Crimean War of 1854-1856.
4. Abraham Lincoln.
5. "Through all the wide border his steed was the best".
6. She was always knitting.
7. Richard Brinsley Sheridan.
8. "Nevermore".
9. He wrote *Robinson Crusoe.*
10. Helen of Troy. "Is this the face that launched a thousand ships, and burnt the topless towers of Ilium"?
11. *Barnaby Rudge.*

12. Seven.
13. Maud Muller, in the poem by Whittier.
14. Henry Wadsworth Longfellow.
15. *Alice in Wonderland.*
16. Pinocchio.
17. In Shakespeare's *Merchant of Venice.*
18. "And be a friend to man". From "The House By the Side of the Road", by Samuel Walter Foss.
19. "Evangeline", by Henry Wadsworth Longfellow.
20. *Hamlet, Macbeth, Othello, King Lear,* and *Romeo and Juliet.*
21. Black Beauty, the Green Goddess, Scarlett O'Hara, Blue Beard. Snow White, Red Pepper Burns, etc. etc.
22. "East is east, and West is west".
23. *Les Miserables,* by Victor Hugo.
24. Robin Hood.
25. One of Shakespeare's famous clowns. He appeared in the *Merchant of Venice.*

ANSWERS TO LITERARY QUIZ NUMBER I-B.

1. They are all pen names of Charles Dickens.
2. "So shines a good deed in a naughty world".
3. Three: Christmas Past, Present, and Yet to Come.
4. Jules Verne.
5. Little Eva, of *Uncle Tom's Cabin* fame.
6. Oliver Wendell Holmes.
7. The principal characters in a novel of the same name by Fyodor Dostoevski.
8. "Something to turn up".
9. James M. Barrie.
10. Petruchio, in Shakespeare's *Taming of the Shrew.*
11. *The Mystery of Edwin Drood.*
12. Robinson Crusoe; it was the footprint of his man Friday.
13. *The Three Musketeers, Tale of Two Cities, Seven Keys to Baldpate, Six Little Peppers, The Thirteen Steps, The Three Comrades,* etc. etc.
14. Grave, Alice, Laughing Allegra, and Edith with golden hair.
15. Meg, Jo, Amy, and Beth March.
16. She found him dying.
17. Road to Lima.
18. Neither; he was an imaginary character in Shakespeare's play of the same name.
19. The Bible is the best seller every year.
20. *The Legend of Sleepy Hollow,* by Washington Irving.
21. Shakespeare, in the last act of *Hamlet.* The Queen says these words as she throws flowers on Ophelia's grave.
22. This aquatic bird that inhabits the southern seas plays an important part in the "Rime of the Ancient Mariner".
23. A gorilla.
24. In *Ben-Hur,* by Lew Wallace.
25. "Barefoot boy with cheek of tan", by Whittier.

ANSWERS TO LITERARY QUIZ NUMBER I-C.

1. The Mississippi River.
2. "The Lady of the Lake", by Sir Walter Scott.

3. John Ridd.
4. Rudyard Kipling.
5. *Treasure Island,* by Robert Louis Stevenson.
6. Thomas Gray, in his "Elegy".
7. One of the chief characters in *Vanity Fair,* a novel by William Makepeace Thackeray.
8. The Holy Grail.
9. Hawkeye.
10. New Hampshire.
11. Brom Bones.
12. S. S. Van Dine, whose real name was Willard Huntington Wright.
13. "I am the Captain of my soul" from the poem "Invictus", by William Ernest Henley.
14. *David Copperfield, Old Curiosity Shop, Little Dorrit.*

15. James Russell Lowell, in "The Vision of Sir Launfal".
16. Caesar's wife.
17. *The Virginian,* by Owen Wister.
18. *Romeo and Juliet.*
19. *Othello,* by William Shakespeare.
20. A character in the French fairy story known as Barbe Bleu, or Bluebeard, because of the color of his beard.
21. The wonderful one hoss shay, which lasted a hundred years to a day.
22. "Locksley Hall", by Alfred Lord Tennyson.
23. *Twenty Thousand Leagues Under the Sea,* by Jules Verne.
24. Nathaniel Hawthorne wrote the story; the letter was an "A".
25. Denmark.

ANSWERS TO LITERARY QUIZ NUMBER I-D.

1. Those of Rip van Winkle and the Sleeping Beauty.
2. Cratchit.
3. *Two Gentlemen of Verona.*
4. Chief Uncas.
5. Paul Revere's ride.
6. Romeo Montague and Juliet Capulet.
7. Women were not allowed on the stage during Shakespeare's day.
8. A section of Westminster Abbey where poets are buried.
9. A water boy in Rudyard Kipling's poem of the same name.
10. A character in Charles Dickens's *Martin Chuzzlewit.*
11. Macbeth was a king of Scotland who died in the year 1057.
12. *Treasure Island,* by Stevenson.
13. "For I'm to be Queen of the May, mother, I'm to be Queen of the May", Tennyson.

14. Shelley's "Ode to a Skylark".
15. Louisa May Alcott, Ralph Waldo Emerson, Nathaniel Hawthorne.
16. *Hamlet.*
17. "The Ancient Mariner", by Samuel Taylor Coleridge.
18. Her beautiful feet.
19. Sherlock Holmes.
20. John Dryden, seventeenth century English poet.
21. *Macbeth,* by Shakespeare.
22. London, England, and Paris, France.
23. Yes; by Friar Laurence in his cell.
24. *Don Quixote,* by Cervantes.
25. "Shall fold their tents like the Arabs,
   And as silently steal away".—Longfellow.

ANSWERS TO GENERAL QUIZ NUMBER I-A.

1. Baltic, Bering, and Black Seas.
2. Isle of Capri.
3. Buenos Aires.
4. New York; St. Louis; Chicago; Detroit; Philadelphia.
5. Rutherford Birchard Hayes and Franklin Delano Roosevelt, both 23 letters.
6. Yule log. Shamrock. Palms.
7. The southernmost tip of South America.
8. Jefferson City.
9. New Year's Eve, marking the end of the Christmas season in Scotland.
10. John Calvin Coolidge. Thomas Woodrow Wilson. Stephen Grover Cleveland.
11. Off the island of Mindanao in the Philippines; depth 35,400 feet.
12. No, it is an island in the Atlantic Ocean, a British possession.
13. The Orkney Islands.
14. Saint Nicholas.
15. Edam.
16. Four. Cuba, Haiti, Puerto Rico, and Jamaica.
17. Come, ye faithful.
18. Over the Connecticut River between Northampton and Hadley.
19. Mecca; all true worshippers still face Mecca at prayer time.
20. In Arkansas.
21. An island; the South Pacific.
22. Colt.
23. Touching glasses together when drinking.
24. Raleigh.
25. Wheeling. Frankfurt. Annapolis. Charlotte. Daytona (date on a). Havana.

ANSWERS TO GENERAL QUIZ NUMBER I-B.

1. Bob gave Dick a punch in the side for cooking the bunny so little.
2. Annapolis, Maryland; Indianapolis, Indiana; Minneapolis, Minnesota.
3. Johnnycake and succotash.
4. They are all types of insects.
5. Colombia.
6. Strawberry. Gooseberry.
7. The Louisiana purchase.
8. Baltimore, the Baltimore Clipper.
9. Faneuil Hall.
10. Almost 1500 feet.
11. The Mississippi River.
12. Hang by your feet.
13. Tennessee.
14. Eat them, they are a hot Mexican dish containing Mexican beans.
15. Eat it, it is an English cheese.
16. Mass of Christ.
17. From the Italian word, meaning tale.
18. Vermont.
19. France.
20. Indian Ocean.
21. Syria.
22. Not until 1752 was the present date of January 1 in general use as the first day of the year.
23. English and French.
24. Six.
25. Quite probably, since pilchards are sardines.

ANSWERS TO GENERAL QUIZ NUMBER I-C.

1. Short wave stations.
2. The tip of South America.
3. No, he puts out his wooden shoes.
4. New York; London; Paris; Venice.
5. It means that the earth has just completed a complete revolution around the sun in 365 1/4 days, and is about to start another one.
6. They are colored red.
7. Golf, polo, baseball, hockey.
8. First footing is a custom in Scotland, and it means that the first person to visit you on New Year's day must bring a bottle, and give you a drink to bring you good luck for the coming year.
9. Bald.
10. Eight. Dasher, Dancer, Prancer, Vixen, Comet, Cupid, Donner, Blitzen.
11. Blue, green, yellow, or orange.
12. Africa, South America, Africa, South America, India, Arctic regions.
13. Colorado.
14. Jersey.
15. You ought to keep it, pelf means money or wealth.
16. Charles-ton, Dan-ville, Frankfort, John-stown, Louis-ville, Jack-sonville, etc. etc.
17. They are both sap from trees.
18. A male ostrich.
19. The Smithsonian Institution, Washington, D.C., where Lindbergh's plane is on view.
20. Flocks, pastures, and wild life.
21. Commute is to travel regularly; compute is to reckon, estimate or number.
22. It means that you are doing a job for which you have already been paid.
23. A place to trade.
24. A song of joy and exultation; old ballads sung at Christmas.
25. Cabbage, as it grows above the ground, and the others grow under the ground.

ANSWERS TO GENERAL QUIZ NUMBER I-D.

1. You should feel complimented, as the rest of the quotation is "your face is so fair that even Time stops to gaze at it".
2. Tap dancing.
3. Foot. Hand. Shoulder. Stomach.
4. Commendation is to praise; condemnation is to censure.
5. Paul Revere.
6. Clement Clarke Moore, wrote it in 1822 for his own children.
7. The Persian Gulf.
8. No.
9. The high hills on either side of the Strait of Gibraltar.
10. February 2nd.
11. Indiana.
12. Labor Day. All other holidays are by state law.
13. On the Adriatic coast of Greece.
14. Indiana and Kentucky, respectively.
15. 19 seconds.
16. When caught it feigns death.
17. A large log of wood used as the basis of the Christmas fire.
18. The Niagara River.
19. Making a decisive or important move that cannot be retracted.

20. With an assumed name or station.
21. A brisk lively dance usually for 8 persons.
22. That part of a ring in which the stone is set.
23. Uruguay, South America.
24. Holland.
25. All the difference in the world.

ANSWERS TO GENERAL QUIZ NUMBER II-A.

1. Caboose and calliope respectively.
2. For its medical specialists.
3. The Happy Hunting Ground.
4. The swing of their bodies and the impact of their feet in rhythm would cause the bridge to swing and eventually to break.
5. A Colonel.
6. France.
7. Atheism.
8. Barber shop, cigar store, pawn shop, and drug store.
9. Ceramics.
10. Alumnus for the men and alumna for the women.
11. A farewell drink.
12. Genealogy.
13. Shakespeare: *Hamlet* Act V, Scene 2.
14. For the favorite wife of the Emperor of India, Sha Jahan.
15. Diamonds, sapphires, emeralds, rubies, and opals.
16. The devil, an unmarried woman, a veteran sailor, and the flag of the United States.
17. Because it is the principal ingredient of smokeless powder and can be best combined with nitric acid to produce a high explosive.
18. The Governor of the state in which the National Guard is located is the only one with this power.
19. In Ecuador, South America.
20. The moustache and long, drooping whiskers worn by the fashionable men of England in the 1860's.
21. Two masts; a brig is square rigged.
22. A postage due stamp.
23. A horse, wife, and a moustache.
24. Dry ice.
25. Amazons.

ANSWERS TO GENERAL QUIZ NUMBER II-B.

1. Theoretically it will never reach the surface because there will always be one half the distance remaining.
2. An audience hears, spectators see.
3. One eighth of a mile.
4. A three stringed Japanese banjo-like instrument.
5. A freshman at West Point.
6. Aaron Burr.
7. Library, atlas, anthology, hymnal.
8. Monsieur, Herr, Señor.
9. One who cuts or polishes gems.
10. The practice of having more than one husband.
11. Rough.
12. Murk, dirk, and lurk.
13. Utopia.
14. All were noted archers.
15. Twenty knots; as the word knots refers to the speed per hour.
16. A duplicate is that which exactly resembles or corresponds to something. A facsimile is an exact and

detailed copy of anything. A replica is a copy of a work of art by the maker of the original.

17. White for China; blue or violet for Turkey; yellow for Egypt.
18. The same four feet; a tree grows in diameter but in height by top branches only.
19. Die.
20. One which results from a high temperature.
21. During the new and full moon.
22. King Midas.
23. You'd find brownstone, and yourself in jail, no doubt.
24. The care of children.
25. The Globe theater.

ANSWERS TO GENERAL QUIZ NUMBER II-C.

1. Mohammedan, Hebrew, Buddhist or Hindu, and Christian.
2. "It's a long time between drinks".
3. Emeritus.
4. Moat.
5. Ten Downing Street, residence of the Prime Minister.
6. April, August, December, February, January, July, June, March, May, November, October, September.
7. In the form of a cross.
8. Your equals.
9. More than seventy-five miles per hour.
10. A shuttle.
11. A mural or fresco.
12. Rhode Island, Maryland, Indiana, New York.
13. A sovereign.
14. A colt becomes a horse at five years.
15. The face is protected by a metal case.
16. It's the guillotine in France, the headsman's axe in Germany, and the firing squad in Russia.
17. Nine floors.
18. The Norfolk Navy Yard is in Portsmouth, Virginia; and the Portsmouth Navy Yard is in Kittery, Maine.
19. Red, purple, yellow, blue, white, and green.
20. There are eight, count 'em.
21. Tobacco.
22. When playing checkers, while swimming, and while playing bridge.
23. Five thousand; "ten thousand eyes were on him—five thousand voices cheered him".
24. It's a shipment by train; a cargo by boat.
25. A hemisphere.

ANSWERS TO GENERAL QUIZ NUMBER II-D.

1. Twenty-four.
2. Daniel was the orator and Noah the lexicographer.
3. Rain before seven, clear before eleven. Rainbow at night, sailor's delight. Rainbow in morning, sailors take warning. A green Christmas, a white Easter.
4. A horse gets up with his front legs first, a cow with her hind legs first.
5. The wheel-barrow.
6. Buckingham Palace.
7. A breed of cattle, fine wool yarn, a close fitting woolen shirt.
8. Romulus and Remus.

9. Ten times.
10. Platinum is the heavier.
11. She talked him green in the face; you could have knocked me down with a feather; she talked his head, or his ear, off; not a leg left to stand on; her eyes dropped to the floor; she flung her arms out of the window.
12. Tonsillectomy.
13. Crazy quilt, loco-motive, buggy ride, screw ball, nut sundae, cuckoo clock, daffy-dill, etc. etc.
14. Daily.
15. Seven hills of Rome, seven ages of man, seven sages of ancient Greece, seven wonders of the world, seven fat years, seven lean years, seven golden years.
16. One out of many.
17. A ghost writer is one who writes stories or articles to be published under another's name.
18. Oxford and Cambridge.
19. Cherry, orange, lime, olive, tangerine, strawberry, lemon, plum.
20. One thousand dollars, five, one hundred, ten.
21. An iceberg for the first, a submarine for the latter.
22. Lady Godiva, Samson, Absalom, Rapunzel, Goldilocks.
23. Master at Arms.
24. The wheelbase.
25. It's called the Privy Council.

ANSWERS TO GENERAL QUIZ NUMBER III-A.

1. The widow's watch is a small piazza enclosed by a railing at the top of many homes on Martha's Vineyard. The outlook faces the sea and there wives of the old whalers waited and watched for the return of their loved ones.
2. It begins on December 13, Santa Lucia's Day, and ends January 11.
3. China, England, Scotland, Turkey.
4. Jacob Coxey led 20,000 unemployed persons in a march on Washington, April 4, 1894.
5. Yes, every year.
6. Golf, polo, tennis, fencing, diving.
7. Laughing gas.
8. Merinos are the most widely distributed breed of sheep.
9. In New York city on April 30, 1789.
10. Play it, it's a famous violin.
11. They are both extinct.
12. Pig.
13. It's a South American animal.
14. If the President and Vice-president should both die, the Secretary of State would become President and the Secretary of State is an appointive office.
15. Because of the red color imparted to it by millions of tiny plants.
16. Pike.
17. The left side as one faces from stern to bow.
18. Because they were the most expensive and valuable gifts available and were customarily associated with Kings.
19. Frankincense is a fragrant resinous gum from certain Arabian trees. Myrrh is an aromatic gum from Arabian shrubs.
20. The Isle of Man, an English possession in the Irish Sea.

21. Arctic, Antarctic, North Pacific, South Pacific, North Atlantic, South Atlantic, and Indian Ocean.
22. Benjamin Harrison.
23. Aye. Aye aye. Cage it, it's a nocturnal animal of Madagascar.
24. An okapi is an animal of the Belgian Congo.
25. Wayside altar reproducing the nativity scene.

ANSWERS TO GENERAL QUIZ NUMBER III-B.

1. A beetle is an insect, a beadle is a messenger or crier, a beagle is a small hound.
2. The Old Year.
3. John Milton.
4. Two tiny bits of gold passed across a bar in '49 bought a drink of rum worth twenty-five cents. A quarter thus became called two bits.
5. John McAdam; the macadam pavement.
6. Fifty, five hundred, and one thousand.
7. Jersey, Guernsey, Alderney, and Sark.
8. A fall guy is one easily tricked into some criminal action for which he alone would seem responsible; a fagin is a fence or receiver of stolen property; the term is also used to denote one who teaches children to steal, as derived from the character Fagin in Dickens's *Oliver Twist*.
9. Live in; it's a Swiss cottage.
10. Off the Alaskan coast, between the Bering Sea and the Pacific Ocean.
11. "Merry Christmas to all, and to all a good night".
12. Maine, Augusta; New Hampshire, Concord; Vermont, Montpelier; Massachusetts, Boston; Rhode Island, Providence; Connecticut, Hartford.
13. The care of children.
14. Oklahoma, whose capital is Oklahoma City.
15. Judea.
16. Connecticut.
17. Houston, Texas, which is connected to the Gulf of Mexico by an artificial ship canal forty-five miles long.
18. St. Nicholas and Kris Kringle.
19. Venice.
20. Carson City.
21. The Greek word Christos uses X for the first two letters, hence the contraction Xmas.
22. An extra ration of rum for all hands.
23. From Antoine Sax, its inventor.
24. This term was used by miners during the gold rush of '49; gold discovered which proved to be only in the top-soil was referred to as "a flash in the pan".
25. No. It was named after its originator, a Mr. Fox who was a New York dancing master.

ANSWERS TO GENERAL QUIZ NUMBER III-C.

1. Buenos Aires, Rio de Janeiro, Santiago, Lima.
2. Death Pledge.
3. South America.
4. The banjo which was invented by Joseph Sweeney, a musical Irishman who was so versatile that he was called a whole band

in himself. Hence "band joe."

5. No, the Hudson river is in New York state and Hudson Bay in Canada.
6. The Pacific.
7. South Carolina does not grant divorce on any grounds.
8. St. Augustine, Florida.
9. The Virginian in Owen Wister's novel of the same name.
    Stonewall Jackson, in Whittier's poem "Barbara Frietchie".
    Thomas R. Marshall, while presiding over a senate debate on the needs of the country.
    Charles Dudley Warner, in an editorial in the Hartford, Connecticut, Courant.
10. Colombia.
11. The highest mountain in Great Britain.
12. Christiania.
13. The North Pole and the Equator.

14. Ohio, Connecticut, Mississippi, Missouri, Colorado, Delaware.
15. Lake Michigan.
16. Holly, poinsettia, mistletoe.
17. Arizona.
18. Wyoming.
19. The Rocky Mountains.
20. Actor.
21. The Himalayas is the highest range, and Mount Everest, at 29,141 feet, is the highest peak.
22. Grosbeak, grouse, greenfinch, goshawk, goldfinch, gull, guinea fowl.
23. A complicated structure with many passages hard to find one's way about without guidance; a maze.
24. A stocking.
25. Seven. Maine, Michigan, Minnesota, North Dakota, Rhode Island, South Dakota, Wisconsin.

ANSWERS TO GENERAL QUIZ NUMBER III-D.

1. In East Java, in the Netherlands Indies.
2. Washington, Wyoming, West Virginia, Wisconsin.
3. Platoon, battery, battalion, regiment, brigade, and division respectively.
4. Topeka.
5. Niagara Falls, Yellowstone Park, Giant Redwood trees, Grand Canyon, Rocky Mountains, and the Palisades along the Hudson River.
6. Time, Bulb, and Instantaneous.
7. In France.
8. There are about five thousand.
9. Stop looking for it.
10. In Asia, between India and Tibet.
11. "The Gift of the Magi", by O. Henry or "The Story of the Other Wise Man", by Henry van Dyke.
12. Frankfort.
13. The chief Hawaiian Islands are 3,400 miles from Yokohama and 2,100 miles from San Francisco.
14. A stockade, peel an apple, a baker's peel, used to take loaves from an oven.
15. Paris.
16. From 150 to 160 feet.
17. Little Jack Horner.
18. Austrian.
19. Brazil, where Portuguese is the official language.
20. Vermont, New Hampshire, Massachusetts, and Connecticut.
21. They are shipped to the Congo, where they are used as tribal thrones.

22. "In Memoriam", by Alfred Lord Tennyson.
23. 1776.
24. Constantinople.
25. Off the eastern coast of New-foundland.

HERE ARE THE QUESTIONS YOU SHOULD HAVE ASKED TO I-A.

1. What is pigeon English?
2. In what state is the United States Cavalry School?
3. What would you use to ride an elephant?
4. What is the Great Divide?
5. When and where was the battle-ship Maine blown up?
6. In hunting, what is a quiver?
7. What is the difference between a cassock and a cossack?
8. Name three well-known flowers beginning with the letter "P".
9. What are the four component parts of an orchestra?
10. What does the word hibernation mean?
11. What English General was called "Gentlemanly Johnny"?
12. What is the wife of a Maharajah called?
13. What is the burial place of the Kings of England?
14. What was the name of the plane flown by Charles Lindbergh in his first trans-Atlantic flight?
15. What bird can fly backwards?
16. What trees are cut by the light of the moon because this is the time they are freest from sap, sounder and of a richer color than during the day?
17. What is an abacus?
18. A fertile spot in the desert is called by what name?
19. What season starts with the vernal equinox?
20. If you were talking to a poilu, a tommy, and a gob, who would you be speaking with?
21. What is Sanskrit?
22. What is the name of the oath all physicians and surgeons take?
23. What is the meaning of the word myopia?
24. What is a stirrup cup?
25. What is meant by carding?

HERE ARE THE QUESTIONS YOU SHOULD HAVE ASKED TO I-B.

1. What does tempus fugit mean?
2. Who were Eng and Chang?
3. How much of a load can a camel carry?
4. What is a blue peter and when is it used?
5. What are mullion windows?
6. What is a cartographer?
7. What is an honorarium?
8. What is the shortest distance between two points?
9. Who was known as the Snow Baby?
10. What is a metronome?
11. What is a spatula?
12. What is a Jolly Roger?
13. What are the seven prismatic colors of the rainbow?
14. Where and what is the Sargasso Sea?
15. Why do teeth require more care and give us more trouble than other parts of the normal body?
16. What was Voltaire's real name?
17. What is a patella?
18. Where is Hell Gate Bridge?

239

19. The Allegheny and the Monongahela rivers unite where to form what?
20. What are jodhpurs?
21. Upon what two famous men did Queen Elizabeth confer knighthood?
22. Birmingham, England, and Birmingham, Alabama, are both famous for what?
23. When may the vice-president vote in the United States Senate?
24. What is a fellah?
25. What is the large red flower used for Christmas decorations?

HERE ARE THE QUESTIONS YOU SHOULD HAVE ASKED TO I-C.

1. What garden implement does an adz most nearly resemble?
2. What Bible character carried off the Gates of Gaza?
3. What is the last word in the dictionary?
4. Who betrayed Christ, and for how much?
5. When God made Eve, why did he take a rib from Adam rather than any other bone of the body?
6. Which is the nearer to the South Pole, Cape Horn or the Cape of Good Hope?
7. What word describes an angel of the highest rank?
8. Between what two continents is the Strait of Gibraltar?
9. What states are officially designated as Commonwealths?
10. What were the ancient Celtic names of Ireland, Scotland, and Wales?
11. What is a printer's devil?
12. What is the capital of the Netherlands?
13. Where did Sheridan make his famous ride?
14. Lake Champlain lies between what two states?
15. What is the English meaning of Rio de Janeiro?
16. What state is called the Badger state?
17. What is the capital of Ecuador?
18. What is a mahlstick?
19. During what queen's reign did Shakespeare write, and what was the name of the theater where most of his plays were first acted?
20. When were the Dionne quintuplets born?
21. What two bodies of water does the English Channel connect?
22. What English King was called "Coeur de Lion"?
23. What was the name of the little lame boy in Dickens's Christmas Carol?
24. Why are dykes used in Holland?
25. What is an isthmus?

HERE ARE THE QUESTIONS YOU SHOULD HAVE ASKED TO I-D.

1. What is the annual sum paid for insurance called?
2. What is ornithology?
3. How are lights measured?
4. What is the name applied to the process of caring for and beautifying the feet?
5. Give the first five words of Lincoln's Gettysburg address.
6. What is an inhabitant of the Isle of Man called?

7. How many knights belonged to King Arthur's Round Table?
8. What is meant by the expression "God's Acres"?
9. What is the name of Punch's dog in the Punch and Judy shows?
10. What does the word gonof mean?
11. For whom was Diogenes looking with his lantern?
12. What do the words "Erin Go Bragh" mean?
13. What are the three Maritime Provinces?
14. What is beautiful about a camel?
15. What was Phineas T. Barnum's middle name?
16. What is the singular of opera?
17. What is a toscophilite?
18. What name is applied to a solid object having twelve plain surfaces?
19. In the song "Coming Through the Rye", what is meant by the word Rye?
20. Could Benjamin Franklin have been rocked to sleep in a rocking chair, as a baby?
21. How are Hope, Faith, and Charity portrayed in art?
22. Who is the patron saint of shoemakers?
23. What is an N-gon?
24. Is a hair's breadth a real unit of measurement or just a figure of speech?
25. Where would you go to get a copy of the British Constitution?

ANSWERS TO SPORTS QUIZ NUMBER ONE.

1. It is square.
2. On ice; rounded stones are hurled towards a tee.
3. At the base of the skull.
4. Tartans-Carnegie Tech, Panthers-Pittsburgh, Wolverines-Michigan.
5. A race in which two or more contestants finish at precisely the same time.
6. That your ball lies directly behind your opponent's.
7. Saint Olaf is so regarded.
8. Horseshoe pitching.
9. Belgium.
10. Lawn tennis.
11. Thirty-two.
12. A period of play in polo is called a chukker.
13. It means pitching at the batter's head.
14. Prizefight—a bell; foot race—a gun; football game—a whistle.
15. Rugby.
16. It is square, measuring fifteen inches on a side.
17. There are six outs to an inning of baseball.
18. Card playing.
19. Rose Bowl—Pasadena, California; Cotton Bowl—Dallas, Texas; Sugar Bowl—New Orleans, Louisiana; Orange Bowl—Miami, Florida.
20. A charlie horse is in an athlete's muscle; it's a cramp or tightening of the muscles.
21. Hurling or hurley and is played similar to our American hockey.
22. Cricket.
23. The winning team moves backward in a tug-of-war.
24. 4.4.4 was Glenn Cunningham's record for the mile run.
25. The Davis Cup is a tennis trophy.

ANSWERS TO SPORTS QUIZ NUMBER TWO.

1. The King of Sweden.
2. Sacrifice hit—baseball; drop kick —football; cross check—hockey.
3. One pair, two pair, three of a kind, straight, a flush, a full house, four of a kind, a straight flush and a royal straight flush.
4. Nightcap is slang for the last game of a doubleheader.
5. Fifty-nine minutes are consumed.
6. Because the white yard lines crossing it resemble a gridiron.
7. Standing in the stirrups distributes the jockey's weight where it will be least felt.
8. Backgammon.
9. Tennis, baseball, golf, squash, hand ball, pool, polo, basketball, lacrosse, and table tennis are a few.
10. The coxswain of a racing crew also uses a megaphone.
11. Four hundred meter run, broad jump, shot put, running high jump, one hundred meter run, discus throw, one hundred meter hurdle, pole vault, javelin throw, and the fifteen hundred meter run.
12. It's sixty feet from the foul line to the head pin.
13. Twelve balls.
14. There are four umpires; one at each base.
15. A small slam means that one side wins twelve tricks. A grand slam means that one side wins all thirteen tricks. The cards rank: ace, King and on down with ten an honor card. The suits rank as follows: no trumps, spades, hearts, diamonds and clubs, in descending order.
16. The Kentucky Derby has been run every May since 1875.
17. Home plate is referred to as the dish.
18. In bowling there are three balls in a box.
19. Standard baseball bats are made of ash.
20. A professional is one who possesses skill he sells for money; an amateur is one who possesses skill but does not accept money for his services; a novice is just a beginner.
21. There are two major baseball leagues in the United States, the National and American leagues.
22. A three gaited horse can walk, trot and canter. A five gaited horse can walk, trot, singlefoot, rack and canter.
23. Golf.
24. A baseball has only one seam but two sections.
25. A horse is handicapped with an impost or extra weight.

ANSWERS TO SPORTS QUIZ NUMBER THREE.

1. Kings, queens, pawns, knights, bishops, castles or rooks.
2. A chukker of polo lasts seven and one half minutes.
3. The center of a standard baseball is made of a piece of cork about the size of a marble and has been aged for fifteen years.
4. Manassa Mauler—Jack Dempsey; Brown Bomber—Joe Louis; Boston Strong Boy—John L. Sullivan; Gentleman Jim—James J. Corbett; Ruddy Robert—Bob Fitzsimmons.

5. Second place—place; third place —show.

6. The National League was founded in 1876, the American League in 1900.

7. In ascending order they are: fly-weight, bantamweight, feather-weight, lightweight, welter weight, middle-weight, light heavyweight, and heavyweight.

8. Resin.

9. Tally-ho is a cry used in fox hunting.

10. The Boston Bees were formerly called the Boston Braves.

11. A half nelson is a wrestling hold.

12. Cribbage.

13. Such a race is called a futurity.

14. Seven.

15. In match play each hole counts a point; in medal play the total strokes for the entire game are counted.

16. Boxing is frequently so described.

17. The gloves weigh more and the purse weighs less.

18. Cornhuskers—Nebraska; Mid-dies—United States Naval Acad-emy; Fighting Irish — Notre Dame; Wildcats—Northwestern or University of Arizona.

19. There is no weight limit in the heavyweight class.

20. Frames.

21. There are six men on an ice hockey team.

22. Yoicks is used in fox hunting; hold 'em in football; slide in base-ball and break in boxing and wrestling.

23. The stroke oar is nearest the stern.

24. Baseball — innings; football — quarters; basket ball—halves; races — laps; prize fighting — rounds; bowling—strings; tennis —sets; bridge—rubbers; hockey —periods; golf—holes.

25. Soccer does not permit the use of the hands.

ANSWERS TO SPORTS QUIZ NUMBER FOUR.

1. Foils, epee, and saber.

2. Select one of linen thread as silk deteriorates rapidly in salt water.

3. Three hundred.

4. A left-handed pitcher is called a "southpaw."

5. It is run counter clock-wise.

6. Gridiron—football; diamond—baseball; rink—hockey; court—tennis, basketball, etc.

7. A can of corn is a high lazy play; a banana stalk is a bat with poor wood in it; a hind snatcher is a catcher.

8. Many people stand up in the home team half of the seventh in-ning, believing it to be lucky.

9. A K.O. is a knockout.

10. The battery.

11. Luff is a sailing term; huff is used in checkers; ruff is used in bridge; and buff in the children's game of Blind Man's Buff.

12. Stalemate means to bring to a standstill; the term is derived from the game of chess.

13. They are all fields of contest.

14. There are eight furlongs in a mile.

15. Rowing is the oldest college sport.

16. Chess is the "game of Kings"; horse racing the sport of kings.

17. A skier calls "track" to get a clear way.
18. We call it checkers.
19. The official marathon distance is 26 miles, 385 yards.
20. Yale, Boston College, Princeton, Dartmouth, Fordham, and Holy Cross in that order.
21. A hand is four inches; a span ten and seven-eighths inches.
22. The Electoral College doesn't go in for athletics.
23. Golf, tennis, baseball, and hockey in that order.
24. There are ten players to a side in lacrosse and fifteen to a side in the game of rugby football.
25. Amherst, Williams, and Wesleyan constitute the famous "Little Three" of the New England Colleges.

JUNGLE LIFE ANSWERS.

1. Chow dogs.
2. The camel and the pig.
3. Another name for the ONE humped camel.
4. Cicero's Cat, Napoleon, Micky Mouse, Dingle Hoofer and His Dog.
5. They are black on white.
6. The animal kingdom.
7. The raccoon.
8. No, only to squirt water into their mouths.
9. A calico horse or pony.
10. Yes, the mandrill answers the description.
11. The leather of full grown goats.
12. This is also the name of a small animal of the Arctic.
13. England, America.
14. No, they are related but are of different species of rodent.
15. The beaver.
16. The Grizzly Bear, the Bunny Hug, and the Turkey Trot.
17. They are found in the North only.
18. Cow, dog, horse, and cat in that order.
19. Dick Whittington, whose cat killed rats in India, twenty at a stroke.
20. The chipmunk.
21. Uphill, because his hind legs are longer than his forelegs.
22. Walt Disney.
23. He pushes.
24. Add the word "dog."
25. The cheetah.

ANSWERS TO ABOUT ANIMALS NUMBER TWO.

1. Saw horse, sea horse, clothes horse, etc.
2. Four—this is also true of the deer, goat, and sheep.
3. It is a proboscis.
4. You can't teach an old dog new tricks; Every dog has his day; Cross as a bear; Mad as a March hare; Grin like a Cheshire cat; Gone to the dogs; Sly as a fox; etc. etc.
5. Horses or cattle; rabbits; pigs; sheep.
6. Forequarters; greenback; two bits; scent; buck.
7. The giraffe's eyes are so constructed.
8. They are all breeds of cats.
9. Wolves.

10. It is the name applied to animals resembling plants, such as corals, sponges, etc.
11. Daisy, Zero, and Sandy.
12. It means that the animal goes into hiding and lives all winter without food.
13. This delicate parchment is made from the skins of calves.
14. India.
15. Another name for andirons.
16. This is a contraction of the French word "marchons" and means to go on. It is used with dog teams.
17. A pouch to carry their young. This trait is also shared by these other marsupials: wombats and bandicoots.
18. Sirius.
19. Strangely enough, the pig.
20. The Koala of Australia.
21. Both chew their cud; the Bactrian camel has two humps on its back, the llama none.
22. Taurus is represented by a bull.
23. The muskrat.
24. Cow, pig, hog, cat, dog, doe.
25. The lion and the lamb.

ANSWERS TO ABOUT ANIMALS NUMBER THREE.

1. After the tree has been cut down.
2. Five and seven. One taken from seven would make six for each flock, and one taken from five would leave four, making the first twice as large as the second.
3. From beef or mutton.
4. The left hind foot and the right front foot.
5. The cat's whiskers.
6. Unless it was cold weather the ermine could not be recognized by its fur, which is usually white. At different seasons the ermine or stoat has reddish brown fur. The tip of its tail will always be black, no matter what the season.
7. Saint Bernard, Scotch Collie, setter, shepherd, police, Boston bull, and Chow.
8. Speak no evil, hear no evil, see no evil.
9. It's another name for the giraffe.
10. Pig, sheep, horse, sheep.
11. Boar, hippopotamus, and walrus.
12. One that has been dehorned.
13. A cosset is a young lamb.
14. Beware of the dog.
15. *Ass* You Like It—*Cow*-medy of Errors; *Hen*-ry the Eighth; Two Gentlemen of Ve-*Roan*-a; Much A-*doe* About Nothing; Merchant of *Venison*; *Ham*-let (Well, that's a little pig, isn't it?).
16. The elephant trumpets and the hyena laughs.
17. A species of monkey.
18. Great Dane, Irish Terrier, Welsh Terrier, Belgian Shepherd, Russian Wolfhound, Pekingese, Skye Terrier (Scotland) German Police, etc. etc.
19. Ride it, it's a donkey.
20. Four legs.
21. Kittens.
22. A gnawing mammal. Rabbits, beavers, squirrels, and porcupines, as well as mice and rats, are all rodents.
23. Happy as a clam, strong as an ox, dumb as an oyster, gay as a lark, stubborn as a mule, brave as a lion, proud as a peacock, meek as a mouse, etc. etc.

24. A dogie is a little calf whose mammy is dead and whose daddy has run off with another cow.

25. That depends on whether you are a man or a mouse.

ANSWERS TO ABOUT ANIMALS NUMBER FOUR.

1. Cow, hen, doe, ewe, sow, lioness, mare, goose, duck, vixen, ewe, hind, doe.
2. Taking it on the lamb, throwing the bull, feeding the kitty, putting on the dog, getting his goat, etc. etc.
3. Tadpoles, goslings, cubs, fawn, calf, pup, kitten, leveret, cub, alevin, colt, shoat, colt.
4. Barbecue.
5. It has no tail.
6. The pelt.
7. Dogs, camels, elephants, reindeer, llama.
8. Yes; upper and lower back teeth, and lower front teeth.
9. Fox, rabbit, lion, elephant, and duck.
10. Pegasus.
11. Wattles.
12. Just above the ears.
13. The sloth.
14. The only place this could happen would be the North pole, therefore, the bear would be white, a Polar bear.
15. A Hallowe'en party, as a grimalkin is an old cat.
16. Fox, lynx, ox.
17. Yes, they are standing face to face.
18. Marsupials.
19. Flock, covey, pack, hive or swarm, school.
20. Straight, the hump is fat.
21. They are said to have fought until only their tails were left.
22. Poults, pullets, cockerels.
23. The joints of an elephant's hind legs bend forward, like those of a human being; most animals' legs bend backwards.
24. In order to increase the evaporating surface. The tongue is the only part of a dog's anatomy that can perspire.
25. Strictly speaking it should be Donald *Drake*, as a male duck is a drake.

ANSWERS TO ENGLISH QUIZ NUMBER I-A.

1. Fourteen.
2. It means "full of".
3. The art or science of developing or improving the memory.
4. Hue.
5. Less and least.
6. Some; used as a suffix you get toilsome, etc.
7. The art of spelling.
8. It means the people.
9. Proantidisestablishmentarianism (31 letters)
10. Cleave.
11. The sending of official postal matter through the mail without payment of postage.
12. A word or words that read the same frontwards or backwards. E.G. Madam, I'm Adam, or Able was I ere I saw Elba.
13. A separate stanza which concludes the poem and which contains either a moral or an address to some individual.

14. Alliteration.
15. It is a figure of speech in which the formation of the letters or words resembles the meaning of the word or phrase, such as "whizz" or "buzz".
16. Naught.
17. Her, him, you, its, our, his.
18. No; translated from the Latin it means "elsewhere" and is a defense.
19. Between signifies that something is to be divided two ways; among infers three or more things.
20. Mistress.

21. Right; not wrong, just, or to rectify.
Rite: a ceremony or act of religion.
Wright: a workman, as a playwright.
Write: the act of writing, as a letter.
22. Pear, pair, pare.
23. Mr. President, Your Eminence, and Your Excellency.
24. "Respondez s'il vous plait" which is French for reply if you please.
25. A verse is a measured line of poetry; a stanza is a number of lines or verses.

ANSWERS TO ENGLISH QUIZ NUMBER I-B.

1. Unquestionably.
2. Monosyllable.
3. It is the capital.
4. A pun.
5. The science of words.
6. Words that are alike in sound, but unlike in meaning.
7. Out of the fight; disabled.
8. Street, Strait, Saint.
9. Period, comma, colon, semi-colon, interrogation mark, exclamation mark, dash, hyphen, single quotation, double quotation, apostrophe, brackets, parenthesis.
10. I is the ninth letter of the alphabet.
11. Five dollars, as there are five lines to a limerick.
12. An aspirin tablet.
13. England.
14. Four hundred and fifty-five thousand.

15. Erred or blundered socially.
16. The first word of a page inserted at the bottom of the preceding page.
17. None, both are pronounced Fee-on-say.
18. Antonym.
19. When clumsy, awkward, or tactless.
20. Verso is the left hand page of a book, bearing even numbers. Recto is the right hand page of a book, bearing odd numbers.
21. Love of offspring; especially love of children.
22. Plural. Datum is the singular.
23. Tattoo, taboo, shampoo, etc. etc.
24. Folio, quarto, octavo, and duodecimo respectively.
25. Bookkeeper.

ANSWERS TO ENGLISH QUIZ NUMBER I-C.

1. Both words are coined. Trylon is from "tri," meaning three sided structure. Perisphere is from "peri," meaning beyond, all round.

2. It is pronounced as if written "sheik".
3. None does.
4. Ampersand.
5. Sir, he is a Knight.
6. The Phoenicians.
7. Four.
8. Because they are regular, irregular, and defective.
9. Beauty is only skin deep.
10. Both mean left or left handed; they are from the French and Latin respectively.
11. Coercion, suspicion, scion.
12. In the fashion of; to the point; in good faith.
13. A tail like twist of hair at the back of the head; the last words of an actor's speech; hint for the succeeding speaker; the stick used in playing the game of billiards.
14. Deny.
15. The letter X.
16. Work. Strictly speaking it is not the past participle of this word, but rather a synonym for the past participle of work which is worked.
17. Flowery English; derived from John Lyly's *Euphues*.
18. To bound by touching the earth or the surface of water, and glancing off, as a shot might do.
19. Tremendous, horrendous, stupendous, hazardous.
20. None does.
21. The flue.
22. Glare, gleam, glisten, glimmer, glitter, glow.
23. Crime doesn't pay.
24. Consonants.
25. Wrong.

ANSWERS TO ENGLISH QUIZ NUMBER I-D.

1. Petrol.
2. Tough, rough, enough; cough; bough, plough; dough.
3. Alphabet.
4. Inability to read and write one's own language.
5. To abstain from food; rapidly or swiftly; to make secure; dissipated or dissolute.
6. His age; he would be eighty.
7. Originally they all meant "son of".
8. She wore a toga on her back, a topaz on her finger, a toupee on her head, and toque on top of that.
9. Foster mother.
10. Showing favoritism to relatives in making appointments.
11. Twenty, ten years, fourteen days.
12. Stroke of mercy; the finishing stroke.
13. Queue.
14. The Leader.
15. A word having the same pronunciation as another but a different meaning—as bear, bare.
16. Red tape, blue laws, black smith (or gold or silver), gold standard.
17. Gnaw, gnu, gnarl, gnome, gnostic, etc. etc.
18. Serge, as it is a woolen cloth and the others are cotton.
19. Yes; he owned a set of the third edition.
20. Each has a silent letter.
21. Eureka, meaning "I have found it".
22. Technically, neither. He is sup-

posed to have sung them. They were set down later.

23. Incorrectly, of course.

24. The study of ancient inscriptions and modes of writing.

25. A versifier rather than a true poet.

ANSWERS TO GENERAL QUIZ NUMBER IV-A.

1. Bastille Day, celebrated on July 14.
2. Three: State, at first called Foreign Affairs; Treasury, War.
3. Center.
4. Melbourne, Australia.
5. The Gulf Stream brings a large body of warm water to England's shores, while the Labrador current flows from the North Pole regions.
6. A swastika.
7. Obverse.
8. Between Asia and Africa.
9. Kentucky, where the United States Treasury keeps most of its gold.
10. St. Helena.
11. England.
12. Mexico City; it is over 7000 feet above sea level.
13. It is regarded as the most cheerful of all the colors.
14. Blue, red, green.
15. Warren G. Harding.
16. Pontiac, Lincoln, La Salle, De Soto.
17. A young hen.
18. A tree.
19. New York. California. Wheatstone Bridge is not a bridge at all, but an electrical instrument named after its inventor, Sir Charles Wheatstone.
20. Monday, Labor Day; Tuesday, Election Day; Wednesday, Ash Wednesday; Thursday, Thanksgiving; Friday, Good Friday; Sunday, Easter.
21. Prince Albert, consort of Queen Victoria.
22. Three; California, Washington, and Oregon.
23. 12.
24. The growth of the automobile, since the whiffletree is the swinging bar to which the traces of a horse's harness are fastened.
25. Harding, in the Presidential Campaign in 1920.

ANSWERS TO GENERAL QUIZ NUMBER IV-B.

1. Yahweh is the old Hebrew for Jehovah.
2. "The children were nestled all snug in their beds,
   While visions of sugar plums danced in their heads,
   And Ma in her kerchief, and I in my cap
   Had just settled our brains for a long winter's nap."
3. Massachusetts, Boston; Louisiana, Baton Rouge; North Dakota, Bismarck; Idaho, Boise.
4. A geometric figure.
5. "Silent Night, Holy Night."
6. Tennessee, Connecticut, Minnesota, Pennsylvania.
7. It is applied to a strong Holland gin.
8. Father Time.
9. A golf club. A boat on an incline. The eye. Pay or risk all one has.

10. Because she has four sea-sons.
11. 360 degrees. Every sphere has 360 degrees in its circumference.
12. Samson's hair. The Gordian Knot.
13. John Adams, Thomas Jefferson, James Madison.
14. The minuet.
15. No, it has five on each front foot, and four on the hind feet.
16. Could be. A hagiographer writes the lives of Saints.
17. The camel, cow, and cat sit with their knees drawn up under them, and a dog with his forelegs straight out.
18. Washington.
19. Seine; Danube; Thames; St. Lawrence.
20. Massachusetts, Michigan, Maine, Minnesota, Missouri, Maryland, Montana, Mississippi.
21. Kansas.
22. California.
23. God helps them that help themselves.
24. Hallowe'en.
25. Press-eedent, accented on the first syllable.

ANSWERS TO GENERAL QUIZ NUMBER IV-C.

1. Two; North Carolina and North Dakota.
2. A cygnet.
3. Asia.
4. Hudson River and Lake Erie.
5. Philadelphia, Pennsylvania.
6. Maple.
7. Flax.
8. Wilson, Tyler, Cleveland.
9. Massachusetts.
10. Tecumseh.
11. John Adams.
12. It simply means treatment while the patient is not in bed.
13. A short clay pipe.
14. One that is no longer manufactured.
15. Cows.
16. Thomas Jefferson, April 13, 1743; Ulysses S. Grant, April 27, 1822.
17. Lawyer.
18. It's bad handwriting.
19. A black cat crossing one's path signifies bad luck. A howling dog means death.
20. Squeeze, bite, gore with horns, kick, quills, odor.
21. Woodrow Wilson.
22. Sir Isaac Newton.
23. Janus was a Roman god having two heads thus enabling him to look backward as well as forward. Likewise a person, having admitted his mistakes during the year just finished, resolves to do better starting January 1 of the coming year.
24. Thomas Jefferson.
25. The sunflower.

ANSWERS TO GENERAL QUIZ NUMBER IV-D.

1. Each is voiceless.
2. They are generally harmless.
3. Taft and Polk.
4. French.
5. A scaramouche is a ne'er-do-well.
6. The eye.
7. All except Kansas and Massachusetts.
8. A fir tree.
9. The Druids.
10. 64 inches.
11. Pitcairn Island.

12. "Auld Lang Syne".
13. Waterway, airway, subway, highway, tramway, railway.
14. Ontario and Erie.
15. Maine.
16. It is an island southeast of Africa.
17. Harrisburg.
18. It is dried unripe fruit from the pimento tree.
19. Basketball, in 1891.
20. In the Pacific Ocean between Australia and South America.
21. A Greek measure of length, approximately 600 feet.
22. Coal or ore.
23. The wooden rim of a wheel to which the spokes and outer iron rim are attached.
24. An indomitable desire to count objects.
25. Overpatriotic; derived from Nicolas Chauvin, whose demonstrative loyalty to Napoleon and the First Empire became ridiculed by his comrades.

ANSWERS TO GENERAL QUIZ NUMBER V-A.

1. A great circle.
2. A bullet, a small snail, a counterfeit, and to smash or swing.
3. White, black, orange, gray, blue, pink, green, purple, yellow, red.
4. A carpenter's hip is the ridge where the two sloping planes of a roof come together, hence a hipped roof. A plumber's elbow is a right angled pipe joint.
5. It is called the gutter.
6. The big story which occupies the best position on the main news page; the tops of columns; the author's signature at the head of a story.
7. Dance.
8. Yes, if he threw it straight up in the air.
9. 18/24ths, or 75%.
10. It was issued and used in Boston in the 17th century, and so-called from the rude figure of a pine tree on one side.
11. The lithosphere.
12. Blonde, a termite is a white ant.
13. It is still white; pinking means to cut or scallop the edge; blueing only whitens it more.
14. To test the presence of alkaline or acid in a liquid.
15. A window on the sloping side of a roof.
16. A blotter.
17. Six rows of eight stars.
18. Possess great power.
19. To deceive or defraud.
20. They are all nicknames of well known railroads.
21. A life saving device, used to take passengers off a boat.
22. Skeezix.
23. Radium.
24. Mother Earth, Lady Luck, Mother Nature, Old Mother Hubbard, Miss Fortune, Mother Goose.
25. 2 pints—1 quart; 8 quarts—1 peck; 4 pecks—1 bushel.

ANSWERS TO GENERAL QUIZ NUMBER V-B.

1. More than 75 miles an hour.
2. By percussion.
3. D.
4. St. Peter's in Rome.
5. Mercury.

6. An Indian or Hindu soldier in the British service in India.
7. To measure specific gravity.
8. United States Military Academy at West Point, New York.
9. Doubt, debt, debtor, dumb, lamb, climb, plumber, comb.
10. Iroquois, Mohicans, Algonquins, Seminoles, Sioux, Aztec, Mayas, Incas, Pueblo.
11. Doric.
12. An active volcano in Hawaii.
13. In prison.
14. It is one of the eight precepts contained in the sermon on the Mount.
15. A student of reptiles.
16. Ferry boats.
17. A password.
18. Alchemy.
19. To the seashore.
20. A leave of absence granted every seven years.
21. Our New Thread.
22. Aladdin's lamp; Diogenes' lantern, which he used when he was looking for an honest man; the Edison Mazda lamp, or electric light.
23. An engraving or figure carved below the surface. A gem carved in relief, the opposite of an intaglio.
24. No, the buoyancy of water does not increase with depth.
25. The family name.

ANSWERS TO GENERAL QUIZ NUMBER V-C.

1. Jack Frost, Santa Claus, John Bull, Uncle Sam, Old Man River, Father Time.
2. A layette; a trousseau.
3. A wizard. A witch.
4. Because light travels more rapidly than sound.
5. Rex Beach is not a place, but an author.
6. A schooner has two or more masts; a sloop only one.
7. Polyandry.
8. Rain; the others are partly or entirely frozen.
9. In the open air.
10. Oil from rose petals.
11. 1100.
12. The keystone. The middle stone at the top of the arch holding the other pieces in place.
13. A favorite, or a popular person.
14. It supplied the key to Egyptian hieroglyphics.
15. Snow.
16. Cantons.
17. Chinese with 214.
18. Definitely, since auriferous means gold-bearing.
19. A dance.
20. Hanging.
21. Dividends.
22. A very rich man.
23. Muskrat, musk melon, musket which is a kind of firearm.
24. Orchard, grove, patch, vineyard.
25. The female side or branch.

ANSWERS TO GENERAL QUIZ NUMBER V-D.

1. A blood pressure recording instrument.
2. A unit of electrical capacity.
3. Perpetual motion.
4. Czar.
5. They are all types of bottles.
6. All three are correct.
7. Unduly particular.

8. 8.
9. Six hooks.
10. Almighty.
11. English.
12. It is a victory gained at enormous cost or loss.
13. 1765.
14. That he has cut his second growth of grass in a season.
15. She is called Dame So-and-So.
16. Mercury.
17. Eleven, including the two in the corner.
18. To allow for expansion and contraction by heat and cold. One solid strip would bulge and crack.
19. To debase, to slander.
20. From the eaves up.
21. A lad between boyhood and manhood.
22. A pigeon is a dove or some similar bird; a widgeon is a river duck.
23. Sir Francis Drake. Pilgrims. Columbus. Henry Hudson. Columbus.
24. Old Mother Hubbard:
"She went to the cobbler's to buy him some shoes."
"She went to the hosier to buy him some hose."
"Deedle, deedle dumpling, my son John,
He went to bed with his stockings on."
25. One of a series of towers erected on the field of an aerodrome to mark the course and guide the aviators.

ANSWERS TO GENERAL QUIZ NUMBER VI-A.

1. A slender cigar.
2. The Gulf of Guinea, where the prime meridian crosses the equator at sea level.
3. Ropes used to hoist sails or flags.
4. A food made of lean meat, fat, and sometimes fruit pressed for easy transportation.
5. Anything that oppresses or burdens; a mental cloud.
6. A platoon is a subdivision of a military unit; a poltroon is a spiritless coward.
7. Argot is a jargon or underworld slang; ergot is a fungus growth on wheat or rye; ingot is a block of cast metal.
8. A facet is the face of a cut gem, and a faucet is a short pipe with a valve used for drawing out liquids.
9. Yes, because peccable means liable to sin, and peccant means corrupt, and peculate means to embezzle.
10. One of a tribe of American Indians tied an amphibian with hemp.
11. Ida-ho; Virginia; Mary-land; Dela-ware.
12. On an island in the St. Croix River sixteen miles south of Calais, Maine, in 1604 by Samuel Champlain and a group of his followers.
13. Chicks, ducklings, goslings, poults, and keets in that order.
14. A platform or fortification from which cannon may be fired over a parapet; a gun platform.
15. The first is a wood wind musical instrument, the second a periodic wind in the Indian Ocean.
16. Saint Nicholas.

17. An office to which no work is attached.
18. A gallon is a unit of liquid measure; a galleon is a large and unwieldy ship formerly used by the Spaniards.
19. An acute tropical disease caused by a vitamin deficiency.
20. A tycoon is a master of industry.
21. Ebenezer Scrooge.
22. Genealogy is the study of the history or descent of a person or family; geology is the study of the earth.
23. A place for keeping or rearing frogs.
24. An English gold coin, called more correctly a sovereign.
25. A barnacle is a shellfish that clings to the bottom of ships; a binnacle is a case which contains the compass and protects it from injury.

ANSWERS TO GENERAL QUIZ NUMBER VI-B.

1. Misanthropy, which means a hatred of mankind.
2. Tom-tom is a native Oriental drum; can-can is a dance introduced in Paris about 1830; haw-haw is a coarse loud laugh; Sing Sing is the New York State Penitentiary at Ossining, New York.
3. A metal pin or rod for fastening; a sliding catch for a door; a roll of cloth; a sudden dashing or darting away; to swallow food rapidly without chewing.
4. Fantan is a Chinese gambling game; fandango is a Spanish dance; a fanfare is a flourish of trumpets.
5. Elizabeth.
6. Because onions contain a volatile oil, similar to that used in making tear gas bombs, which is released when the skin is removed.
7. Braces.
8. Six dozen dozen is the greater number.
9. All stars are in motion. Fixed stars are so called because they appear to change their positions slowly in comparison to the others.
10. To the Swiss guards who died defending Louis XVI from a mob during the French Revolution.
11. A woman's tears.
12. Whaling.
13. Heave the lead.
14. Elephants, alligators, turtles, poll parrots.
15. A form of pudding.
16. Because more vibrations per second reach the eardrum.
17. Peach, lemon, apple (of his eye).
18. The bicycle business.
19. Research shows that each package averages about 93 yards.
20. Trading on margin, or with very little capital.
21. The Secretary of State.
22. Absent Without Official Leave.
23. Summer.
24. No; it was a slave chained to the oar of a galley ship.
25. One who follows an army and sells provisions to the troops.

ANSWERS TO GENERAL QUIZ NUMBER VI-C.

1. The Marine Corps, authorized by act of Congress in 1775.
2. The walnut tree is native to Persia. It is now cultivated mostly

254

in Southern Europe and California.

3. Logic.
4. "Hang a lantern aloft in the belfry arch of the North Church tower as a signal light."
5. One hundred and forty-four.
6. Norway. Norwegian miles are seven times as long as the American mile.
7. Pineapple. (Ananas)
8. A breed of pigeon.
9. A pitcher or jar.
10. Eat it; it's a flat fish resembling a flounder.
11. Ordnance is artillery used in warfare; an ordinance is a law or religious rite.
12. A garland.
13. In water; a manatee is a sea cow.
14. Eat it; it's a fish.
15. Trickery or artifice.
16. A kind of drum or tabor.
17. Wear the calot, as it is a small skull cap; put the jabot at your neck, as it is a ruffled ornament of lace; put the sabot on your foot, as it is a wooden shoe.
18. A faker is a cheater; a fakir is an Oriental ascetic.
19. A native of Tartary. The word is also used to describe a person of violent temper, and the word tartar, uncapitalized, refers also to acid potassium tartrate.
20. The difference is in spelling only; both words refer to a small glass bottle or vessel.
21. A wild dog, native to Australia.
22. One in which no other address is given except a box number at the office of the publication in which the ad appears.
23. Whoopee refers to an hilariously jolly time; a rupee is a silver coin of British India, worth about thirty cents.
24. From the engineer Clifford M. Holland.
25. A dupe, or one who can be easily tricked.

ANSWERS TO GENERAL QUIZ NUMBER VI-D.

1. No; Franklin was the fifteenth in a family of seventeen.
2. Sound.
3. An easel.
4. The good egg would sink, the bad egg would rise to the surface of a pail of water because of the gas it contained.
5. Nine; eight associate justices and one Chief Justice.
6. To wash the eye of irritating particles.
7. Because it contains a high percentage of salt which makes it impossible for anything to live in the water.
8. A Bible.
9. A balloon with the skin taken off.
10. A ship's galley smoke stack.
11. Six.
12. No, the color of the dye makes no difference in warmth.
13. A sod which can be cut and burnt; it is extensively used in Ireland.
14. Mileage.
15. The Amazon.
16. Stalk, tuber or root, fruit.
17. Eat it; a flitch is a cured side of bacon.
18. A dentist, as it is a toothache.
19. Yes, Charles Evans Hughes ran against Woodrow Wilson.

20. Turkish.
21. Kansas.
22. Saint John.
23. Rhode Island, Delaware, Connecticut, New Jersey.
24. Calais, Maine, which derives its water supply from across the border in Canada.
25. New Hampshire, Maine, Oregon.

ARISTOLOGY QUIZ ANSWERS.

1. Cow, goat, reindeer, yak, zebu, buffalo, camel, llama, and sheep.
2. A pudding of flour, oatmeal, or Indian meal.
3. They grow in clusters like grapes, hence their name.
4. It's haddock that has been cured with the smoke of green wood, turf, or peat.
5. They are formed by the gases that result from the chemical action of fermentation.
6. Popeye would want Spinach, Wimpy hamburgers, and Jack Horner a Christmas pie.
7. The missing words are cucumber, two peas, and an egg.
8. It's eaten in the open; the term derives from the Low countries and there means an outdoor festival or fair.
9. Beets.
10. Beef, mutton, veal, and venison in that order.
11. At the age of one year.
12. Baldwin, pippin, and Gravenstein are apples. Bartlett and Seckel are pears.
13. Caviar is the prepared and salted roe of the sturgeon or other large fish.
14. Bananas, figs, strawberries, currants, blackberries, blueberries, etc., etc.
15. Truffles.
16. Roast beef.
17. The questions can be answered in this order: sole, crab, sword, bluefish, and red salmon.
18. Usually made of calf's head.
19. It's sour milk which has been separated; the curds being the thick part and the whey the liquid.
20. Cabbage, corn, and plums.
21. Formosa black, Congou or English breakfast, Java, Japan Black, Japan green, Japan Dust, Scented Canton, Canton Oolong, Formosa Oolong.
22. Because the fish are cheaper than olive oil, and less sardines would require more olive oil.
23. You should think of China, Russia, Japan, and Scotland.
24. Pod, peel, rind, husk, and skin.
25. Molasses completes the sentence and the recipe.

ANSWERS TO FOOD QUIZ NUMBER TWO.

1. According to statistics rice is more extensively grown and more widely used than any other foodstuff.
2. Corned beef and cabbage.
3. Crackers.
4. It is a strong scented herb of the mint family.
5. Before it's cut it's white, when it touches the air it oxidizes and turns red.
6. Table salt to you.

7. It's a welsh rabbit according to both Webster's and Funk and Wagnall's Dictionaries.
8. The lily family.
9. A young trout.
10. A calorie is the amount of heat required to raise the temperature of one gram of water one degree Centigrade.
11. Buy them in this order: Marble, loaf, and sponge.
12. That's a baby's formula.
13. White pepper is well ripened black pepper.
14. Yes, it is one form of vinegar.
15. They are edible decapod crustaceans, or more briefly shrimp.
16. Tea.
17. Belgium is the country.
18. The shin bones of beef cattle.
19. Beet.
20. It's a small cube of fried or roasted bread usually served with soup.
21. It should have been cooked in a covered dish with scant water.
22. The apple Adam ate; the apple that fell on Newton's head and gave him the idea of the law of gravity; and the apple that William Tell shot from his son's head.
23. Only two *legs* of lamb from one animal; the front legs are called fores.
24. Oats, rye, millet, corn, wheat, rice, barley, and buckwheat.
25. Pig's feet.

ANSWERS TO FOOD QUIZ NUMBER THREE.

1. Here are the countries in order: Mexico, Italy, Hungary, England, and France.
2. A seedless raisin never had a seed; a seeded raisin has had the seeds removed.
3. Puree—a thickened soup; fondant —a soft icing; roti—roasted; souffle—any dish mixed with eggs and baked.
4. Apple, peanut, date, cocoa.
5. All are herbs used in cooking.
6. Hamburg, Bologna, and Frankfurt.
7. Here are the answers in the correct order: mint, weeds, briar, bay.
8. They are all fruits but cauliflower, which is a flower.
9. No; tapioca is the product of the root of the cassave, a tropical plant grown extensively in South America.
10. Onions, potatoes, carrots, beets, parsnips, turnips, etc.
11. You'd get lemonade.
12. Chopped mixed pickles.
13. Mint sauce.
14. The Parker House for its rolls of the same name.
15. It's a variety of fish.
16. It points upward.
17. To keep it from being soggy.
18. Apples.
19. You could eat it but you probably wouldn't want to because it would be leathery.
20 Vitamin D.
21 Fruit; a small purple plum.
22. The banana tree.
23. Peas, beans, and corn.
24. Three.
25. Sure, they're one and the same thing—peanuts.

ANSWERS TO FOOD QUIZ NUMBER FOUR.

1. There are two.
2. The bud of broccoli, the blossom of cauliflower, the root of salsify, and the leaves of the endive.
3. It's a biennial plant of the celery family.
4. The American plan includes lodging and meals for the guest. The European plan charges for lodging only.
5. Eat it. It's a pudding the chief ingredient of which is the pluck of a sheep or calf.
6. The herring.
7. White of eggs—not angels.
8. Albumen.
9. It's an earthen baking dish.
10. Corned beef, cabbage, potatoes, carrots, turnips, and onions.
11. Caffeine is found in all three, but only a small amount is in cocoa.
12. It's a fruit.
13. It's a small vegetable tasting similar to a cabbage.
14. Stilton—England; Edam—Holland; Roquefort—France; Parmesan—Italy.
15. Salting, freezing, canning, and smoking.
16. They are neither fruit nor vegetables, but are classified as berries.
17. The bean of the cocoa tree.
18. A hand.
19. A normal ear has an even number of rows.
20. It is a pork loin or chop.
21. A minimum charge of, say two dollars, means that you must spend that much at least while a cover charge is an amount paid in addition to whatever you spend.
22. Yellow perch, red snapper or red salmon, and bluefish.
23. The hazel tree.
24. An olive is a true fruit.
25. It's another name for a grapefruit.

ANSWERS TO NURSERY QUIZ

1. Peter, Peter Pumpkin eater.
2. The Queen of Hearts.
3. Jack be Nimble, Jack Spratt, Jack and Jill, Little Jack Horner.
4. "Plastered his knob with vinegar and brown paper".
5. "Deedle, deedle dumpling, My son John".
6. The dish ran away with the spoon.
7. "The Queen was in the parlor eating bread and honey".
8. The butcher, the baker and the candlestick maker.
9. Jack, of Jack and the beanstalk fame.
10. "Along came a spider and sat down beside her."
11. The big bad wolf.
12. Scissors and snails, and puppy dog's tails.
13. Snow White.
14. Jack Spratt, who could eat no fat, and his wife, who could eat no lean.
15. "Simple Simon went a-fishing, for to catch a whale,
    And all the water that he had was in his mother's pail."
16. Flopsy, Mopsy, and Cottontail.
17. Peter Piper.
18. The lark.
19. The maiden, all forlorn.
20. A very fine gander.
21. A crooked six-pence.

22. Little Tommy Tucker sang for his supper.
23. Simple Simon.

24. One o'clock.
25. Georgie Porgie.

ANSWERS TO NURSERY QUIZ NUMBER TWO.

1. Goldilocks.
2. Three bags full.
3. His Christmas pie.
4. Twenty-four.
5. London Bridge.
6. Wynken, Blynken, and Nod.
7. She cut off their tails with the carving knife.
8. Old King Cole.
9. Sugar and spice and everything nice.
10. A piece of beef, some tarts, a pig, in that order.
11. Bo-Peep.
12. Silver buckles on his knee.
13. An egg.
14. Wee Willie Winkie.
15. Mary's little lamb.
16. Cinderella, Puss in Boots, Goody Two Shoes, the Old Woman Who lived in a Shoe, the Shoemaker and the Elves.
17. The sparrow, with his bow and arrow.
18. In a bowl.
19. Silver bells, and cockle shells, and pretty maids all in a row.
20. Straw, sticks and twigs, and bricks.
21. Little Red Riding Hood.
22. Jack and Jill.
23. Four and twenty blackbirds baked in a pie.
24. Old King Cole.
25. To sweep the cobwebs off the sky.

ANSWERS TO NURSERY QUIZ NUMBER THREE.

1. Quite contrary, simple, habitually late, careless—they lost their mittens.
2. Under the haystack, fast asleep.
3. "Be he alive, or be he dead, I'll grind his bones to make my bread."
4. The little dog laughed to see such sport.
5. The fly.
6. Little Miss Muffet, Tom, the Piper's Son, Old Mother Hubbard, Jack and Jill, Little Boy Blue, Little Jack Horner.
7. Sing a Song of Sixpence; A Dillar a Dollar, a Ten O'clock Scholar; Hot Cross Buns, one a penny two a penny hot cross buns.
8. Goldilocks.
9. To visit the Queen.
10. Four and twenty.
11. The Cat and the Fiddle, Little Boy Blue, Old King Cole, Little Tommy Tucker, Four and Twenty blackbirds, etc. etc.
12. Until the clock struck ten.
13. "Mary had a little lamb,
    Its fleece was white as snow,
    And everywhere that Mary went,
    The lamb was sure to go."
14. Little Boy Blue, Little Tommy Tucker, Little Jack Horner.
15. Tradition has it that the Mother Goose rhymes were written by Mistress Elizabeth Goose who was born in Boston in 1665 and died

in 1757. She is buried in the Old Granary Burying Ground on Tremont Street, Boston.

16. "A garden full of weeds."
17. The Queen of Hearts, who made some tarts.
18. One for my Master, one for my dame, and one for the little boy who lives in the lane. (Some versions account for only two bags with the concluding line reading: "but none for the little boy who cries in the lane".)
19. Cock Robin to Jenny Wren.
20. He tossed the dog.
21. Jump over the stile.
22. Humpty Dumpty.
23. Banbury Cross.
24. Upstairs and downstairs and in my lady's chamber.
25. Little Bo Beep has lost her sheep.
   Tom, Tom the Piper's son stole a pig and away he run.
   Hey, diddle diddle, the cat and the fiddle,
   The cow jumped over the moon.

ANSWERS TO NURSERY QUIZ NUMBER FOUR.

1. Old Mother Hubbard.
2. Three.
3. An inkstand and a three legged stool.
4. Georgie Porgie; Taffy was a Welchman and This Little Pig had roast beef; Jack and Jill; King and Queen of hearts; Little Jack Horner; Little Tommy Tucker; Old Woman Who Lived in a Shoe.
5. Cinderella and the glass slipper.
6. "Not a creature was stirring, not even a mouse."
7. The Arabian Nights.
8. The Pied Piper of Hamelin.
9. "Will you walk into my parlor, said the spider to the fly".
10. The dormouse, in *Alice in Wonderland*.
11. He entered by the use of the magic password, "Open Sesame".
12. This is the popular child's term for sleep.
13. The Pied Piper of Hamelin.
14. Dick Whittington.
15. A Cheshire cat.
16. Dasher, Dancer, Prancer, Vixen, Comet, Cupid, Donder, Blitzen.
17. To her grandmother's house.
18. "Nipped off her nose".
19. To Banbury Cross, and back.
20. Cock-a-doodle-doo.
21. Among the cinders.
22. "The lion and the unicorn were fighting for the crown."
23. Seven; man, mile, sixpence, stile, mouse, house, cat.
24. "And what they could not eat that night, the Queen next morning fried."
25. Yellow.

WHERE HAVE YOU BEEN? ANSWERS TO QUIZ NUMBER I-A.

1. The Sahara Desert, in Africa.
2. Mecca.
3. Holland; practically all of the best tulip stock originates there.
4. Kentucky, United States.
5. It is the scene of the Passion play, result of a vow taken by the inhabitants on the cessation of a plague in 1633.
6 Denmark.
7. Huron, Ontario, Michigan, Erie, Superior.

8. The North Pole is water; the South Pole is a land plateau.
9. France, Italy, England.
10. It's a mountain peak in the Alps.
11. Switzerland and Scotland.
12. Atlantic, Pacific, Indian, Arctic, and Antarctic.
13. The Adriatic.
14. Ottawa.
15. Belgium, Germany, Switzerland, Italy.
16. Larger.
17. Massachusetts, Virginia, Pennsylvania.
18. San Juan.
19. Indianapolis.
20. England, Egypt, Ecuador.
21. Ontario.
22. Paris. It is in the Louvre.
23. It is the name of a mountain peak in Switzerland.
24. In France; the inhabitants are called Bretons.
25. The United States of Brazil.

WHERE HAVE YOU BEEN? ANSWERS TO QUIZ NUMBER I-B.

1. In the southeastern part of New Mexico.
2. The entrance to San Francisco harbor.
3. The Danube River.
4. In southern Africa.
5. Switzerland, Ireland, and Spain.
6. Russia, the Argentine, South Africa.
7. Lima.
8. From west to east.
9. Persia.
10. The Luray Caverns in the Shenandoah Valley, Virginia.
11. Dover and Calais.
12. South America.
13. Cape Elizabeth, Portland, Maine; Cape Ann, Rockport and Gloucester, Massachusetts; Elizabeth's Island, Buzzard's Bay, Massachusetts; Martha's Vineyard, off southeastern Massachusetts; Point Judith, southern Rhode Island.
14. In northern Russia.
15. Turkey.
16. In the St. Lawrence River, between New York State and Ontario, Canada.
17. The Appalachians.
18. The Amazon.
19. Over the Hudson River in uptown New York City.
20. Fifteen hundred miles.
21. At the South Pole.
22. Territory of Hawaii.
23. It is the longest river in Alaska.
24. Because the country is below sea level.
25. On the border between Europe and Asia.

WHERE HAVE YOU BEEN? ANSWERS TO QUIZ NUMBER I-C.

1. California; Florida; off the coast of Newfoundland; Tibet; North of Ireland, in that order.
2. St. Augustine, Florida.
3. *Tale of Two Cities*.
4. Portugal.
5. Bedloe's Island, and strictly speaking it's in the state of New Jersey.
6. Lake Superior.
7. It's a city in central Burma, India.
8. Red, White, Black, Yellow.
9. British West Indies.
10. North pole.

11. The Indian Ocean.
12. It's a famous park just outside of Paris.
13. Monaco.
14. Mediterranean and Red.
15. Port-au-Prince.
16. The United States.
17. Buffalo, New York.
18. The petrified forest in Northeastern Arizona.
19. Honolulu.
20. Maine, Pine Tree State; New Hampshire, Granite State; Vermont, Green Mountain State; Massachusetts, Bay State; Rhode Island, Little Rhody; Connecticut, Nutmeg State.
21. Russia and Japan.
22. Caribbean.
23. A little over fifty miles.
24. China, Russia, India.
25. Guatemala, Nicaragua, Honduras, San Salvador, Costa Rica.

WHERE HAVE YOU BEEN? ANSWERS TO QUIZ NUMBER I-D.

1. In County Kilkenny, Ireland.
2. Belgium.
3. Rome, Ireland, and Agra, India.
4. The Pyramids of Egypt.
5. Juneau.
6. England, Ireland, Scotland, Switzerland, Iceland, Greenland, Poland.
7. Salem, Sudbury, and Billerica, Massachusetts.
8. Cuba.
9. In Quebec, Canada.
10. Mountainous.
11. Vineyard, Peninsula, Islands, Springs, Caves.
12. Portugal, Netherlands, Great Britain, France, Great Britain, at the present writing.
13. New York, London, Paris, Venice.
14. United States, India, China, Russia, Germany, Japan.
15. South Africa.
16. Norway, Japan, Africa, Egypt, Rome, America.
17. Boston, New York, Chicago, Detroit, Pittsburgh, Philadelphia, Minneapolis and St. Paul, and San Francisco.
18. The Dead Sea in Palestine.
19. New York, New Hampshire, Vermont, Tennessee, California.
20. Wash., Ill., Ore., Miss., Ark., Mass.
21. The Pacific Ocean.
22. Michigan.
23. London, Washington, D.C., Rome, Paris.
24. Texas, Ohio, South Carolina.
25. The shops of dressmakers, milliners, jewelers, and perfumers.

PRESIDENTS QUIZ . . . ANSWERS TO SET NUMBER ONE.

1. Herbert Hoover, from Palo Alto, California.
2. Calvin Coolidge, upon the death of Warren Harding.
3. Virginia.
4. Abraham Lincoln in 1865; James A. Garfield in 1881 and William McKinley in 1901.
5. John Adams.
6. The one with the largest head, of course!
7. In Theodore Roosevelt's administration.

8. Grover Cleveland.
9. Abraham Lincoln.
10. Martin Van Buren; the United States was founded in 1776 and Van Buren was born in 1782.
11. John Adams and Thomas Jefferson both have this distinction.
12. The bull moose; the Progressives were sometimes referred to as the Bull Moose Party.
13. Thomas Jefferson was president at that time.
14. Andrew Jackson.
15. Gettysburg is in Pennsylvania.
16. John Adams lived to be the oldest, he died at the age of ninety; James A. Garfield died at the age of 49.
17. They don't seek out this honor, they have to die to get their likeness on a postage stamp.
18. John Adams, the second president of the United States, had a son John Quincy Adams who became the sixth president.
19. The U. stood for Ulysses and the S. stood for Simpson. He was sometimes called United States Grant.
20. George Washington is buried at Mount Vernon, in Virginia.
21. No president has the power to declare war; it is done by Congress.
22. Washington, Jackson, William Henry Harrison, Taylor, U. S. Grant, and Garfield all were generals and later presidents of the United States.
23. George Washington did not occupy the White House at all as it was not completed during his term of office. John Adams was the first president to live there.
24. Abraham Lincoln was a lawyer in private life, Woodrow Wilson was an educator, Warren G. Harding was a newspaper publisher, and Herbert Hoover was an engineer.
25. No pension is granted ex-presidents of the United States.

ANSWERS TO PRESIDENTS QUIZ NUMBER TWO.

1. None.
2. Abraham Lincoln.
3. The Senate has the sole power to try all impeachments.
4. It was adopted by act of Congress in 1931 during the term of office of Herbert Hoover.
5. The Federalist party with only two, George Washington and John Adams.
6. Woodrow Wilson.
7. The president has the power to pardon only those persons who have been convicted of crimes under Federal law.
8. No one: Washington was elected unanimously both times.
9. Taylor, Pierce, and Grant all served in the Mexican War.
10. Both George Washington and James Madison signed the Constitution.
11. In 1861 Abraham Lincoln in the North and Jefferson Davis in the South.
12. Theodore Roosevelt, Millard Fillmore, and Martin Van Buren were all from New York state.
13. The line would reach from Washington to Cleveland.
14. To become president a man must

be: thirty-five years old, a natural born citizen of the United States, a resident of the United States for fourteen years, and, of course, he must win the election.

15. During the term of Theodore Roosevelt.
16. Taylor, Lincoln, Garfield, McKinley and Harding.
17. Abraham Lincoln.
18. Martin Van Buren, who was inaugurated in March of 1837.
19. Slow methods of communication and transportation made this length of time between election and the taking over of office essential.
20. The custom was inaugurated by President McKinley.
21. As presidents they were all cabinet makers.
22. Franklin Pierce.
23. Washington, he was the father of his country.
24. The president's salary is paid to him by check twice a month. It is delivered personally by a messenger from the Treasury Department.
25. Abraham Lincoln.

ANSWERS TO PRESIDENTS QUIZ NUMBER THREE.

1. He was their step-father.
2. James Madison, James Monroe, James K. Polk, James Buchanan, James A. Garfield.
3. Woodrow Wilson.
4. William Henry Harrison was the grandfather of Benjamin Harrison.
5. The Federalist party.
6. Andrew Johnson, seventeenth president, because he vetoed so many bills.
7. William Henry Harrison, the ninth president of the United States, served one month. He was inaugurated March fourth 1841 and died April fourth 1841.
8. No, he is immune from arrest.
9. The president precedes everyone.
10. Thomas Jefferson was the first to be inaugurated there.
11. James Buchanan.
12. Washington lived at Mount Vernon, Jefferson at Monticello, and Andrew Jackson at the Hermitage.
13. There were no cameras in his time.
14. John Adams, Thomas Jefferson, Martin Van Buren, John Tyler, Millard Fillmore, Andrew Jackson, Calvin Coolidge and Theodore Roosevelt.
15. Warren G. Harding.
16. Abraham Lincoln, 16th president.
17. No, he was born in Virginia which at that time was a British colony.
18. F. D. Roosevelt went to Harvard, Wilson to Princeton, and Coolidge to Amherst.
19. The barber.
20. President Andrew Johnson.
21. Theodore Roosevelt, before he became president.
22. Woodrow Wilson, in 1918.
23. Only one, the state of Washington.
24. George Washington was inaugurated in New York city.
25. Woodrow Wilson.

ANSWERS TO PRESIDENTS QUIZ NUMBER FOUR

1. Zachary Taylor.
2. Theodore Roosevelt in 1906 and Woodrow Wilson in 1919.
3. He had no middle name.
4. William Howard Taft. Arizona was the last state to be admitted in February of 1912 during Taft's administration.
5. Benjamin Harrison, twenty-third president.
6. "Hail to the Chief".
7. Washington, Jefferson, Madison, Monroe, Harrison, Taylor, Tyler, and Wilson.
8. Seven; Jefferson, Madison, Jackson, W. H. Harrison, Johnson, Benjamin Harrison, Wilson.
9. George Washington, Thomas Jefferson, Theodore Roosevelt, and Abraham Lincoln.
10. Washington had red hair. He usually wore a white wig however.
11. The full name was Warren Gamaliel Harding.
12. Warren G. Harding.
13. 1861—Abraham Lincoln—Civil War.
    1898—William McKinley—Spanish American War.
    1914—Woodrow Wilson—World War.
14. Madison, Wisconsin; Lincoln, Nebraska; Jackson, Mississippi.
15. George Washington: February 22, 1732.
    Abraham Lincoln: February 12, 1809.
    William Henry Harrison: February 9, 1773.
16. Taft became Chief Justice of the United States Supreme Court and swore in Hoover as president.
17. Millard Fillmore; Franklin Pierce; Chester A. Arthur.
18. Only one; Herbert Hoover.
19. George Washington, with the possible exception of Herbert Hoover. Washington's estate, at the time of his death, was valued at five million, three hundred thousand dollars.
20. George Washington, John Adams, Thomas Jefferson, James Madison, James Monroe.
21. Seventy-five thousand dollars per year. William Howard Taft was the first to receive this amount.
22. Taft, Tyler, Pierce, Hoover.
23. James Madison; Dolly Madison introduced the custom which has been observed ever since except during the Civil and World Wars.
24. Lincoln was assassinated at Ford's Theater, Washington, D.C., April 14th, 1865.
25. Washington, McKinley, Adams, Monroe, Madison.

ANSWERS TO GENERAL QUIZ NUMBER VII-A

1. They are all wheeled vehicles or carriages.
2. Outside. The explosion causes a vacuum, therefore the presence of the air inside the building forces the glass outside.
3. There were no slaves at the time of the Fifteenth Amendment; they were made citizens by the Fourteenth Amendment.

4. About 50 pounds.
5. The term for a shoemaker.
6. 12.
7. 555 feet.
8. Wong, which is used by at least 150,000,000 Chinese.
9. "How much territory do you control?"
10. 21 years. He began in 1807 and finished in 1828.
11. France.
12. 18. (1,000,000,000,000,000,000)
13. The Jack of Spades and the Jack of Hearts, because they each have only one eye.
14. Nosebleed.
15. The archaeologist, because the Rosetta Stone was of great help in deciphering Egyptian hieroglyphics.
16. 13.
17. Speech.
18. In your Sunday dinner, if you had chicken . . . it is the wishbone.
19. Hydrochloric acid; water; sulphuric acid; sodium chloride or salt.
20. Papoose; bambino; bucaroo.
21. A stolen car.
22. The cells of the body.
23. The heart.
24. She's a nut; it's the berries; she's a peach.
25. It was the ten dollar bill that led to the arrest of Bruno Hauptmann.

ANSWERS TO GENERAL QUIZ NUMBER VII-B

1. Sweep the floor; a besom is a broom, usually of twigs.
2. A warm wind which is very harmful to the cattle owners in the west.
3. Sunday.
4. Maggie and Jiggs; Dagwood and Blondie; Andy and Min Gump; Joe and Vi Green; Toots and Casper.
5. Wool.
6. Above, since the scapula is the shoulder blade, and the femur (the largest bone in the human body) is in the thigh.
7. 60 cents, as only two cuts and welds are necessary.
8. From the bark of a species of oak tree.
9. A kibitzer.
10. No, because it is a race for three year olds only.
11. It rests about 8/10 second between contractions which are about 1/10 second in length.
12. 7 years, from 1919 to 1926.
13. Tennis; rowing; golf; yachting.
14. On March 21st, and September 23rd.
15. A headdress worn by desert tribesmen to protect them from the sun.
16. From the book by Edmund Hoyle, an authority on games.
17. Miniature golf.
18. It is the four year period intervening between the games.
19. All are implements used in gathering and flailing wheat.
20. Racquet, bat, and mallet.
21. They are both mammals.
22. The condor of the Andes, with wing spreads ranging from 8 ft. 8 inches to 9 ft. 9 inches.
23. India.
24. From coal-tar.
25. In 1932.

1. Thrown; it is a rod hurled like a javelin.
2. A large, clumsy flightless bird now extinct.
3. No mallets are used in water polo.
4. A hole made in one stroke less than par.
5. It is a fish, generally known as a herring.
6. Churchill Downs in Louisville, Kentucky.
7. About three miles.
8. Fly.
9. Ice hockey.
10. Linseed oil.
11. Fencing.
12. Goal posts; they pertain to hockey, polo, or football, while the others are all baseball terms.
13. They are all card games.
14. Aberdeen-Angus; the others are breeds of sheep.
15. Madison, War of 1812; Wilson, World War; McKinley, Spanish-American War; Lincoln, Civil War.
16. Monrovia, Liberia, is named after James Monroe.
17. In a museum, as they are now extinct.
18. Fire cracker; nut cracker; safe cracker; Georgia cracker.
19. No, except in captivity. Tigers are native only to Eastern and Southern Asia and their adjacent islands.
20. Calorie.
21. Pod, rind, husk, skin, or peel.
22. Eat it, it is a cross between a peach and a plum.
23. Animal, plant, animal.
24. A peanut.
25. False. True.

1. A bell tower.
2. The cheetah of Africa, and the jaguar of Central America.
3. One that lives entirely on vegetables.
4. 6; 11; 9; 5.
5. Chess.
6. From the bottom up.
7. Three minutes.
8. Rustlers.
9. A birdie.
10. Badminton.
11. Mule, Bulldog, Goat.
12. Angora.
13. Dates.
14. One, then it's a dead one.
15. Buck, doe and fawn.
16. Fox, bear, lion, horse.
17. Football, ice hockey, archery, badminton, horseshoe pitching.
18. Newfoundland; the dog is on the 14-cent stamp.
19. A Natural History museum, as they are both extinct.
20. Pepper (black, red and white), cayenne, mustard, mace, nutmeg, cinnamon, ginger, paprika, allspice, curry.
21. Striped.
22. He wrote his famous farewell address, crossed the Delaware, retired from active service to his country, and died.
23. A grilse.
24. Sugar cane and sugar beet.
25. True. True. False.

ANSWERS TO GENERAL QUIZ NUMBER VIII-A

1. Milk.
2. Its rear paw.
3. Star.
4. He would be over 500 years old.
5. A piece of turf displaced by a player when he makes a stroke.
6. John Bull; Charley Horse; Peter Rabbit; Cheshire Cat.
7. Apple, peach, pear, cherry.
8. A cockroach.
9. They are used to direct a team of oxen; "gee" means to the right, and "haw" to the left.
10. Adam and Eve in the garden of Eden; William Tell; Sir Isaac Newton discovering the law of gravity.
11. True.
12. A star is billed above the title of the production, while a featured player's name comes after the title of the production.
13. A chocolate factory.
14. None; if she were full rigged she would have them all.
15. Half full, because the lower at-mospheric pressure of the upper altitude causes the ink to expand.
16. The seagull, because he is equally at home on land or sea, and subsists on fish, while the eagle is a land bird and cannot fly over vast stretches of water because he would die of exhaustion since he cannot alight on water.
17. Fir, oak, elm, ash, yew.
18. Flogging with rods.
19. You can turn green with envy; the leaves turn red; you can also turn red or purple with rage; or pale with hunger; jewelry turns when it tarnishes; milk turns sour.
20. Estivation.
21. Mickey Mouse, Donald Duck, Snow White, the Seven Dwarfs.
22. Capable of being elongated or drawn out, as into wire or threads.
23. China, silver, glass.
24. The earth moves around the sun.
25. The hurricane signal.

ANSWERS TO GENERAL QUIZ NUMBER VIII-B

1. Cloth. Pinking shears are designed to cut cloth so that it doesn't ravel.
2. A low water animal growing mostly on the bottom of the ocean.
3. Jack Benny and Mary Livingstone; George Burns and Gracie Allen; Fibber McGee and Molly.
4. They are the four basic types of clouds.
5. The "mike" (microphone).
6. Knack, knee, knave, kneel, knead, knew, knell, knife, knit, knoll, know.
7. Locomotive engines.
8. They were all curious.
9. Wear it, it is a halo.
10. Dartmouth College.
11. Pyrrhic victory.
12. You could do all three, because a fillet is a little band with a special significance as a headdress; it is also a piece of lean meat without bone; and a flat molding.
13. The Zodiac.
14. The sense of smell.
15. A species of grass.
16. Today, yesterday, day before yes-

terday, tomorrow, day after tomorrow.
17. Midshipman.
18. Pappous means downy, as the
    seeds of certain plants are. This-
    tle and dandelion.
19. A gosling.
20. A charm.

21. The sessions for jury trial held
    periodically in England.
22. Mulberry.
23. One who wilfully sets fire to
    property.
24. No, it is a small jumping rodent.
25. A whale.

ANSWERS TO GENERAL QUIZ NUMBER VIII-C

1. Eat it, it is a breed of turkey.
2. A flower.
3. 1600 Pennsylvania Avenue.
4. Napoleon; Bismarck; an irresponsible person.
5. Put it in a cage; it is a small
   bird somewhat like a goldfinch.
6. The reindeer. The killdeer is a
   bird.
7. Hydrogen is inflammable, helium
   is non-inflammable.
8. About 98 cents.
9. Supine.
10. The window will be completely
    closed.
11. Joseph; The Pied Piper of Hame-
    lin; Sir Walter Raleigh.
12. Indian. Buffalo. Covered wagon.
13. Indian, Scotch, Italian, Negro.

14. All of them would, because they
    are all lighter than mercury.
15. Bole.
16. A barber shop; a cigar store; a
    pawn shop; a drug store.
17. They are all types of sailing
    vessels.
18. Flax.
19. The next to the last day.
20. Banking and finance.
21. 12 letters.
22. A European bird.
23. A supernatural being in Celtic
    folklore, whose wail or shriek at
    night is believed to foretell the
    death of a member of the family
    visited.
24. On a stalk.
25. Acorn.

ANSWERS TO GENERAL QUIZ NUMBER VIII-D

1. Wedding, Christmas, peace.
2. Antiseptics.
3. All are famous diamonds.
4. No ignition system.
5. Boots. Slippers.
6. It will remain the same.
7. They are styles of type used in
   printing.
8. Geranium.
9. Lower.
10. Financial.
11. Measure with it.
12. They are all types of boats.

13. A star with a tail.
14. A dormer window.
15. Medicine.
16. To have a watch or clock re-
    paired.
17. Pewter is an alloy of tin, lead,
    etc.
18. No two are alike.
19. The direction *from* which the
    wind is blowing.
20. A serving tray.
21. Lunula, which is derived from the

Latin word "luna", meaning moon.

22. No particular country; Esperanto is an artificial language invented for universal use.

23. A liter contains 1000 cubic centimeters, while a quart contains only 960.

24. The limbs of the tree.

25. The House of Commons.

ANSWERS TO GENERAL QUIZ NUMBER IX-A

1. Look before you leap.
2. A dollar made of silver, brass, and pewter, designed by Benjamin Franklin in 1776.
3. The earth.
4. The American bison or buffalo, of which there are only about 4,000 in the United States now.
5. Hind feet.
6. Yellow.
7. Lieutenant Colonel.
8. Pythagoras.
9. The seizing of the Bastille by the people of Paris.
10. "Trees," by Joyce Kilmer.
11. When a vessel is becalmed it is said to be in the doldrums; when it cannot sail owing to lack of wind.
12. It returns to its thrower.
13. Red lead.
14. Snakes have as many as 300 pairs.
15. "Bean-eaters."
16. 48 ounces.
17. Noon.
18. The Atlantic Ocean. One ton of Atlantic water yields evaporated 81 pounds, the Pacific, 79 pounds of salt.
19. A hat. An overcoat. A coarse shoe. A cloak like a blanket with a slit for the head.
20. Pyramid.
21. An extension of time for the payment of a debt.
22. One who writes what another dictates, or copies what another has written.
23. They were a famous fighting regiment of Canada during the Great War.
24. A musical instrument.
25. Eat it, it is a duck.

ANSWERS TO GENERAL QUIZ NUMBER IX-B

1. Yes, but only with the permission of Congress.
2. A bed of roses.
3. In Russian it means little grandmother, but as we know it, it is a scarf used as a headdress.
4. The douglas fir.
5. Thoughts. Gold. Broth.
6. A trifling affair or misdemeanor.
7. Smile, smirk, snicker, simper.
8. Butterscotch, butter milk, butter nut, butter bean, butterfly, buttercup.
9. Small bubbles of air blown into the soap in the process of manufacture.
10. A monster which is a man from the head to the waist, and a horse from the waist downward.
11. A grotesque figure.
12. It is found in the copy of almost any advertised product from cigarettes to sheets. It is a thin transparent sheeting, air and grease proof, made from the cellulose of wood.

13. None; in total darkness it is impossible to see anything.
14. That of Liberia with alternating red and white horizontal stripes, with a white star in a blue field.
15. Columbus.
16. "Close cover before striking."
17. To the place where it's high tide!!!
18. Silver.
19. Women may not vote in France.
20. About 8 to 10 years.
21. 7.
22. A series of columns.
23. "Left blooming alone."
24. A wooden Indian.
25. Dane, dalmatian, dachsund.

ANSWERS TO GENERAL QUIZ NUMBER IX-C

1. Mostly from the hair of squirrel tails.
2. Baltimore and Washington.
3. A restaurant in the basement of a German town hall.
4. 6¼.
5. ". . . that come back shorn".
6. A telescope.
7. Quarter Master.
8. Plum, pear, persimmon, pomegranate.
9. A music box.
10. Cinderella.
11. Eli Whitney.
12. Neither; it is a fabulous monster with the aspect of a horse upon whose forehead is a single straight horn. It is generally found on a coat of arms in Britain.
13. A real person, a Swiss patriot who lived in the 14th century.
14. Pine, fir, spruce, hemlock, cedar.
15. Hook, needles, and shuttle.
16. To change the baser metals into gold.
17. The Big Dipper and the Little Dipper.
18. The ship's carpenter.
19. Readin', 'ritin', and 'rithmetic.
20. Crude rubber, sugar cane, coffee.
21. Pippins, Russet, Northern Spy, Baldwin, MacIntosh, Gravenstein.
22. 16.
23. Run, pitch, slide, score, tie, base (bass).
24. The Vice President, as the President is the Commander in Chief of the United States army.
25. Vegetable; pressed vegetation from thousands of years ago.

ANSWERS TO GENERAL QUIZ NUMBER IX-D

1. Norway, Sweden, Denmark, and Iceland.
2. French.
3. Life insurance.
4. The president's salary is not taxable, but any other income he may have is taxed.
5. A signalling instrument which uses the sunlight to transmit messages.
6. The United States Congress.
7. Much like common table salt.
8. New York, New Jersey, Pennsylvania, Ohio, Indiana, and Illinois.
9. The Order of the Garter.
10. Bachelor of Arts; Doctor of Divinity; Doctor of Philosophy.
11. 12 seconds, as there must be 10 intervals of 1 1/5 seconds each.

12. The eagle. United States, Mexico, Poland, Rumania. Yugoslavia, Albania, Bolivia, Chile, Colombia and Czechoslovakia. It once flew over France, Germany, and the old Austria.
13. One made to individual measurement.
14. In Holland; it is the seat of the World Court.
15. Carol II of Rumania.
16. Use it for holding magazines.
17. 10 to 20 paces.
18. A jail, or a house of correction.
19. The flag of Maryland bears the Calvert arms.
20. An instrumental band. A rubber band. An identification band.
21. Horace Mann.
22. When a harpooned whale tries to escape it tows the boat carrying the sailors. This is referred to as a Nantucket sleigh ride.
23. Two; a Zulu is an African tribesman.
24. Pearl White.
25. Portrait painting.

TRUE AND FALSE ANSWERS—NUMBER ONE

1. True.
2. True.
3. False; $10,000 is the largest denomination of U.S. currency.
4. True.
5. False; a necrologist is one who writes obituaries.
6. False; Pocahontas married John Rolfe.
7. False; an archipelago is a group of islands.
8. True.
9. False; it is colder at the antarctic.
10. True.
11. False; hyperbole is the use of exaggeration.
12. True.
13. True.
14. False; a fathom is six feet.
15. True.
16. True.
17. True.
18. True.
19. True.
20. True; the word is also used to describe a wig.
21. False.
22. True.
23. False; it's in Northern Africa.
24. False; he was the first.
25. True.

TRUE OR FALSE? NUMBER TWO

1. True.
2. False—it has six legs.
3. True.
4. True.
5. False—a fortnight is fourteen days.
6. False—a hogshead is a measure of 63 gallons.
7. True.
8. True.
9. False—a bibliophile is a lover of books.
10. True.
11. False—an amanuensis is one who writes from dictation.
12. True.
13. False—both legs are the same length.
14. False—it's a colloquialism for water.

15. False—a necropolis is a cemetery.
16. True.
17. False—there are 24 sheets to the quire.
18. False—a stallion is a male horse.
19. False—it's in the foot.
20. True.
21. True.
22. False—it's a leave of absence.
23. False—off the coast of South America.
24. False—there are 96.
25. False—Sweden does.

TRUE OR FALSE? NUMBER THREE

1. True.
2. False—there are seven.
3. False—it rotates from west to east.
4. False—he has twelve pair.
5. True.
6. False—cream floats on milk.
7. False—hatching larvae do the damage.
8. True.
9. True.
10. False—33 years are usually considered a generation.
11. False—the Sahara is larger.
12. False—a meter is 39.37 inches; a yard 36.
13. False—candytuft is a flower.
14. True.
15. False—Omega is.
16. False—sheep and goats also do.
17. True.
18. False—there are ten.
19. True.
20. False—they're red, yellow, blue.
21. False—it's gold or silver in bars.
22. False—it's a hoop-skirt.
23. False—it has only six sides.
24. True.
25. True.

TRUE OR FALSE? NUMBER FOUR

1. False—there are three.
2. True.
3. False—it equals 87 years.
4. False—a pedagogue is a school-teacher.
5. True.
6. True.
7. False—she was his wife.
8. False—it takes 10 inches.
9. True.
10. False—Charlie McCarthy is the dummy.
11. False—it usually has only four prongs.
12. True.
13. False—it is a type of window.
14. False—a sheriff is a county officer.
15. False—the word means individual or eccentric.
16. True.
17. False—Madame Curie received it twice.
18. True.
19. False—the goldenrod is.
20. False.
21. False—Edward Everett Hale wrote the story.
22. False—it's the study of pottery or the art of making it.
23. True.
24. False—it is an island resort near Venice.
25. True.

1. Alexander the Great was born in Macedonia, died in Babylon, and was buried in Egypt.
2. Marie Antoinette.
3. Sir Francis Drake.
4. French.
5. Governor Winthrop.
6. Mary Stuart.
7. Thomas Jefferson, over 125 years ago.
8. Yes, President Madison agreed to declare war on Great Britain in 1812.
9. He was a nephew.
10. Alexandria.
11. Frederick, Maryland.
12. Louis XV of France.
13. Harry Lee. Benjamin Franklin. Anthony Wayne.
14. Edward Everett.
15. War, the Revolutionary War.
16. Dewey at the battle of Manila Bay, May 1, 1898.
17. Richard the First of England.
18. Rhode Island. Pennsylvania.
19. She was the first white child to be born of English parents in America.
20. Benjamin Franklin.
21. Louis IX.
22. Minnehaha.
23. The Mexican War.
24. William Bligh.
25. Barnum's circus.

ANSWERS TO MEN AND WOMEN QUIZ NUMBER I-B

1. Robert E. Lee and Ulysses S. Grant.
2. Daniel Webster.
3. King John in 1215.
4. The Battle of Bunker Hill, June 17, 1775.
5. Paul Revere.
6. William Dawes.
7. Theodore Roosevelt. Richard III. The Three Musketeers.
8. She was beheaded by order of Queen Elizabeth in 1587.
9. Millard Fillmore, 1851.
10. Pythias. Cleopatra. Sullivan.
11. They were two maids who lived at Light House Point, Scituate, Massachusetts, during the War of 1812. They were called the Army of Two, because with fife and drum they frightened away the British as they were about to enter Scituate Harbor during the war.
12. Queen Victoria, 1837-1901.
13. Rembrandt; his name was Rembrandt van Rijn.
14. Austrian.
15. Leonardo da Vinci.
16. Rhea Silvia.
17. John Adams.
18. Their first names are Henry.
19. Americus Vespucius, a map maker.
20. Napoleon; Josephine had been previously married to Beauharnais.
21. No, at Domremy.
22. Great-grandfather.
23. The leader of the mutiny on board the Bounty which sailed from England in 1787.
24. Benjamin Franklin; as Richard Saunders he started "Poor Richard's Almanac" in 1732.
25. Titian.

ANSWERS TO MEN AND WOMEN QUIZ NUMBER I-C

1. He was the Duke of York.
2. Alexander the Great.
3. A wooden leg.
4. Socrates.
5. Priscilla, the Puritan maiden, in "The Courtship of Miles Standish", by Longfellow.
6. Plato.
7. Finley Breese.
8. George Spelvin is the name placed on the program cast for the player's name when the player takes two or more parts in the same play and does not want his name to appear twice in the cast.
9. It was spoken by John Wilkes Booth when he shot Lincoln.
10. He was an old soothsayer.
11. Georges Clemenceau.
12. Nicolette. Lord Nelson. Melisande. Beatrice.
13. Disraeli.
14. All are actors or actresses, and their last names pertain to water.
15. Yes, in his earlier years.
16. Ethan Allen.
17. Attila the Hun.
18. Thomas Marshall, Vice-President of the United States.
19. They all have the first name William.
20. The New York Herald, to locate Dr. David Livingstone.
21. Phineas Taylor. James Joseph. William Frederick Cody.
22. Dean. Bennett. Astaire. Barrymore.
23. Italy.
24. William Kidd was a Scotch navigator born in 1650, who was tried for murder and hanged in 1701. Originally sent against the pirates on the high seas, it is claimed he became one himself.
25. Juliet. Paris. Marc Antony. Lancelot. John Smith. John Alden.

ANSWERS TO MEN AND WOMEN QUIZ NUMBER I-D

1. Tom Thumb.
2. Mount Vernon, Virginia. Springfield, Illinois.
3. Columbine. Joan. Jonathan. Eve. Naomi.
4. General Sherman in 1864.
5. Wolfe and Montcalm.
6. Oliver Hazard Perry at the battle of Lake Erie in the War of 1812.
7. Prussia. Russia. England.
8. Thomas Gainsborough, an English artist, 1727-1788.
9. The building of the Panama Canal. He was the engineer.
10. Martha Washington, Whistler's Mother, Susan B. Anthony.
11. Alexander Hamilton. Goliath. Desdemona.
12. Benjamin Franklin, electricity; James Watt, steam engine; Sir Isaac Newton, the law of gravity.
13. Edison, Jefferson, Hardy, Mann, Carlyle, à Becket.
14. It was the name of the airplane in which Admiral Byrd flew over the North Pole in 1926.
15. Charles II of England said it, referring to Nell Gwynn.
16. Millet.
17. Auguste Rodin, French sculptor of the 19th century.
18. Rembrandt van Rijn, the famous Dutch painter.

19. Fred Astaire, Al Jolson, W. C. Fields, Robert Taylor, Edward G. Robinson.
20. Grant, Sherman, and Sheridan for the North. Lee and Jackson for the South.
21. John Wilkes Booth, Czolgosz, Zangara.
22. They were all vice-presidents of the United States.
23. George Washington. Herodotus.
24. Pierce; all the others had the first name of Oliver.
25. Graham. Cabot. Cullen. Jennings.

ANSWERS TO LAW AND ORDER QUIZ NUMBER ONE

1. A post card is any unstamped privately printed card for mailing. A postal card is a government printed and stamped card for mailing.
2. The maximum amount of a money order is $100, but as many $100 money orders may be issued to an individual as desired.
3. They are a fifty-fifty blend of the Union blue and Confederate gray.
4. Vesting legislative authority of a state in a legislature of one chamber.
5. Grand larceny.
6. Identify yourself, a Congressman is immune to arrest for traffic violation.
7. To die without making a will.
8. Perjury.
9. It all goes to the country in which the letter is mailed.
10. Department of Agriculture.
11. Homicide simply means killing a man. Murder means killing a man with malice aforethought.
12. Fourth class.
13. These letters stand for the mints where the coins were made, at either San Francisco or Denver.
14. Probably read it, it is a notice filed with the Patent Office by an inventor.
15. The ending of debate by a majority vote.
16. "Let the buyer beware".
17. That the judge hears the case in his private quarters.
18. One to whom a legacy is bequeathed.
19. Usury.
20. In good faith.
21. 3 miles.
22. A warrant of commitment to prison; a writ for removing records from one court to another.
23. No, although most of them have had a legal training.
24. Duties leveled on goods according to value.
25. Extradition.

ANSWERS TO LAW AND ORDER QUIZ NUMBER TWO

1. Yes.
2. Oyer is a hearing or an inspection in open court which a party might demand of certain instruments. Oyez is a cry used by court criers to procure silence before a proclamation.
3. Finally.
4. Department of the Interior; De-

partment of Agriculture; Department of Commerce.

5. Conservatives.
6. Louisiana, whose statutes are based on the Napoleonic Code.
7. Yes, if he mails an absentee ballot—and then dies before election day.
8. Involuntary manslaughter.
9. Possession is said to be nine points of the law.
10. A document ordering the presence of a person in court under penalty for non-appearance.
11. Mail which cannot be delivered, usually because of incorrect address.
12. Comptroller General, with a term of 15 years.
13. The Department of State.
14. Executive: President; Legislative: Congress; Judicial: Supreme Court.
15. Wives of United States presidents.
16. United States mail carriers.
17. Libel is written abuse or defamation, and slander is oral.
18. Six cents an ounce, and six cents for each additional ounce.
19. Yes.
20. Atlanta, Georgia; Alcatraz, California; Leavenworth, Kansas; McNeil Island, Washington; Lewisberg, Pennsylvania.
21. Specie.
22. Killed a king.
23. Administratrix.
24. One written wholly in the hand of the testator.
25. The United States mail truck has the right of way at all times.

ANSWERS TO LAW AND ORDER QUIZ NUMBER THREE

1. John is always the plaintiff, and Richard the defendant.
2. It is the abbreviation of the Latin word "uxor" meaning a lawfully wedded woman, used in civil law.
3. 12, as there is a ½ cent stamp, as well as 1½ cent stamp besides the denominations from one to ten inclusive.
4. If they were smooth, it would be easy to file off some of the precious metals without changing the appearance of the coin. Nickels and pennies are not milled, as their metals are not very valuable.
5. An administrator is appointed by the court when no executor is named in the will; an executor is named in the will by the testator.
6. Neither; it only says "This side of card for address."
7. Interest charged in excess of a legal rate to the borrower of money.
8. "We, the people of the United States . . ."
9. Three.
10. Of stealing and using as one's own another's ideas and designs.
11. An addition or change in a will.
12. Juris Civilis Doctor, or Doctor of Civil Law.
13. The Treasury Department.
14. Treason.
15. The Bill of Rights.
16. The Executive Mansion, meaning the residence of the head of the executive branch of the government.

17. By a Governor appointed by the President of the United States.
18. Latin.
19. An unfair arrangement of voting districts intending to favor one candidate.
20. Word for word, and letter for letter.
21. Secretary of the Treasury, Henry Morgenthau, Jr. and the Treasurer of the United States, W. A. Julian.
22. Woman Suffrage.
23. That persons convicted of a felony for the fourth time are automatically sentenced to life imprisonment, and are not eligible to pardon or executive clemency.
24. The right of the government to take property and pay the market value for the use of the land for public utility.
25. A body of 23 citizens.

ANSWERS TO LAW AND ORDER QUIZ NUMBER FOUR

1. A sufficient number of members who when gathered together are legally able to conduct business.
2. 48 guns, one for each of the 48 states.
3. 12 buttons.
4. They all have the same number, 2.
5. The Attorney General.
6. Being put on trial twice for the same offense.
7. A direct, violent, sudden and irresistible act of nature which could not by any means have been foreseen or resisted.
8. It means "you may have the body".
9. A fair claim or right.
10. The Treasury Department.
11. From Lincoln's Gettysburg address.
12. Diet.
13. The Pony Express.
14. The President; no length of time in office is specified.
15. 0, zero degrees.
16. Yes, for Cuba.
17. Do nothing; it merely means to be of age.
18. A slip of the tongue.
19. Yes, all except one: he cannot become President of the United States.
20. A gynarchy.
21. Blue.
22. From the Latin, "I forbid".
23. From the Royal Observatory of Greenwich, England, which stands on the first meridian; hence, Greenwich time.
24. Admiral; Vice Admiral; Rear Admiral; Commodore.
25. They are all penitentiaries.

ANSWERS TO SUPER QUIZ NUMBER I-A

1. It is a general pardon for offenses against the government.
2. 39.37 inches.
3. Chemistry, physics, literature, medicine, the Promotion of Peace.
4. They were the four fairies in Shakespeare's "Midsummer Night's Dream".
5. To shelter the bodies of the rulers of Egypt against the day of resurrection.
6. Seventy-one.

7. General, Lieutenant General, Major General, and Brigadier General.
8. The keystone.
9. Welkin means the sky or the vault of heaven. The far fetched meaning of the phrase would therefore be to imply a noise that would seem to reach to the sky.
10. Three; identical, unlike, Siamese.
11. The width is determined by the Panama Canal and the height by that of the Brooklyn Bridge.
12. "Maintain the Right".
13. A flatterer of great men.
14. The battle of Brandywine.
15. Twelve.
16. It is an angle.
17. Louisiana is divided into parishes.
18. The throwing of goods overboard to lighten a ship in distress.
19. An ascian is one who casts no shadow; this would happen in the torrid zone where the sun was shining vertically.
20. It is a cask containing forty-two wine gallons.
21. Battleships after states, destroyers after naval heroes, submarines after fish, and cruisers after cities.
22. Twenty-four.
23. Ornithology.
24. Centigrade, Fahrenheit, and Reaumur.
25. Here are the missing words in order: Santa Fe, Twelfth Night, Sir Walter Scott, and Hawaii.

ANSWERS TO SUPER QUIZ NUMBER I-B

1. One hundred.
2. Longitude.
3. An armada is a fleet of war vessels and an escadrille is a squadron of war planes.
4. A picture expressing an idea.
5. Bucks and does.
6. In a dairy; it's an instrument for measuring the richness of milk.
7. A bull.
8. The Ohio River.
9. To protect the life of the president and to suppress counterfeiters.
10. From end to end; from head to foot; from stem to stern; from top to bottom; etc. etc.
11. A funeral, inasmuch as a threnody is a song of lamentation or a dirge.
12. She "fell into the foamy brine".
13. A small kangaroo.
14. They are all types of shoes.
15. "I knew him, Horatio". From Shakespeare's "Hamlet".
16. By being sullen or dull.
17. What type and arrangement of windows do you want?
18. The first is a sleep-walker; the second a tightrope walker.
19. The pupil of the tiger's eye is vertical, that of the lion is round.
20. Seventy-seven years old.
21. It means "capable of being steered".
22. Two minutes. One minute to enter and one to exit.
23. It is a unit of weight, a hundredweight. It is used in computing the tonnage of fish.
24. This is four, and that is two-thirds.
25. Westminster Abbey.

1. "Our American Cousin".
2. They are found exclusively in the Antarctic.
3. The fifteenth of March, May, July and October and the thirteenth of the other months.
4. A canoe made from a log or tree.
5. The Holy Grail; its quest formed the basis for Tennyson's Arthurian legends and Wagner's drama, "Parsifal".
6. Fill the five gallon can and empty it into the three, thus leaving two in the five gallon can. Pour the three gallons away and then pour the two gallons back into the empty three gallon can. Fill the five gallon can and the total is seven.
7. A man who inspects the railroad ties for loose rails and bolts.
8. The President of the United States and the Governor of Massachusetts.
9. Equally in all directions.
10. Never; as the boat rises with the tide also.
11. The popular name for the French stock exchange.
12. Catacombs.
13. A liquid measure of eighty-four wine gallons.
14. Solomon, Orpheus, and Gabriel.
15. A person employed at auctions to make bids in collusion with the owner of the property to be sold.
16. The Suez Canal is 108 feet wide and 31 feet deep; the Panama Canal is 300 feet wide and 45 feet deep.
17. Since the year 1902, after President McKinley was assassinated.
18. Yes; Belva Lockwood was nominated in both 1884 and 1888 by the Equal Rights Party.
19. It is the study of beards or a treatise on the subject.
20. A non-alcoholic drink made of milk and wine.
21. Marianne.
22. Seven. I V X L C D M
23. The Punic Wars.
24. In the middle of the Pacific Ocean, running North and South.
25. The lighter part of a shadow.

1. A caduceus, pronounced ka-DU-se-us.
2. An inclusive term meaning all the American republics.
3. Norway.
4. By Pope Gregory XIII in 1582.
5. A pin in the gunwale of a boat to support an oar.
6. Aurora Australis.
7. *The Tempest*.
8. Nineteen billion miles.
9. The latitude of the North pole is ninety degrees North. All degrees of Longitude pass through that point.
10. The Navy.
11. The sloe.
12. A candidate receiving more votes than any other receives a plurality. One receiving more votes than the other contestants combined, that is, more than one half

of all the votes cast, receives a majority.

13. Stamp collecting. A blot, blur, or misprint makes a stamp more valuable to collectors.
14. Anyone married legally the second time.
15. A time of calm and peacefulness.
16. Tiller man.
17. A trick.
18. It isn't the smoothness of the ice that admits of skating. The weight of the body melts the ice, and one is really traveling on a film of water which freezes as the weight is removed.
19. A painting done in different shades of the same color.
20. Ten thousand.
21. Disraeli, in a speech in London on July 27, 1878, referred to Gladstone in those words.
22. British Thermal Unit; it is the standard measure of heat.
23. In Pullman cars; it is a registered phrase.
24. Autumn.
25. The installment plan.

ANSWERS TO ENGLISH QUIZ NUMBER II-A

1. Profession of law; a bank of sand or rock; the verb meaning to shut out; a counter over which food is served; a slender rigid piece of wood or metal; a piece of some substance, as a bar of soap; in music the vertical line across a staff before the initial accent; a broad band or stripe; any tribunal, as the bar of public opinion.
2. Talkative.
3. An encyclical is a general letter sent to many persons, especially by a Pope; an encyclopedia is a work in which all the branches of learning are treated in separate articles.
4. A doughnut, bread, a tall silk hat, a pawnbroker.
5. A bag; a kind of Spanish wine; to plunder or pillage; and in England it means also to fire from a position.
6. The transposition of the first and last letters or syllable of two or more words. e.g. Please, sass the palt, for Please pass the salt.
7. Gray and grey.
8. Combustible means inflammable and comestible means edible or pertaining to food.
9. Shingle.
10. A dialogue is a conversation between two or more persons; a monologue is a soliloquy.
11. A piece of timber; the deck of a ship; furnished with food and lodging; a number of persons elected for the management of an office; a table on which games are played.
12. Domino.
13. You are being bored to death.
14. Plug hat; plug of tobacco; fire plug; plug, the horse; plug along; light plug; etc. etc.
15. A talesman is a person summoned to make up a jury; a talisman is a charm.
16. On credit; straightforward or honest; with the compliments of the management.
17. A warehouse; chamber in a gun; a periodical.
18. It means self.

19. A public stage coach and the quality of being attentive.
20. Unable to endure punishment or wear and tear of life.
21. One who steals from the writings of another and passes them off as his own.
22. A line of people; an instrument with a rough edge for smoothing; an arrangement of material for reference.
23. A mannequin.
24. A pair of trousers (in this instance pronounced britches); the rear or firing part of a gun; a breeches buoy used for rescue work on ships.
25. It means after.

ANSWERS TO ENGLISH QUIZ NUMBER II B

1. Auf Wiedersehen.
2. No, since it only means that you cast a shadow.
3. Rays—as rays of the sun; raise—to lift or grow; raze—to tear down.
4. Opaque.
5. Dispossesses.
6. A linguist.
7. Telephone, telegraph, teletype, television.
8. "I have found it".
9. Rustic.
10. Suffering with.
11. An American Thanksgiving bird, the name of an empire, a brilliant red color, a dance, a buzzard (the American black vulture).
12. Crooked, distribute, reject, pleasure, debit, ascend, shallow, gather, guilty.
13. Fish story.
14. Tack.
15. Three. An ancient vessel with banks of oars; a kitchen in a boat; a flat rectangular tray for holding type.
16. Biennial means occurring once in two years. Biannual means occurring twice a year.
17. One who makes an ostentatious display of learning.
18. Publish it.
19. United: untied.
20. To cease to live, singular of dice, a tool used in cutting the threads of screws or bolts, a knife used by envelope makers.
21. God be with you.
22. One who observes or notes very carefully.
23. A cord fastening on dress or coat; the horny substance on the bottom of a horse's foot; the joining of ties on a railroad; the loop for carrying a sword.
24. A very short one.
25. Anonymous is without name; pseudonymous is with a fictitious name.

ANSWERS TO ENGLISH QUIZ NUMBER II-C

1. To conceal the real meaning of something under some pretext.
2. Zenith.
3. Refuse, retard, subtraction, scatter or dissipate.
4. A cat-tail is an aquatic plant, the bulrush; a cat-o-nine-tails is an instrument of punishment, a whip made of nine pieces of knotted cord fastened to a handle.
5. The term is frequently applied to mean a simpleton, but it is

really not slang but a perfectly respectable Latin word meaning "we do not know".

6. An epoch is an important time in history, it is the beginning of an era, which is any notable period of time. e.g. The Christian Era.
7. To climb, to weigh, to measure, a musical term, the particles on the outside of a fish.
8. Yes, both mean to excrete through the pores.
9. Quarrelsome.
10. Stationery.
11. Rain, precipitation from the clouds; reign, to rule or to exercise authority; rein, the strap of a bridle.
12. On the contrary, it means to go over point by point, to look closely at or into, to examine with care.
13. A football player; a loss or an objectionable feature; a breed of pig.
14. Indolent.
15. Abusive.
16. A case of close equality, as between two runners.
17. It would be possible to do all three; a mule is a form of house slipper, an animal, and a textile machine.
18. Cheap talk.
19. A stereotyped phrase.
20. Tearful.
21. Opponent, near, interesting.
22. Candid means frank or outspoken; candied means prepared with sugar, as candied fruit.
23. The bonnet.
24. Actor, dancer, magician.
25. Drowsy.

ENGLISH II . . . ANSWERS TO D

1. Oblige.
2. Acid, dark, beneficial, thin, thorough.
3. Bare—bear; wait—weight; know—no; new—knew; real—reel; etc. etc.
4. To hit hard; a monetary measure of Great Britain; a weight; an enclosure for stray animals.
5. Bangs.
6. The doing of something against opposition.
7. No. Impish means mischievous while impious means irreverent.
8. Vocation, calling, job, profession,
9. An insect, an outdoor game, a low wooden stool.
10. Bragging or loud voiced talk.
11. Unmarried.
12. Lipstick.
13. Personal name, to tap or rap gently, a small mass beaten into shape, as a pat of butter; exactly suitable or fit or exactly at the same time; to stick to one's guns, as to stand pat.
14. Fre-kwent', meaning to be seen in a certain place regularly.
15. Swift, secure, abstain from food.
16. A hiccough.
17. Entirety. Saber.
18. A vegetable of the gourd family; a game played with racquets and a soft ball; to crush or squeeze into a pulp.
19. Kilt, the same as the singular.
20. Secretary, second, secrecy, secure, section, secret, sect.

21. Any of the numerals; the measure of a finger's breadth; one of the fingers or toes; in astronomy a unit of measure equal to one half the diameter of the sun or moon.
22. Dictaphone, telephone, vitaphone, saxophone, xylophone.
23. A tie; a nautical mile; a round hard place in a piece of wood where the limb joined the trunk.
24. A number of persons associated for a common purpose; one of a suit of cards; a joint expense; to beat, as with a club.
25. Healthy.

ANSWERS TO GENERAL QUIZ NUMBER X-A

1. Mocha coffee comes from Arabia, and is known by the small grayish beans inclining to greenish.
2. The St. Louis Cardinals.
3. Hannibal Hamlin; Schuyler Colfax; Levi Morton.
4. Eat it; it is a sweet roll.
5. Two. John Adams and John Quincy Adams.
6. Clark.
7. Foods with moisture evaporated; eggs with moisture evaporated.
8. A yellow turnip.
9. Pegasus.
10. Baseball, football, golf, tennis, field hockey, polo, soccer, handball, pingpong, bowling, basketball.
11. Vitamin C.
12. Animals that live in flocks or herds.
13. Below ground.
14. "My kingdom for a horse." "You can lead a horse to water but you cannot make him drink." "That's a horse of another color."
15. Uncle.
16. Eat it; it is a clear meat jelly.
17. Hippocratic oath.
18. Cornucopia.
19. Dried salt cod.
20. The states of which they are the capitals all begin with the letter 'M'.
21. December and January.
22. Horseshoe, rabbit's foot, wish bone, four leaf clover.
23. A light frothy dessert.
24. Music, painting, sculpture and architecture.
25. A leather strap fastened to the leg of a hawk or a falcon, to which the leash is attached.

ANSWERS TO GENERAL QUIZ NUMBER X-B

1. The book lists only the living.
2. Sheldon, it is a pear; the rest are apples.
3. John Quincy Adams.
4. Yellow.
5. It is the dyed fur of the muskrat.
6. A nose straight in profile.
7. The science of bird's eggs.
8. Gander. Drake. Gobbler.
9. Solomon Grundy.
10. The bean family.
11. Herbert Hoover, Calvin Coolidge, Woodrow Wilson.
12. They are all breeds of horses.
13. Angora goat.
14. Alligator pear.
15. A vegetable.
16. Clarendon, agate and pearl all denote styles of type.
17. Golf.

18. In a barrel.
19. From the Latin word septem, meaning seven.
20. It is derived from the Gatling gun which was used before the modern machine gun.
21. 4 inches.
22. Two strokes under par for a given hole.
23. One entered in a race but withdrawn before the race is run.
24. Hardly! Jersey lightning is a kind of applejack home brewed in New Jersey.
25. It is mined.

ANSWERS TO GENERAL QUIZ NUMBER X-C

1. A dice game.
2. Windsor.
3. Skiing, bowling, tennis, polo.
4. Hot Cross buns and crullers with dough, the rest with batter.
5. Dog tired, hot dog, my dogs are tired, in the dog house, doggone it, work like a dog, leading a dog's life.
6. Woodchuck and groundhog.
7. Boxing.
8. Play it. It is a field game played with racquets.
9. A hot drink prepared from port wine, water, lemons, sugar, and nutmeg.
10. A novice is a beginner, while an amateur may be highly skilled.
11. From the city of Marathon, Greece. The distance is judged by the distance Pheidippides ran from Marathon into Athens to tell of the victory at Marathon.
12. 90 feet.
13. Mush, nuts, applesauce, bologna.
14. To sleep.
15. Fishing.
16. Poker; a hand in bridge or whist; dice shooting; golf.
17. It is a wrestling term.
18. It stands for the high explosive trinitrotoluol, of the nitro-glycerine class.
19. Killing venomous snakes.
20. Andrew Johnson.
21. A score of zero.
22. The fine, minute stroke which often distinguishes one letter from another in the Hebrew alphabet.
23. False. Newfoundland is controlled by the British Empire and governed by a commission appointed by the British government.
24. They were not held in 1916 because of the World War.
25. Sheep.

ANSWERS TO GENERAL QUIZ NUMBER X-D

1. A species of cabbage.
2. Neigh, bray, grunt or squeal, trumpet, hiss, cackle.
3. A turned up nose.
4. Joe Humphreys. Joe Walcott. Rube Marquard.
5. From the heart.
6. A millet is a grain bearing plant of the grass family, and a mullet is a food fish.
7. A moat.
8. It is a dummy piece of artillery or a wooden gun mounted to deceive the enemy.
9. Forbidden.
10. A 'ham'.

11. A collector of postage stamps.
12. A harem.
13. Quinine.
14. Each can move one eye without moving the other, and they can move each eye in opposite directions at the same time.
15. Male, the female is called the peahen.
16. It is false. Mount Everest has never been climbed.
17. Black coffee.
18. Fencing.
19. Ghizeh, with an estimated weight of 5 million tons.
20. A saddle horse.
21. It is a shell fish.
22. A pogonotoist.
23. It is an abbreviation for engine.
24. Water power.
25. Fireworks.

ANSWERS TO OFF THE RECORD QUIZ NUMBER ONE

1. Twenty.
2. There are seven red bars and six white bars.
3. Twenty.
4. Usually on the right side.
5. He faces left.
6. About thirty gallons.
7. Yes, he's wearing a bow tie.
8. It's on the left side.
9. Three fourths of an inch.
10. Sixty-four squares; 32 black and 32 red.
11. Blue, black and green.
12. Two feathers.
13. He faces right on the one; left on the two and front on the three.
14. United States of America.
15. DeWitt Clinton.
16. Twelve.
17. Thomas Jefferson.
18. A sheaf of arrows in one claw, an olive branch in the other, and a banner bearing the words "E pluribus unum" in its beak.
19. There are 88 keys; 52 white and 36 black.
20. The head of an Indian.
21. Twelve, of course.
22. Eight.
23. Nine months, but it never lasts us that long.
24. Nathan Hale is on the half cents stamp and Warren G. Harding on the one and a half cents stamp.
25. There are 42, not including the backspacer, shifts, and margin releases.

ANSWERS TO OFF THE RECORD QUIZ NUMBER TWO

1. It measures three inches in circumference.
2. The standard page is twenty-three inches long and seventeen inches wide.
3. The one is green, the two is red, the three is purple.
4. It would take seventeen.
5. There are two.
6. The standard gauge is four feet, eight and one half inches.
7. It appears twice on a dollar bill.
8. The standard newspaper measures two inches in width.
9. The average typewriter ribbon measures twenty-five feet.
10. The King of Hearts has no moustache.

11. Benjamin Franklin.
12. Martha Washington.
13. It measures two and three-fourths inches.
14. September with nine letters tops the list.
15. Nine, count 'em!
16. Twenty-six; thirteen on each side.
17. Ours all measure six and one eighth inches by two and five eighths.
18. F-G-H and J-K-L!
19. The star on a bill indicates that there is a substitute bill issued to replace one that was worn or defective.
20. It's always made with the four strokes (IIII); not with the letters IV, as might be supposed. Take a look.
21. The great seal appears only on the one dollar bills.
22. $10,000 gold certificate, Federal Reserve Note.
23. There's a woman on the fifty cent piece and the dime; a man on the nickel and the penny.
24. Here's the list: one—George Washington; two—Thomas Jefferson; five—Abraham Lincoln; ten—Alexander Hamilton.
25. Statistics say that the average number of trips is thirty-four.

ANSWERS TO OFF THE RECORD QUIZ NUMBER THREE

1. One thousand.
2. $5,368,709.12.
3. One hour.
4. One hour.
5. They are trade names of pencils.
6. Left side.
7. If not, then what follows the third?
8. A five cent stamp, it will take a message to any part of the world.
9. $1.80.
10. No; it would remain at a constant temperature.
11. Thirteen, they represent the thirteen original states.
12. On most doors, either way.
13. Pyramid.
14. Only one; the others are merely anniversaries of his birth.
15. Twenty-four; the hundredth year is not a leap year.
16. Number three; the numbers on opposite sides of a die always total seven.
17. Forty pennies, eight nickels, and two dimes will do it.
18. The sash is raised.
19. Liberty.
20. The match, of course.
21. Nine times.
22. They all have.
23. K T; D K.
24. The Fasces.
25. Only half way; after that he's running out.

ANSWERS TO OFF THE RECORD QUIZ NUMBER FOUR

1. Thirteen.
2. One half dollar, one quarter, and four dimes.
3. There is no difference, both times are the same.
4. Twenty-four dollars.
5. March twenty-fourth, because one day is dropped from the calendar reckoning when crossing the International Date Line.

6. One quarter of an inch, the thickness of the two covers.
7. One hour.
8. Seventy-eight times.
9. Nine days, he doesn't fall back the last time.
10. Between pages fourteen and fifteen, as they are separate pages; thirteen and fourteen are opposite sides of the same sheet of paper.
11. It would take the same number of pickets but more fence rails.
12. Left side.
13. Yes.
14. No, since length is the name applied to the greater of the two dimensions.
15. The bottom of the picture would be farthest from you as you entered the room.
16. After seven hundred and twenty days.
17. At the North Pole.
18. B is eighteen years old.
19. Inward, because of the vacuum.
20. Fourteen. Every day during the journey a fresh train is starting from the other end, and there are already seven trains on the way to begin with.
21. Twenty-two times.
22. Three.
23. L or M, B, T, P, J.
24. At exactly twenty-one and nine elevenths minutes past four.
25. Seventy-eight times.

ANSWERS TO FAMOUS ORIGINS NUMBER ONE

1. It is formed by the first letters of the words North, East, West, and South.
2. In the old days a traveler carried with him a piece of "journey cake" from which derived our johnny cake.
3. From the goddess Juno, the wife of Jupiter.
4. Louis XIV.
5. From beginning to end. They are the first and last letters of the Greek alphabet.
6. God be with you.
7. Because it follows the line of the palisaded wall or stockade built in 1652 across the southern end of Manhattan Island.
8. In war times the enemy would have the range after the second cigarette was lighted and the third smoker would thus be an easy target.
9. It is the day of Thor, the thunderer and war god of Norse mythology.
10. Julius Caesar was warned that he would be killed during the Ides of March.
11. It was originally used by titled ladies at court to help conceal marks or scratches on the face.
12. From Pontius Pilate and Judas Iscariot.
13. It is derived from the Latin word fidus, meaning faithful and loyal.
14. That was the time when Abraham Lincoln was assassinated. This set-up also allows the most free space for advertising.
15. Shakespeare in "Hamlet".
16. It was prepared by the Earl of Sandwich to save him the necessity of having to leave his card games. His valet brought him a slice of meat with two slices of bread.
17. King Louis of France warned all

bakers who gave under measure that they would be beheaded. As a consequence they tossed in an extra article just to be on the safe side.

18. Benedict, from Benedick, who married Beatrice in Shakespeare's play *Much Ado About Nothing*.
19. Sir Walter Raleigh.
20. Both derive from the Latin word Caesar.
21. From the initials of an old dietetic society called: "Society for the Prevention of Unwholesome Diet".
22. Because this was the width of the original surveyor's chain.
23. According to a tradition dating back to the Egyptians, it was believed that a nerve ran from that finger to the heart.
24. Washington Irving in "The Creole Village".
25. King David, the Psalmist; Charlemagne, Alexander the Great, and Julius Caesar.

ANSWERS TO FAMOUS ORIGINS NUMBER TWO

1. Kowtow is a Chinese form of greeting from an inferior to a superior by touching the ground with the forehead.
2. Augustus Caesar.
3. From the Roman word "salarium", meaning salt-money, since Roman soldiers received a part of their pay in salt.
4. Cleopatra, Queen Esther, Queen of Sheba, Boadicea.
5. In allusion to the carved figure on the prow of wooden ships which had no function and were called figureheads.
6. From Ceres, the Roman goddess of the harvest.
7. In the old days, when swords were carried, it was the custom to extend the right hand to indicate a friendly feeling and to show that there was no sword or knife therein for attack.
8. Calico is named after Calicut, in the East Indies; Damask after the city of Damascus; Muslin for Mosul, in Mesopotamia; Khaki is a Hindustan word meaning "dust colored".
9. Because it was originated in Hamburg, Germany.
10. It was the ancient coat of arms of the Lombards, the money lenders of the Middle Ages.
11. One of the early kings of England, returning from a hunting excursion, so enjoyed his loin of beef that he knighted it Sir Loin, hence our sirloin.
12. It means that the game is played according to the rules set forth in a book of games by the English writer and authority on games Edmond Hoyle, 1672-1769.
13. The common claim is that the U.S. symbols were worked together to form that sign.
14. In the early days the mail was carried over these roads by post.
15. They are interested in archery. The word toxophilite comes from two Greek words and means "love of the bow". In 1781 a group of archery enthusiasts organized the Royal Toxophilite Society which is still in existence.
16. It is named after Josiah Wedgwood, a celebrated English potter.

17. Shakespeare, in his play "Macbeth".
18. Those in the Royal Navy. In olden times the cabins aboard ship were not high enough to permit them to stand up.
19. It is an imaginary country in South America, fabled to be very rich in gold and precious stones; hence the term refers to an inexhaustible treasure.
20. This is a sailor's term for a region of the great Southern Ocean lying between the latitude of forty degrees to fifty degrees South. In this region strong west-northwest winds prevail.
21. Admiral Nelson at the battle of Trafalgar.
22. From two Anglo-Saxon words meaning "day's eye", in other words, the sun, which the flower resembles with its yellow center and white rays.
23. Sir Walter Scott in *Redgauntlet*, Mark Twain, Jonathan Swift in *Polite Conversation*, and Charles Dickens in *David Copperfield*.
24. Brother Jonathan, a personification applied to citizens of the United States. Its traditional origin is that whenever Washington wanted to ask the advice of his friend Jonathan Trumbull, Governor of Connecticut, he would say: "Let's ask Brother Jonathan."
25. William Shakespeare in *Much Ado About Nothing*.

ANSWERS TO FAMOUS ORIGINS QUIZ NUMBER THREE

1. Our Easter is a Christianization of the pagan festival welcoming the coming of spring. Ancient civilizations regarded rabbits and eggs as symbols of a new birth and adopted them to symbolize resurrection.
2. It was a pilot's cry to mark a sounding on the Mississippi River.
3. It used to be Milaner, as Milan, Italy, was at one time the center of women's finery.
4. Because the Yankee pedlars were supposed to have come from Connecticut and to sell to unsuspecting housewives in other states imitation wooden nutmegs for the genuine.
5. They are the initials of Timothy Dexter, an eccentric capitalist, who left a large sum of money for the manufacture of such pipes. After being defeated in politics he vowed that he'd have his name in every man's mouth and succeeded with his famous pipes. He also wrote a book entirely without punctuation.
6. To determine the wind direction and to lie with his nose to the wind so as to be immediately warned of strange enemy scents.
7. Peeping Tom of Coventry was an inquisitive tailor who peeked at Lady Godiva during her ride through the streets, and was struck blind for his curiosity.
8. From the bird of the same name whose shrill cry suggests the laugh of a maniac.
9. It means to make a definite decision. The Rubicon is a small river between Italy and ancient Gaul;

when Caesar crossed it he had invaded enemy territory and could not help but continue his campaign.

10. This is a hangover from the custom of knights wearing a scarf or kerchief of their ladies' when going into battle or combat.

11. John Wanamaker, the famous merchant prince.

12. It is derived from the word fanatic.

13. It was introduced in ancient times as a protective measure. Long beards were easy for opponents to seize and thus enable them to cut off the head.

14. There are two theories, one that honeymoon derives from the old custom of wedding parties being entertained on successive days at the house of neighbors, and the other that it derives from the drinking of mead at wedding feasts. Mead was made from honey and moon is always associated with romance.

15. It comes from the Dutch word yanku, meaning to snarl. It was first used as a term of derision.

16. The phrase applies to something that causes the recipient more trouble than it is worth. It derives from the method of ancient Indian Princes who gave a sacred white elephant to those whom they wanted to ruin. The person could not refuse the royal gift, and had to keep it in such splendour that he was eventually ruined.

17. A rap was a counterfeit Irish coin in the days of George I. It passed for a half penny, though not really worth a fourth of that value.

18. Playing cards originated in Hindustan, early in the seventh century. In 1392 Gungoneur, a Frenchman, fixed the number of cards at fifty-two, for the number of weeks in a year. Four suits stood for the four seasons, red and black for day and night, and thirteen cards to a suit denote the number of weeks per season.

19. In 1833 the population of New Orleans was mostly French, so when the bank issued ten dollar bank notes, the Americans interpreted the French word for ten as dix and the people came to be known as Dixies, and their land as Dixieland.

20. Stage glare caused by the artificial lighting of a theater affects the eyes of the players. Green is a soothing color to the eyes, and therefore the walls of the actor's waiting room were colored green.

21. Old English Inns had small boxes with the inscription "To Insure Promptness" into which patrons dropped coins. Tip came from the first letters of these three words.

22. From the first two letters of the Greek alphabet, alpha and beta.

23. Eric the Red gave Greenland its name in 985 A.D. to make the inhabitants of Iceland think this new country was fertile so they would leave their own colony and settle there.

24. Because of its dull yellowish color and thick consistency.

25. It dates back to medieval times when honored guests were served

hot foods, but when they over-stayed their welcome they were served a cold shoulder of beef or mutton.

ANSWERS TO FAMOUS ORIGINS NUMBER FOUR

1. During an epidemic of scurvy they were served lime juice.
2. Because the first thimble was worn on the thumb, it was shaped like a bell. Thumb bell became thimble.
3. Compounded from the French and German words for yes.
4. It means no choice at all. Thomas Hobson, an English liveryman, attained notoriety by his stubborn refusal to let out his horses except in their proper order. Hence, you could take your choice of the one he offered or none at all.
5. The crocodile was fabled to weep as it ate its victim.
6. It stands for the Latin meaning "Take Thou."
7. It was Frederick the Great's idea to keep his soldiers from wiping their noses on their sleeves.
8. Because it is equi-distant from both the North and South poles.
9. Because when first made they were either round or pointed at the bottom and would not stand when filled, hence the name tumblers.
10. Gob comes from a Chinese word meaning sailor and came into use when the fleet was in the East.
11. A Samuel Wilson supplied the American troops with meat during the War of 1812 and it became known as Uncle Sam's meat. Later all government property became known as Uncle Sam's. In 1854, after Wilson's death, cartoonists commenced using the now famous caricature in referring to the United States government.
12. Because Columbus thought that he had reached the Indies.
13. Steve Brody made a jump from Brooklyn Bridge on November 9, 1888.
14. Louis XII of France, whenever he wanted to evade a distasteful duty, said "let George do it", George being his obliging minister.
15. In England they are called Bobbies and in Ireland they are called Peelers. Both derive their name from the same man, Sir Robert Peel.
16. A south-paw is a left handed baseball pitcher. This name derived because most baseball diamonds are laid out with home plate in the west corner, therefore the pitcher's left arm is on the south side.
17. Lime was once used in the foot-lights of a stage because it burned with a bright glow. Hence the expression.
18. Because its original purpose was to make or sharpen quills for pens.
19. They were originally worn to support the sword belt.
20. Shakespeare's play *Julius Caesar*.
21. A1 is a term used to denote highest quality of merchandise and integrity in business. The symbol originated with Lloyds of London who use it to indicate quality of insurance risks and seaworthiness of ships. A is the symbol for best

rating on the hull and 1 on the rigging.

22. In ale houses, when scores were chalked up on the wall, or behind the door it was customary to put these initials, p and q, at the head of every man's account to show the number of pints and quarts for which he was in arrears. It was thus very important that the host mind his p's and q's.

23. The early American colonists, wishing to get as far removed as possible from things British, named their monetary unit after the Spanish piece of eight.

24. It is named for the ancient Roman god, Janus, whose two heads looked one back into the old year and one forward into the new.

25. Although this expression is generally interpreted to mean "the larger share", its true meaning is the whole. This expression is taken from an old fable in which, when an animal was killed, the lion claimed the first quarter because he was King of the beasts, the second quarter because he was the animal most feared, the third quarter because he had killed the animal, and the fourth quarter because no one dared take it away from him.

ANSWERS TO GENERAL QUIZ NUMBER XI-A

1. Animals that live in flocks or herds.
2. Eight sides, five sides, six sides.
3. One designed for two people in which one rides in front of the other.
4. A dog, with forty-two teeth.
5. A base-ball club.
6. A revolving mechanism is employed to enable the user to fire several shots without reloading.
7. A non-English student at Oxford University who receives a scholarship from a fund established by the provisions of the will of Cecil Rhodes.
8. China.
9. A natural cavern in the earth or rocks.
10. They are all located off the Orange River, in South Africa.
11. Whales, grampus, sawfish, dolphin, seal, walrus.
12. Have your shoes shined.
13. The House of Lords sits as supreme judicial authority as the highest court of appeal of all the courts of Great Britain.
14. A depot is properly a station where goods are stored. A station is the place where railway trains stop for passengers.
15. A drink which has had a dash of spirits added.
16. A wooden post or block of wood, a supply of goods, domestic animals, to lay up food, the capital of a company.
17. None, they are all egg shaped.
18. Purposeless dreaming or imagining.
19. One hundred and eighty degrees.
20. The distance above the ground in which visibility is clear and the height which an airplane can reach.
21. The American flag.
22. A sanatorium is an institution for the care of invalids and the treatment of certain diseases. A sani-

tarium is an institution where one is guarded and protected from disease.

23. A unit of electrical resistance.
24. You, ewe, yew.
25. Nonagon.

ANSWERS TO GENERAL QUIZ NUMBER XI-B

1. No.
2. Eight.
3. Socrates, Plato, Aristotle.
4. It's a part of the brain.
5. Towards the stem.
6. A flare used for signalling at sea.
7. A Russian tea urn with an interior heating unit.
8. The track left by the ship when passing through the water.
9. One of different colors, mottled, especially black and white.
10. Quaker.
11. From a goat-like animal called the chamois, but most of our ordinary commercial chamois comes from sheep or lambs.
12. To cut apart and to hold fast.
13. Igloo.
14. In a frown fifty muscles are active; only thirteen are required to smile.
15. Sorrel is yellow or reddish brown; roan is brown with gray or white; bay is a reddish brown.
16. Boston.
17. A quarter and a dime.
18. A thief gains possession of the stolen goods by stealth and secrecy, and a robber by violence or force.
19. Yes, the volume only would be slightly greater.
20. Moustache, van dyke, goatee, sideburns, muttonchops.
21. It derives from university.
22. A road made of logs.
23. Pledges of stock, notes or chattels as security for the payment of a debt.
24. An allergic person is one who is particularly sensitive to certain foods or conditions.
25. Up stage.

ANSWERS TO GENERAL QUIZ NUMBER XI-C

1. A written word.
2. To the point.
3. Sound travels through water at the rate of 4700 feet per second and through air at the rate of 1090 feet per second.
4. It is not a bone but a nerve, the ulnar nerve, located on the inside of the elbow.
5. One who offers to the public for a price transportation of persons or goods or both.
6. The flying of any national flag upside down.
7. Weaving.
8. As the tombs of the rulers.
9. Down the front they're cut vertically and the collar and cuff buttonholes are cut horizontally.
10. A sea gull; a male swan; a corncob; a lump or piece of anything, as coal or stone; a short-legged, stocky horse; and in obsolete English a big man or leader, as a chief.
11. A book.
12. The Postal Law places the weight at fifty pounds per trip.
13. The customs and arts of ancient people.

14. A progressive tax.
15. Demosthenes.
16. Nothing, it means that you have the power to provoke laughter.
17. A set of chimes played mechanically from a keyboard.
18. A body of water, the bark of a dog, a position one is held at when pursued, the color of a horse, a tree, a place for storing coal in the forepart of a ship between decks.
19. An unbranded steer.
20. A short poem on one subject ending in a witty thought.
21. They refer to magazines, viz. the type of paper on which they are printed.
22. Acrid means sour, acid means bitter.
23. Pigeon English is a mixture of French, English, and Portuguese. Pigeon-hearted means timid. Pigeon-hole is a compartment in a desk in which papers are kept.
24. January, garnet; February, amethyst; March, bloodstone; April, diamond; May, emerald; June, pearl; July, ruby; August, sardonyx; September, sapphire; October, opal; November, topaz; December, turquoise.
25. A black eye.

ANSWERS TO GENERAL QUIZ NUMBER XI-D

1. A decade is ten years, a century one hundred years, and a chiliad is one thousand years.
2. Berry, smacker, simoleon, greenback, bill.
3. The ace of clubs.
4. First Families of Virginia.
5. Satan, Beelzebub, Lucifer, Mephistopheles, Belial, Apollyon, Abaddon.
6. Death, War, Famine, and Pestilence.
7. By the height of the Brooklyn Bridge and the width of the Panama Canal.
.8. The upper.
9. Scotland.
10. The highest possible religious state in the Buddhist religion.
11. A cave dweller.
12. The mahogany tree, because then the tree is freer from sap and of a richer color.
13. All of them.
14. A liter, as it contains 1000 cubic centimeters, while a quart contains only 960.
15. It is made from metal taken from the guns captured in the Crimean War.
16. Thirteen, for the thirteen original states.
17. Men, as it is the name given to submarines.
18. Threes would be the best buy. In threes one gets ninety cents worth for a dollar; in ones and twos only eighty cents worth for a dollar.
19. One thousand.
20. A thief or highway robber.
21. Sixteen. Four each for the brougham, surrey, and victoria; and two each for the hansom and gig.
22. Pumpkin coach, horse, flying trapeze.

23. Herbert George.
24. One hundred and forty pounds, as a stone is fourteen pounds.

25. To steal a train ride on the rods underneath the carriages; to drive an auto very fast; to go on foot.

ANSWERS TO GENERAL QUIZ NUMBER XII-A

1. Flyweight.
2. An unreasoning fear of cats.
3. Shetland, the rest are breeds of dogs.
4. All are fruits except bayberry, which is a wax myrtle tree.
5. A pot of gold.
6. He did not hit his opponent as hard as he was capable of hitting.
7. Gulp. Palm. Leap.
8. Mt. McKinley, in Alaska.
9. The letter "Q".
10. Spinach.
11. Two; the sheep have hooves and the dog has paws.
12. It is a fresh water fish.
13. A chain of mountains with serrated or notched ridges.
14. Martha, Mary Lou, Rosalie, Margie, Juanita, Ramona, Sylvia.
15. Green peas.
16. The eastern hemisphere.
17. A tropical tree whose fruit is used for making jellies.
18. The sea shore. The heavier the atmosphere, the more baking powder.
19. Mace is the dried outside covering of the nutmeg.
20. It is a shade of red, so called because the painter Titian used it extensively in his portraits.
21. It is young cod fish split and prepared for cooking.
22. The Erie Canal.
23. James I of England.
24. Rabbits.
25. New Hampshire, with only 18 miles of coastline.

ANSWERS TO GENERAL QUIZ NUMBER XII-B

1. Lemons, limes, oranges, grapefruits.
2. Spotted.
3. Australia; it is entirely British.
4. Tuna.
5. Baking, boiling, broiling, braising.
6. Shoat is a young hog; the other three are poultry.
7. A Scotch village once famous for eloping couples.
8. Snowy range.
9. That between the Brooklyn and Boston Nationals, May 1, 1920, in Boston. The game was called on account of darkness with a 1-1 tie, after running 26 innings.
10. 18 miles from Dover to Calais.
11. For baking food in an oven.
12. Egypt (sacred beetle); Australia (weapon); Russia (drink); China (public officer); Mongolia (desert); London (district); America (Indian).
13. In Norse mythology, the heaven of heroes.
14. In his own country.
15. Cairo, Egypt.
16. Its wine.
17. Indian corn.
18. The science of dining.
19. Golf, football, tennis.
20. They are berries.
21. "In the Spring a Young Man's

Fancy"; "In the Good Old Summer Time"; "Autumn in Paris"; "Winter Wonderland".
22. Unter den Linden.
23. Brazil; and the Portuguese language is still spoken there.
24. Herodis, the Greek historian, who recorded the travels of the Phoenicians.
25. Lake Superior.

ANSWERS TO GENERAL QUIZ NUMBER XII-C

1. 50 miles.
2. An inhabitant of the western Pyrenees.
3. The one in Missouri.
4. Overcoat and red flannels, for when we have summer in the northern hemisphere, it is winter in the southern hemisphere.
5. The Iberian Peninsula.
6. Flyweight, Bantam, Feather, Light Welter, Middle, Light Heavy, Heavy weight.
7. Philadelphia, Denver, San Francisco.
8. Chicago.
9. At the International Date Line.
10. Cur, rat, pig, skunk, (big) horse, etc.
11. A gam.
12. Not by the ears, but preferably by the scruff of the neck.
13. The pupil of the tiger's eye is vertical, that of the lion is round.
14. All three.
15. Wednesday. September.
16. Harrison, Hayes, Harding, Hoover.
17. (Thomas) Woodrow Wilson; (John) Calvin Coolidge; (Stephen) Grover Cleveland.
18. A fish, especially a young salmon.
19. Walnuts and castinas; peanuts are a root.
20. St. Paul.
21. Mark Twain.
22. California, Sacramento; Illinois, Springfield; Minnesota, St. Paul; New Mexico, Santa Fe; Oregon, Salem; Utah, Salt Lake City.
23. They couldn't have held them on Lake Mead because it is a great artificial lake over 100 miles long formed by Boulder Dam, holding back the water.
24. Frugality and industry; blindness; slyness; hypocrisy; innocence and peace; strength; grace.
25. Lincoln; Grant; Cleveland; McKinley; Theodore Roosevelt.

ANSWERS TO GENERAL QUIZ NUMBER XII-D

1. United States, Soviet Russia, and Venezuela.
2. There are only three: Alabama, Arkansas, Arizona.
3. Speak a cordial greeting; a tycoon is a prominent business man. (Originally the name assumed by the commander of the Japanese army.)
4. Politics.
5. A cat's jaw moves up and down, not sideways. A dog's jaws move in either direction.
6. Water; it is colorless.
7. Red for courage, white for liberty, blue for loyalty.
8. Thirty-six square miles.
9. A person who raises frogs for market use.

10. St. George, St. Andrew, St. Patrick, and St. David.
11. The Egyptians.
12. A bag.
13. A guppy is a small tropical fish; a duppie is a ghost.
14. It's a black eye.
15. The pathological term for seasickness.
16. A prison sentence.
17. The layer of dead vegetation on the forest floor.
18. 101. (100 plus 13 minus 12.)
19. One fathom; one nautical mile; one league; one degree.

20. Merely indulged in explosive, hysterical or immoderate laughter.
21. Any currency which can be lawfully used in the payment of a debt.
22. A kind of raft made of logs.
23. It is a situation or action where one congressman agrees to vote for another congressman's bill, if the latter will vote for the former's bill.
24. The three estates of the realm are: the nobility, clergy, commons. Radio is frequently referred to as the fifth estate.
25. An elephant and a pelican.

ANSWERS TO GENERAL QUIZ NUMBER XIII-A

1. The Stars and Stripes, the flag of the United States.
2. A line with a lead weight on the end used to measure the depth of water.
3. Land which is plowed but not seeded for a season.
4. A wood carver.
5. A dock is the water between two piers, not the pier itself. Hence, drydock.
6. A coward.
7. Steeple-jack, building wrecker and parachute jumper.
8. Seismograph.
9. Occipitofrontalis.
10. Alaska is more than twice the size of Texas.
11. January 1, 1901.
12. A tunnel worker.
13. Duke.

14. Manicuring, police, painting, weaving.
15. Germany.
16. At exactly noon, when the sun is directly overhead.
17. It's an Indian pipe of peace, so smoke it.
18. Paper is vegetable, and parchment animal in origin.
19. From the latex, or milk.
20. The sapphire.
21. Mistletoe. The rest are trees, while mistletoe is a parasitic plant growing on trees.
22. 1 A.D.
23. Avoirdupois weight, Apothecary weight, Troy weight.
24. Charlie Chaplin.
25. Fan yourself with it, it is a large fan used in Eastern countries.

ANSWERS TO GENERAL QUIZ NUMBER XIII-B

1. The science of guns, pistols, bullets, etc.
2. Marionettes.

3. Marriage between a person of a royal family and a commoner.
4. Head, Heart, Hands, Health.

5. They are all imaginary beings.
6. Sulphur and molasses.
7. Two million.
8. Eight.
9. Radium.
10. Nickname.
11. Laughing gas.
12. A woman.
13. A widow who enjoys some property, especially a title coming from her deceased husband.
14. Hope.
15. Hypotenuse.
16. Ape-like.
17. The principal character in Washington Irving's story "The Legend of Sleepy Hollow".
18. 1800.
19. New York, Pennsylvania, Illinois.
20. The United States dollar.
21. It means that the body has become adjusted to the demand made on it for more oxygen.
22. Aesop.
23. A frame on a ship's table to keep articles from falling off in stormy weather.
24. Longitude.
25. In Athens, Greece.

ANSWERS TO GENERAL QUIZ NUMBER XIII-C

1. A name derived from a father or ancestor.
2. As far as the Constitution is concerned, she can.
3. St. Crispin.
4. An elevated place in the open.
5. The science of fingerprint identification.
6. "It fell to earth I know not where."
7. March 22 to April 25. Easter is always the first Sunday after the full moon which happens on or next after March 21.
8. The receiver of a gift.
9. A juggler, or one versed in sleight of hand.
10. A thick one.
11. Ratlins.
12. They are all types of crosses.
13. Those who went to California in 1849 following the discovery of gold there.
14. Manipulate means to operate by hand, and pedals are for the feet.
15. All are names of rugs.
16. An inscrutable or enigmatic smile.
17. Hottentots.
18. Cardinal numerals are 1, 2, 3, 4. Ordinal numerals are 1st, 2nd, 3rd, 4th.
19. No; it is caused by the glare of the snow reflected from the sun.
20. From tapioca.
21. Wasteful.
22. The Gregorian.
23. Architecture.
24. They are all names of old English china.
25. When he is an earl. Earl's wives as well as count's wives are called countesses.

ANSWERS TO GENERAL QUIZ NUMBER XIII-D

1. One of two baskets suspended across the back of a horse to carry produce.
2. Barrel; Certified Public Accountant; hundredweight; His or Her Imperial Highness; cash on delivery.
3. Because sand smothers a fire

without causing electrical short circuits as water might.

4. One purchased in Canada, as the Canadian Imperial gallon contains almost five quarts.

5. Folded in eight, against, in secret, by the grace of God, at liberty or discretion, by the hundred, by the value of.

6. Gun. Butter. Saddle. Pestle. Beast. Found. Ink. Eggs.

7. Nine cuts, as the last cut leaves two pieces.

8. Rich.

9. He makes barrels.

10. Italian flag.

11. When you are knighted by the King of England, you are a "Sir" just for the rest of your own life, but when you are made a baronet you can pass the title down to your eldest son.

12. The west wind, used poetically.

13. The horizontal part is called the tread, and the vertical part is called the riser.

14. Coast Guard.

15. At night, because you can see the stars then.

16. A fog is a cloud on the earth; a cloud is a fog in the sky.

17. Neither. A spitfire is a violent tempered or quarrelsome person.

18. Neither. He means to issue a large amount of free passes so that there will be few vacant seats.

19. In lighting a cellar. A Hyatt light is a steel frame set into the sidewalk with heavy glass to allow daylight to enter into a cellar which extends under a sidewalk.

20. The Bank of England, located on Threadneedle Street.

21. Read it. It is a daily journal or newspaper.

22. A large bird.

23. Cotton.

24. Whale, walrus, manatee, dugong.

25. Food. Drink. Flower. Game. Overcoat.

ANSWERS TO PROVERBS AND MYTHS QUIZ NUMBER ONE

1. . . . is a penny earned. . . . wait for no man. . . . is like a garden full of weeds.

2. A rolling stone gathers no moss. A bird in the hand is worth two in the bush.

3. A church mouse. A berry. A poker.

4. Performing a task right away. Doing two tasks with time and energy for but one.

5. ". . . rules the world."

6. Beggars would ride if wishes were horses.

7. Look before you leap. He who hesitates is lost.

Many hands make light work. Too many cooks spoil the broth. Absence makes the heart grow fonder. Out of sight, out of mind.

8. Benjamin Franklin.

9. A barking dog never bites. Let sleeping dogs lie. Every dog has his day. You can't teach an old dog new tricks.

10. Do not cry over spilled milk.

11. Imitation.

12. He's lost.

13. Long. Tuck. Sailor. Hills.

14. When time passes it is gone for good.

15. As good as a mile. (As good as

her smile.) Saves nine. Three's a crowd. There's a way.
16. It will make one "healthy, wealthy and wise."
17. Runs deep. The best policy. A multitude of sins.
18. In a haystack.
19. Hearty. Snow, a ghost, or a sheet. Ice. Pours. Brass.
20. Practice what you preach.
21. A rolling stone. Stepping stones. The Blarney stone.
22. As handsome does. Is a friend indeed. Than never.
23. Benjamin Franklin.
24. Invention. A feast. Fair lady.
25. Barrel. Forty. Wide.

ANSWERS TO PROVERBS AND MYTHS QUIZ NUMBER TWO

1. Weep and you weep alone. To forgive divine. Shall rise again.
2. Time and tide.
3. Lion. Silk or satin. The driven snow.
4. "Let the little colt go bare, bare, bare."
5. Don't count your chickens before they're hatched.
6. Than to receive. That glitters. As thyself.
7. Still water runs deep. We never miss the water till the well runs dry. Water always runs down hill. Water always seeks its own level. You can't tell the depth of the well by the length of the pump handle.
8. But woman's work is never done. Poverty you'll never lack.
9. A feather. A picture. A whip.
10. Pound foolish. Dreads the fire. Is the shortest way home.
11. Too many cooks spoil the broth.
12. Baggage. Kin. Sane. Substance.
13. Tomorrow will take care of itself. Fools think alike.
14. Whistle. Rail. Pin.
15. As strong as its weakest link.
16. All is not gold that glitters.
17. Give me death. Divided we fall. And all for one.
18. Benjamin Franklin.
19. A bee. Bat. A lark.
20. Lives to fight another day. From a turnip. Out of a sow's ear.
21. Two in the bush.
22. A kitten. A pancake. Toast.
23. Haddock. A cricket or cat. An oyster or an ox.
24. Thoth was the Egyptian's scribe of the gods and the measurer of time.
25. Thor was the Norse god of thunder.

ANSWERS TO PROVERBS AND MYTHS QUIZ NUMBER THREE

1. The goddess of Wisdom.
2. The nine goddesses of the arts and sciences.
3. Juno.
4. Morpheus.
5. Ambrosia. Nectar. Mount Olympus.
6. His right heel.
7. He had two faces looking in opposite directions.
8. Clotho, who spins the thread of life; Lachesis, who draws out the thread of life; and Atropos who cuts the thread of life.
9. Prometheus.
10. The Rock of Gibraltar.

11. Mercury, the messenger of the gods.
12. Hygeia.
13. A creature half man, and half goat; a god of the woods.
14. Atlas.
15. Snakes.
16. It is a mythical river said to flow around the lower regions.
17. The Apple of Discord.
18. The god of the sea. The god who punished crime. The goddess of the hunt.
19. Mars.
20. Their eyes. Argus had one hundred, and Cyclops had one.
21. Hercules.
22. He fell in love with his own reflection.
23. It turned to stone every living thing that saw it.
24. Ceres was the goddess of vegetation; Flora, the goddess of flowers; and Pomona, the goddess of fruit, in Roman religion.
25. Love.

ANSWERS TO PROVERBS AND MYTHS QUIZ NUMBER FOUR

1. A muscle close to the heel.
2. Dactylology, the art of communicating ideas with the fingers. The statue of Venus is minus arms.
3. Hippolyta.
4. In German folklore, a siren of the Rhine who lured boatmen to destruction by her singing.
5. Pygmalion fell in love with the statue of Galatea.
6. The hearth.
7. Ovid and Vergil.
8. The spot where mortals who were favored by the gods were transported after death to enjoy an immortality of happiness.
9. Apollo.
10. Vulcan.
11. Diana.
12. Pan.
13. The winged horse of Greek mythology.
14. The city of Troy.
15. The shrine of Neptune.
16. Hebe, cup bearer to the gods, and goddess of youth.
17. To Apollo, and they left him many sacrifices when healing took place.
18. Europe is named for Europa.
19. Thomas Bulfinch.
20. The ears of an ass.
21. Aphrodite.
22. Achilles.
23. Mercury.
24. The bright and burning one.
25. In Greek religion the God of medicine and healing; a son of Apollo slain by Zeus for attaining such skill that he raised the dead.

ANSWERS TO FLORA TO REPTILIA NUMBER ONE

1. The carnation.
2. The lily.
3. Yes; a whale being a mammal cannot breathe under water.
4. River horse.
5. Bob white, Phoebe, whip-poor-will, cuckoo, bob-o-link.
6. Crow, eagle, owl.
7. Whistler.
8. She was called the Swedish nightingale, and nightingales feed on ant eggs.
9. Bats, flies, fowls (fouls).
10. Drones, queens, workers.

11. Oklahoma.
12. Three very heavy frying pans of different sizes.
13. Mulberry leaves.
14. Bamboo.
15. United States Lighthouse tenders.
16. Cowslip, dandelion, tiger lily, foxgloves.
17. Two on each foot.
18. Baltimore oriole, Carolina cuckoo, Australian weaver bird, English sparrow.
19. A drake does not quack.
20. The male.
21. No, they give birth to their young alive.
22. The sparrow has twice as many vertebrae as the giraffe. All birds have fourteen while all mammals have seven.
23. Small birds closely related to the kingfisher.
24. Surely, it's a sponge.
25. The pheasant family.

ANSWERS TO FLORA TO REPTILIA NUMBER TWO

1. A nye.
2. Jackdaw.
3. Fish.
4. The parrot.
5. In its stomach.
6. His own weight in food every day.
7. Cardinal, lark, cat bird, blue bird, loon.
8. An upholstered worm.
9. By the pound; there are approximately five thousand honey bees to the pound.
10. A grasshopper.
11. The mosquito.
12. Switzerland, Scotland, France, Ireland, Egypt, Germany, England, and Italy.
13. Eight; spiders belong to the arachnid group which is characterized by four pairs of walking legs.
14. Egg, caterpillar, cocoon, adult.
15. It is a term used by biologists to classify sponges; strictly speaking it means provided with pores.
16. A wading bird of the heron family.
17. The penguin.
18. A flea can jump one hundred and fifty times its length. If a flea were as long as a six foot man he could jump nine hundred feet, or clear over a ninety story building.
19. Plant, distant, remnant, merchant, slant.
20. A bunch of wild flowers.
21. Defeated congressmen still holding office from their unexpired term.
22. The giant tortoise, which has been known to live as long as three hundred years.
23. A crocodile is man-eating and has a pointed nose; an alligator (not the rug cutting type) does not eat man and has a rounded nose.
24. A large lizard of the desert region of the southwest United States.
25. A bird whose feathers were formerly used for hat decorations.

ANSWERS TO FLORA TO REPTILIA NUMBER THREE

1. Eight.
2. Ten.
3. Hardly, as an alewife is a fish which is akin to the herring.

4. A variety of duck.
5. Because it is able to imitate the call of almost any species of animal.
6. Six, the titmouse is a bird.
7. A bird similar to a woodcock or a snipe.
8. It's a bird, he's a nighthawk, a jay walker, on a lark, etc.
9. That they ascend the river to breed at definite seasons.
10. The orange blossom.
11. The beaver.
12. A water animal of the same name.
13. A species of lizard.
14. Gull, goose, duck, coot, loon.
15. An insect; it is the fastest and most powerful of the running insects.
16. Boa constrictors and the regal python.
17. It is easier to obtain food swimming upstream.
18. A species of alligator.
19. No, they are unable to swallow unless completely submerged.
20. The ostrich.
21. Forget-me-not.
22. A tadpole.
23. Oysters.
24. They are all flowers.
25. An ostrich.

ANSWERS TO FLORA TO REPTILIA NUMBER FOUR

1. They are all names of birds.
2. A bird, better known as the robin red breast.
3. Blubber.
4. The King cobra.
5. Because a snake has no eyelids.
6. Because it saved the early settlers from starving, and was also their first export, their first source of revenue.
7. Oysters.
8. A fresh water fish of the salmon family found in clear streams.
9. The frog.
10. Yes, a long eared one.
11. Tortoise, crocodile, snake, lizard.
12. Yes, it cannot strike unless coiled.
13. Rome, according to the ancient legend.
14. In a wedge shaped V.
15. Tobacco.
16. Laudanum, opium, paregoric, morphine.
17. Fungi.
18. White oak, white ash, black oak, red cedar, white elm, redwood, blue spruce, black walnut, etc. etc.
19. The plant and animal life of a given region.
20. It would be impossible for them to do either inasmuch as pineapples are a fruit of a plant and not a tree.
21. Chlorophyll.
22. Pick it up; if you get stung it's a worker, a drone cannot sting.
23. An aerie.
24. The falcon.
25. Poppy, marigold, aster, orange blossoms, bachelor buttons, snapdragon.

ANSWERS TO LITERARY QUIZ NUMBER II-A

1. *Julius Caesar*.
2. Jonathan Swift.
3. "Backward, turn backward, O time, in your flight," "The boy stood on the burning deck," "Where ignorance is bliss."

4. "The Nautilus."
5. Barbara Frietchie, in the poem by Whittier.
6. Rafael Sabatini.
7. "The Village Blacksmith" by Longfellow.
8. *The Tempest.*
9. Don Quixote.
10. *The Merchant of Venice.*
11. David Copperfield, Wilkins Micawber, Uriah Heep, Mr. Barkis, Mr. Steerforth, Dr. Strong.
12. "Who never to himself hath said . . ."
13. *The Scarlet Letter* by Nathaniel Hawthorne.

14. *Henry IV, Richard III, Hamlet.*
15. Cervantes.
16. John Bunyan.
17. Aesop.
18. Julius Caesar.
19. "Mighty Casey has struck out."
20. The Ancient Mariner killed an albatross.
21. A boarding school.
22. *Henry VIII* in 1611.
23. Louisa May Alcott.
24. She was the daughter of Shylock. and she appears in Shakespeare's play *The Merchant of Venice.*
25. Herman Melville.

ANSWERS TO LITERARY QUIZ NUMBER II-B

1. *Candida, Pygmalion, Saint Joan, Androcles and the Lion, Fanny's First Play, Arms and the Man,* etc.
2. *Oliver Twist* by Charles Dickens.
3. Aunt Polly.
4. "The Vision of Sir Launfal".
5. *Scarlet Sister Mary, Riders of the Purple Sage, So Red the Rose, The Green Bay Tree, The White Sister.*
6. Dickens's *David Copperfield.*
7. "The Children's Hour" by Henry Wadsworth Longfellow.
8. The 18th Century.
9. *The Vicar of Wakefield.*
10. He was a German, Rudolph Raspe, an exile who wrote in England.
11. *As You Like It, The Merry Wives of Windsor* and *King Henry the Fourth, Julius Caesar, Macbeth.*
12. *A Christmas Carol, The Tale of Two Cities, Uncle Tom's Cabin, Vanity Fair.*
13. He struck out.
14. Washington Irving.
15. Mark Twain.
16. "Nor any drop to drink". From "The Ancient Mariner".
17. In Stevenson's *Treasure Island.*
18. *Anthony Adverse* by Hervey Allen; *Captains Courageous* by Rudyard Kipling; *Nicholas Nickleby* by Charles Dickens.
19. "All in the valley of death, rode the six hundred." From Tennyson's "The Charge of the Light Brigade".
20. Charles Hamilton, Frank Kennedy, Rhett Butler.
21. Rudyard Kipling.
22. "The Courtship of Miles Standish."
23. "Tell me not, in mournful numbers, Life is but an empty dream!"
24. Paul.

25. Paul Revere's ride. The landing of the Pilgrims. The battle of Concord. Sheridan's ride to Winchester.

ANSWERS TO LITERARY QUIZ NUMBER II-C

1. "Abou Ben Adhem" by Leigh Hunt.
2. A pen name.
3. Marc Antony in his oration over Julius Caesar in Shakespeare's play of the same name.
4. John Greenleaf Whittier in "Maud Muller".
5. "And he stoppeth one of three."
6. "Twinkle, twinkle, little star."
7. "And many goodly states and kingdoms seen." From Keats' "On First Looking into Chapman's Homer".
8. They are all characters in Shakespeare's *The Tempest*.
9. "Snowbound" by John Greenleaf Whittier.
10. A description of Cleopatra in Shakespeare's *Antony and Cleopatra*.
11. *The Merchant of Venice, Alice in Wonderland, The Christmas Carol*.
12. Charles Dickens, Reverend C. L. Dodgson, Charles Lamb, W. Sidney Porter, Washington Irving, Samuel L. Clemens (Isaiah Sellers), Benjamin Franklin, Joel Chandler Harris.
13. "And all the men and women merely players".
14. "Under a spreading chestnut tree The village smithy stands."
15. Victor Hugo. Jean Valjean.
16. Tiny Tim.
17. *Uncle Tom's Cabin*.
18. In prison.
19. A character in Dickens's *David Copperfield*.
20. General Munroe, Major Heyward, General Montcalm, Alice, Duncan, Webb, Uncas.
21. *The Merchant of Venice*.
22. Elbert Hubbard.
23. *Uncle Tom's Cabin*.
24. The Three Musketeers.
25. Sir Walter Scott's "Lady of the Lake".

ANSWERS TO LITERARY QUIZ NUMBER II-D

1. Shakespeare in *Hamlet*.
2. Mr. Hyde.
3. 3000 ducats.
4. *Oliver Twist* by Charles Dickens.
5. Simon Legree was the brutal slave master in *Uncle Tom's Cabin*. Little Nell was a precocious and phenomenally good child in Dickens's *The Old Curiosity Shop*. Cordelia was the youngest and only faithful daughter in Shakespeare's *King Lear*.
6. They are all characters in Dickens's *David Copperfield*.
7. "In a kingdom by the sea". "Annabel Lee", by Poe. "But spare your country's flag, she said." "Barbara Frietchie", by John Greenleaf Whittier. "But I go on forever". "The Brook", by Tennyson.
8. The Parish Beadle so named them in *Oliver Twist*.

9. The Bible, the 23rd Psalm.
10. In *Sherlock Holmes* by Arthur Conan Doyle.
11. A boy.
12. Parson Weems, the first biographer of George Washington.
13. *David Copperfield*. Barkis sent this message to Peggotty.
14. John Greenleaf Whittier.
15. "The Ride of Paul Revere" by Longfellow; "And I on the opposite shore will be."
16. Charles Dickens.
17. Macduff. (*Macbeth*, V, viii.)
18. James Whitcomb Riley, the Hoosier poet.
19. Shakespeare, Washington Irving, Margaret Mitchell, Arthur Conan Doyle.
20. Luke and Revelation from the New Testament; Psalms, Daniel and Jonah from the Old Testament.
21. Robert Louis Stevenson.
22. Adolf Hitler.
23. *The Old Curiosity Shop*.
24. "—spider to the fly."
25. Medusa, Rapunzel, Samson, Lady Godiva, Absalom, Lorelei.

ANSWERS TO HOW'S YOUR HISTORY QUIZ NUMBER I-A

1. The purchase of Alaska, which took place under Seward's administration as Secretary of State, was thought to be a foolish investment.
2. Columbus made his landing in the fifteenth century; the Pilgrims made theirs in the seventeenth century.
3. Oklahoma in 1907; New Mexico, January 1912; Arizona, February 1912.
4. Northerners who sympathized with the South.
5. 1871, 1872, and 1906, in that order.
6. Louis the XVI.
7. Edward VIII of England abdicated as King and Emperor.
8. Commander Robert E. Peary on April 6, 1909. It was not announced however until October of that year.
9. This was the signal code for Paul Revere's ride.
10. President McKinley was shot.
11. Yes.
12. George I, King of England from 1714-1727, was German.
13. Confederate money was called shin plasters during the Civil War.
14. Vermont.
15. "Liberty, Equality, Fraternity".
16. Alexander the Great.
17. 1898.
18. Ferdinand Foch.
19. Eleven states were in the Confederacy. Virginia, North Carolina, South Carolina, Georgia, Florida, Alabama, Mississippi, Louisiana, Tennessee, Arkansas and Texas.
20. 1773.
21. 1900.
22. August 3, 1914.
23. It announced that the Declaration of Independence had been ratified by the thirteen states.
24. Her Golden Jubilee in 1887, and her Diamond in 1897.
25. The assassination of Archduke Ferdinand of Austria-Hungary by a Serbian youth.

ANSWERS TO HOW'S YOUR HISTORY QUIZ NUMBER I-B

1. England. George V died in January of 1936; Edward VIII abdicated in December of the same year, and George VI became the new King.
2. The shot fired by the American colonists at Concord at the beginning of the Revolutionary War.
3. Patrick Henry, Nathan Hale, Captain John Parker.
4. Thomas Jefferson was the pen, Patrick Henry the tongue, and George Washington the sword.
5. Miles Standish.
6. Great Britain and the United States.
7. Ulysses S. Grant, Philip Sheridan, and William T. Sherman.
8. At Yorktown, Virginia, on October 19, 1781.
9. The House of Rothschild.
10. Only one, the 18th, Prohibition.
11. The Battle of New Orleans.
12. Denmark.
13. France.
14. France, on February 6, 1778.
15. Constitutional Monarchy.
16. None; Holland remained neutral.
17. Twelve years before the Revolution, in 1763.
18. Most all of our wars have started during that month.
19. France has never had a sovereign Queen.
20. Yes. In 1794 Congress decreed that after May 1, 1795, the flag should have fifteen stripes and it remained that way until April 1, 1818.
21. He returned it to General Lee.
22. The death of John Marshall in 1835.
23. A soldier is holding an American flag in the stern of the boat and the flag had not been designed at that time.
24. They were called hieroglyphics, meaning picture writing.
25. Of having divulged state secrets of France to a foreign power.

ANSWERS TO HOW'S YOUR HISTORY QUIZ NUMBER I-C

1. Mexico, from 1864 to 1867.
2. England, Spain and France.
3. Julius Caesar, Alexander the Great, and the Iron Duke of Wellington.
4. He made four.
5. He crowned himself, saying that "no one is great enough to crown Napoleon".
6. Chief Sitting Bull.
7. Pony express rates were ten dollars an ounce.
8. Moses, Caesar, Shakespeare, Washington, Lincoln.
9. Viscount Horatio Nelson.
10. The Civil War, The Revolutionary War, and the World War.
11. "Remember the Maine!"
12. A short route to India and the East.
13. The Continental Congress.
14. The Olympia.
15. They were both beheaded.
16. The Trojan War.
17. The right to sub-divide into not more than four additional states.
18. Texas. United States, Confederate States, Texas State flag, Spain, Mexico, and France.

19. When there is a new state added to the Union.
20. "It's a long time between drinks".
21. There was only one naval battle in the World War, the Battle of Jutland.
22. The House of Lancaster, whose symbol was a red rose, and the House of York, whose emblem was a white rose.
23. Ferdinand and Isabella.
24. The Battle of Verdun.
25. Lancaster, Pennsylvania.

ANSWERS TO HOW'S YOUR HISTORY QUIZ NUMBER I-D

1. The Civil War.
2. A council called in 1521 by the Emperor Charles V to try Martin Luther for his heretical teachings.
3. He was a gold and silversmith.
4. Plymouth, England.
5. Yes. Napoleon lived from 1769-1821, and Washington from 1732-1799.
6. 1620, the year the Pilgrims landed.
7. 1607.
8. Nina, Pinta, and the Santa Maria.
9. General John Burgoyne.
10. The Bill of Rights.
11. ". . . shall not perish from the earth."
12. Fifty-six.
13. In Westminster Abbey.
14. They were a group of Colonial fighters led by Robert Rogers against the French and Indians.
15. Persia.
16. Napoleon divorced Josephine to marry Marie Louise of Austria.
17. The Civil War, the Spanish American War, War of 1812.
18. Napoleon.
19. John Bull.
20. Queen Victoria's Birthday.
21. The British. We are the only nation which celebrates a defeat.
22. Eleanor, Beaver, and Dartmouth.
23. Philadelphia, New York, Boston.
24. The first letters of the names of Argentine, Brazil, and Chile which have acted together in international affairs, and are hence referred to as the A-B-C powers.
25. Richard Coeur de Lion, or Richard the Lion Hearted.

ANSWERS TO GENERAL QUIZ NUMBER XIV-A

1. From 50 to 100 years.
2. Ride on it. It is a cable railway, used especially on a mountain.
3. A purplish brown color.
4. Massasoit, better known as King Philip; Samoset, first to greet the Pilgrims; Powhatan, father of Pocahontas; Squanto, who taught the colonists about food; Pocahontas, Indian princess who saved John Smith.
5. The Ohio River.
6. One of the largest diamonds in the world.
7. Zoo, zinc, zero, zone.
8. A plane with five angles and five sides.
9. It is four times as large. Circles are to each other as the squares of their diameters.
10. A catastrophe.
11. Regiment, battalion, company, platoon, squad.
12. An old style flat-iron.

13. Kapok is found in advertisements of furniture. It is the mass of silky fibers found in the seed pod of a tropical tree, and is used extensively for stuffing mattresses and pillows.
14. Copper, because it is not a gas.
15. A signal, usually sounded at sunrise to awake sailors and soldiers.
16. An eccentric old man.
17. The alligator.
18. An animal which spends half its life on land, and half in water.
19. "To be in another's shoes." "To die with one's shoes on." "If the shoe fits, put it on."
20. White, the same as any other candle. The color of the wax makes no difference.
21. Bowling.
22. Sell it; it is a waxy substance from the sperm whale, used largely in perfumery. It is scarce and very expensive.
23. The members of the white race have from 40,000 to 60,000 hairs in a full head of hair. Women have as many as 70,000. Other races have fewer hairs than the white race.
24. A bad egg.
25. Profitable.

ANSWERS TO GENERAL QUIZ NUMBER XIV-B

1. The glass.
2. 29 days, 12 hours, 44 minutes and 5 seconds.
3. More chlorine.
4. A fortress.
5. Because they are the most easily distinguished.
6. The orchid.
7. A carriage.
8. All are names of knots.
9. Stands perfectly still.
10. Test it with your elbow.
11. Giraffes.
12. Cutting stone.
13. No, it is straight as any other animal's. The hump of a camel is chiefly fat which is stored there and then re-absorbed when needed as food.
14. Yes, a Hebrew coin worth about 60 cents.
15. It is a new issue of a stamp put on an envelope and canceled at the post office with the postmark dated the same as the date the stamp was first put on sale.
16. Water.
17. McGinty. Dan McGrew. Danny Deever. Humpty Dumpty. Casey Jones.
18. Because it takes one year for the earth to go around the sun, and a year is not an exact number of days but about 365 and a quarter. so every four years an extra day is added to make the calendar even.
19. Wanderer.
20. Franz Lehar.
21. Four. Telemark or downhill; slalom for a course requiring turns; touring model for general cross country work; jumping skis, up to 8 feet in length.
22. She "fell into the foamy brine."
23. 2.
24. The jugular vein.
25. Probably not; a cubic foot of gold weighs about 1200 pounds.

ANSWERS TO GENERAL QUIZ NUMBER XIV-C

1. One day.
2. It is the internationally chosen symbol used in radio for distress of a ship, and is not an abbreviation of 'save our ship', but was chosen for its ease in transmitting.
3. A poisonous plant.
4. A peculiarity of character.
5. 120 different combinations.
6. A rip-saw.
7. Abraham Lincoln.
8. A perennial lives several years while an annual must be planted anew each season.
9. June. January. May.
10. Century plant; morning glory; day lily.
11. It is a short dagger.
12. It has no head.
13. Two and a half feet.
14. Because it is a donkey.
15. Kentucky.
16. Rarely higher than 50 feet, but they have been known to be as high as 80 feet.
17. 15 years service.
18. The development of rayon, the radio, the automobile, the airplane, the telephone, and motion pictures.
19. 72%.
20. A large stone mug for beer or ale.
21. Two, the Tropic of Cancer, and the Tropic of Capricorn.
22. The sun.
23. Train, tractor, trailer, tank, taxi, toboggan, torpedo boat, trireme, trolleycar and truck.
24. One of the mythical inhabitants of the planet Mars.
25. To distinguish it from the smaller Brittany in France.

ANSWERS TO GENERAL QUIZ NUMBER XIV-D

1. Glue is composed of hard brittle brownish gelatin obtained by boiling to a jelly the skins, etc., of animals. Mucilage is a gelatinous substance produced in certain plants by the action of water on various celluloses. Glue is a product of animals, and mucilage a product of plants.
2. Henna leaves; used for centuries in Egypt and Asia to color the hair, nails and skin.
3. To portion out.
4. A sun room.
5. You have a head cold.
6. A shako.
7. An inn.
8. Grand Old Party.
9. "The Jazz Singer" starring Al Jolson.
10. Talkative.
11. Yes, for one short period, from 1835 to 1837, the National Debt was lifted.
12. Setter, sealyham, spaniel, spitz, shepherd.
13. The large post at the foot of a flight of stairs used to hold the stair railing or balustrade.
14. Benjamin Franklin.
15. A sickle.
16. White, brown, white, brown.
17. $999,999.90.
18. Pyramids of Egypt.
19. Play it; it is a fanfare or flourish.
20. A root growing underground, a potato. A brass wind instrument with a low pitch.
21. There is no difference.

22. Switzerland, Japan, Alaska.
23. You would be going east.

24. The lakes of Killarney.
25. Union of South Africa.

ANSWERS TO GENERAL QUIZ NUMBER XV-A

1. Central America.
2. Sweet pea, Sweet William, Sweet Alyssum, Sweet Briar Rose.
3. The longest day is June 22, and the shortest December 21.
4. Because a billion in England is a million million, but in the United States a billion is considered to be a thousand million.
5. The break actually occurred on July 8, 1835, while tolling during the funeral of John Marshall, Chief Justice of the United States.
6. 6 hours and 20 minutes fast.
7. They are airplane carriers.
8. A rich ore deposit.
9. The left side.
10. They are all dress goods.
11. Horse. Fish. Bird.
12. 1.
13. Cabbage, lettuce, parsley, spinach.
14. The white becomes the chick, and it nourishes itself on the yolk.
15. Angling, archery, autoracing, aviation.
16. Clams, oysters, scallops, mussels.
17. The Secretary of State.
18. Sage, thyme, dill, mint, chives.
19. James Abram Garfield.
20. Gaspar, Melchior, and Balthasar.
21. A police patrol wagon.
22. Of no country; it is a charm or token of good luck.
23. It occurs about three times in a century; the last time was in 1920, the next time will be 1942.
24. Antilles.
25. There are 27 east and 21 west of the Mississippi.

ANSWERS TO GENERAL QUIZ NUMBER XV-B

1. He would take the goat first. Then he would return and take the wolf over and bring back the goat. Then he would take the hay over and return for the goat. Remember that the wolf will not eat the hay.
2. A vegetable, a kind of onion.
3. Madison, Wisconsin; Jackson, Mississippi; Lincoln, Nebraska.
4. Oxford, Ohio.
5. 2700 acres.
6. New Scotland.
7. An Arab kingdom, the state of Mesopotamia.
8. Yes, several.
9. Oklahoma.
10. The right bank of the stream as one faces downstream.
11. A rat or a mouse. A cow. A pig or hog. A deer.
12. Miscellaneous.
13. One whose motto is Mañana. Mañana means tomorrow, and a procrastinator is one who puts off doing things until 'tomorrow'.
14. Bullock, ram, stag or hart, wizard, buck.
15. On the seal of the State of Pennsylvania, the 13 original states are represented as stones of an arch, with Pennsylvania being the keystone of this arch.
16. In da Vinci's painting "The Last Supper" the salt dish is overturned and the salt spilled out. This picture is also the origin of the "13 at table" superstition.

17. His name is now used to identify a type of whiskers worn by him.
18. Canal Zone; Territory of Hawaii; District Federal.
19. The Angora goat market.
20. California.
21. You could go hunting with it, because a nimrod is a hunter.
22. Finished her stewed fruit.

23. A Chinese fruit cultivated for making preserves and confectionary; also the name of the tree which bears it.
24. None; acorns do not grow on elm trees.
25. Red and blue. Black and yellow. Yellow and blue. Yellow and red.

ANSWERS TO GENERAL QUIZ NUMBER XV-C

1. It is the boundary line between Pennsylvania and Maryland. Originally set up to settle a boundary dispute, it later came to be accepted as the dividing line between slave and free states, or the North and the South.
2. Chess.
3. An isotherm is an imaginary line connecting all points having the same temperature, and an isobar is an imaginary line connecting all places having the same barometric pressure.
4. North Atlantic, South Atlantic, North Pacific, South Pacific, Arctic, Antarctic and Indian Oceans.
5. Switzerland.
6. Haiti.
7. A belt or zone of calm, 15 degrees north and south of the Equator.
8. Yes, it is in the British Museum.
9. In Minnesota, or in Texas, Arkansas, and Louisiana.
10. An isosceles triangle.
11. Eat it, it is a small cucumber pickle.
12. Red.

13. The end nearer the vine has no seeds; this is the bitter end.
14. Ace, King, Queen, Jack, and ten of the same suit.
15. An athlete, a discus thrower.
16. Bulls.
17. Its long neck; a camelopard is a giraffe.
18. Grapes.
19. Yes. It is a tropical American fruit, oval shape, of a greenish yellow color.
20. It is a kind of pancake originating in France.
21. It is a yellow, oval, plum-like fruit, sometimes called the Japanese plum.
22. Rook, knight, bishop, king, queen, pawn.
23. The Pony Express.
24. Philadelphia Phillies; Brooklyn Dodgers; Cincinnati Reds; Chicago Cubs; New York Giants; Boston Bees; St. Louis Cardinals; Pittsburgh Pirates.
25. San Diego in California; Santiago in Chile.

ANSWERS TO GENERAL QUIZ NUMBER XV-D

1. Jack Johnson.
2. Ask for a new deck, as there would be five aces.
3. Rams, Crusaders, Eagles, Blue Devils, Trojans.

4. 11, 6 on each team.
5. The mutinous sailors from H.M.S. Bounty.
6. Delaware.
7. Los Angeles, California.

8. Animal and vegetable.
9. Rhode Island, the smallest state has the longest name. Its official title is State of Rhode Island and Providence Plantations.
10. Vermont maple syrup, Cape Cod cranberries, Maine potatoes, Gloucester fish products.
11. It is a rich cheese.
12. The lily family.
13. They are all varieties of nuts.
14. George Washington, John Adams, Thomas Jefferson, James Madison, James Monroe, John Quincy Adams.
15. Goslings.
16. Gaseous, liquid, solid.
17. One out of three.
18. Homes.
19. Luzon.
20. Stuff it, for it is a young chicken.
21. No, it is located on the island of Oahu.
22. The quick brown fox jumped over the lazy dogs. Pack my box with five dozen liquor jugs.
23. Common salt.
24. The pheasant family.
25. A soubrette.

ANSWERS TO GENERAL QUIZ NUMBER XVI-A

1. Milk—there is more fat in the cream, which is lighter.
2. The inner ear, or labyrinth.
3. To the painting of inanimate objects.
4. It's an old fashioned dance.
5. Colored prints.
6. Just before dawn and just before dark.
7. In advertisements for furs. Lapin is the trade name for rabbit fur.
8. Three is the numerator and four the denominator.
9. After nine years of age.
10. The larva of a moth which is inside it.
11. There are about three generations to a century, which means that one generation is about thirty-three years.
12. The trading of one commodity for another.
13. A descending plane.
14. A check whose payment is guaranteed by the bank on which it is drawn.
15. Liberia.
16. Lava is a deposit from volcanic eruption; larva is the first stage of an insect after leaving the egg.
17. Al Capone, Nelson, Diamond.
18. In the middle ear.
19. A metal cap on a cane handle, etc. to strengthen it or prevent splitting.
20. The American Indians, who used this type of sled to haul packs.
21. The Department of Commerce.
22. Tie her with a rope or chain for grazing within a restricted area.
23. Athena to the Greeks, Minerva to the Romans.
24. To cover the cow.
25. A periodical wind in the Indian Ocean.

ANSWERS TO GENERAL QUIZ NUMBER XVI-B

1. Women who retain their maiden names after marriage.
2. Attend it, as it's an evening party.
3. Wanderlust.

4. On the right in Canada, and on the left in both Sweden and England.
5. The Knight Bachelor.
6. About three pounds.
7. A dark horse is a relatively unknown or unsuspected contestant who comes out ahead. A charley horse is a muscle injury.
8. The cow reindeer.
9. A soft nosed bullet which spreads on striking.
10. The dance.
11. The fountain of perpetual youth.
12. The common personification of jealousy, an analogy originated by Shakespeare.
13. One who settles on public or unimproved land without permission.
14. New moon, First quarter, Full moon, Last quarter.
15. Men; forty men out of every thousand as opposed to four women out of every thousand.
16. Hair spring and main spring.
17. One who guides the first pair of a set of horses in a coach; also one who rides post.
18. Dots and dashes when printed, long and short sounds when heard.
19. Because it contains air bubbles and is lighter than water.
20. New York.
21. They are all carpenter's tools.
22. No; honey derives its flavor from the nectar of the different flowers used by the bees.
23. The King of England.
24. October thirty-first.
25. Pigeons.

GENERAL QUIZ NUMBER XVI-C

1. The width of the vessel at its widest point.
2. Maltese, Persian, Angora, Siamese, Cheshire, and Kilkenny.
3. Black.
4. Autumn.
5. No; translucent means partially transparent.
6. A Hindu title of respect equivalent to "Lord".
7. Decoration Day.
8. At West Point.
9. A tooth or spike, as the tine of a fork.
10. None; it's a covered wagon.
11. In state prisons.
12. A boy servant or page, because of the many buttons on his livery.
13. A catacomb is a subterranean burial place; a cataclysm is a deluge or flood; a catamount is the wild cat, puma, cougar or mountain lion.
14. The Roman circus was the arena or place where the show was held; the present day circus is the show itself.
15. Dog, cat, horse, cow.
16. An atheist denies the existence of God; an agnostic neither denies nor affirms it but says "I do not know".
17. The forelock; the fetlock is a tuft of hair just above the hoof at the back of the foot.
18. A wasp, a sailor, and a sailor's short coat, respectively.
19. A hob is a seat at a fireplace; a hobble-de-hoy is an inexperienced or awkward youth.

20. On a weather map or chart. Isobars are lines connecting places of equal barometric pressure.
21. One of the largest lizards in southwestern United States.
22. A typhoon is a violent wind; a buffoon a clown; and a pontoon a flat bottomed boat.
23. One who works in tin.
24. A bull, a cow, and a pup.
25. The matador is the one appointed to kill the bull. The picador is a horseman who excites the bull by prodding it with a lance.

ANSWERS TO GENERAL QUIZ NUMBER XVI-D

1. He is the one who attends to all of the necessary repairs of a ship while it is in port.
2. You'd probably bury it, as a zoril is a South African skunk.
3. A concave surface is like the inside of a sphere, and a convex like the outside.
4. A covered cup shaped vessel pierced with holes, in which incense is burned.
5. He is cross-eyed.
6. A baby kangaroo.
7. A diplomatic dispatch.
8. Eruption is a breaking out; irruption is a bursting in.
9. An animal, a South American antelope.
10. A breed of pigs, reddish brown in color.
11. Eat the flapjack, pull off your boots with the bootjack, and raise a wagon with the wagon jack.
12. The flight of Mohammed from Mecca September 13, 622 A.D.
13. A sea trip, ships' companies, and a small cup.
14. A latitudinarian is a free thinker in religious matters; valetudinarian is a sickly person; a valedictorian is a student orator on class day who delivers the farewell.
15. A vessel with a perforated bottom used for straining or as a sieve.
16. A rodent, the gray squirrel.
17. The first is a male goat, the second a short love note.
18. After he has destroyed five enemy planes.
19. Light green with a yellowish cast, brilliant red, deep violet blue, and crimson or purplish red in that order.
20. It is named for the palace of St. James which was formerly the Royal Residence.
21. It is above because the bullet begins to fall in an arc as soon as it leaves the barrel.
22. White reflects heat rays and black absorbs them.
23. The gypsies.
24. A crosspiece over a doorway.
25. Baltimore, Maryland.

ANSWERS TO HOMO SAPIENS SET II-A

1. He was better known as Buffalo Bill.
2. George Bernard Shaw.
3. Roald Amundsen.
4. Isaak Walton, Joe Miller, Andrew Jackson, Abraham Lincoln, Attila, king of the Huns, and Jenny Lind in that order.

5. Julius Caesar.
6. Alexander Hamilton.
7. Florence Nightingale.
8. Katherine Cornell, actress; Madame Frances Perkins, Secretary of Labor; Helen Hayes, actress; and Dorothy Thompson, newspaper correspondent, in that order.
9. Hans Christian Andersen.
10. Alexander the Great.
11. Thomas Jefferson.
12. Mary Stuart.
13. James Whitcomb Riley.
14. Louisa May Alcott.
15. An American Army scout and mail carrier. She was an aide to Generals Custer and Miles.

16. Dr. Samuel Johnson, famous English writer.
17. Sir Walter Raleigh for Queen Elizabeth.
18. John Rolfe; she saved John Smith's life.
19. Benjamin Disraeli.
20. John Masefield.
21. Napoleon Bonaparte.
22. Cecil Rhodes.
23. Benjamin Franklin.
24. No.
25. Giacomo Jocante Casabianca. His father commanded the French ship Orient in the battle of the Nile, against Lord Nelson. The boy, who was ten years old, died with his father on the burning vessel.

ANSWERS TO HOMO SAPIENS SET II-B

1. James Buchanan, Michelangelo, Raphael, Charles Lamb, Voltaire, John Burroughs, Lewis Carroll, Cecil Rhodes.
2. The man without a country.
3. They are all masculine pen names of women writers.
4. Track, hockey, golf, tennis, baseball, and boxing in that order.
5. Benjamin Franklin. (Poor Richard's Almanac.)
6. Jacob Ludwig Felix; Ludwig van; Johannes.
7. Priscilla Mullens, when John Alden was bespeaking her love for Myles Standish.
8. Theodore Roosevelt, Hoover, Coolidge, Franklin D. Roosevelt.
9. Kenneth Roberts, Victor Heiser, and Dale Carnegie.
10. Charles Francois Gounod.
11. Catherine of Aragon, Anne Bo-leyn, Jane Seymour, Anne of Cleaves, Kathryn Howard, Katherine Parr.
12. The Mississippi River.
13. Baseball: Rick and Wes Ferrell or the Deans. Hockey: Lyn and Murray Patrick. Track: The Rideout twins.
14. They were all classical composers.
15. Cooper, Stevenson, Andersen, Browning.
16. Calvin Coolidge.
17. John Philip Sousa.
18. Hiawatha's grandmother.
19. William Shakespeare.
20. Alice Roosevelt; the color was Alice Blue.
21. Martha.
22. Guinevere.
23. Mark Twain.
24. Eugene O'Neill.
25. Maid Marian.

ANSWERS TO HOMO SAPIENS SET NUMBER II-C

1. Lew Wallace who wrote "Ben-Hur". Wallace was a Union General.
2. Athos, Porthos, and D'Artagnan.
3. Edward Everett Hale.
4. Ludwig van Beethoven.
5. Golf, polo, and baseball.
6. Oliver Wendell Holmes.
7. Sir Francis Drake.
8. Willard Huntington Wright.
9. Ben Jonson.
10. Oliver Goldsmith.
11. Jacques Cartier.
12. Lord Byron.
13. Stonewall was Thomas Jackson, an American General. Old Hickory was Andrew Jackson, President.
14. Ralph Waldo Emerson.
15. Maxwell Anderson.
16. Baseball, wrestling, golf, and tennis.
17. They were all assassins of American presidents.
18. Henrik Ibsen.
19. Raphael Sabatini.
20. Sir Galahad.
21. Flagg, Christy, and Gibson.
22. The Pacific Ocean.
23. John Greenleaf Whittier.
24. Charles Dickens and his illustrator, Hablot K. Browne.
25. Helen of Troy, the wife of Menelaus.

ANSWERS TO HOMO SAPIENS NUMBER II-D

1. They were all American painters.
2. They were all religious reformers.
3. Stowe, Poe, and Emerson.
4. Geoffrey Chaucer.
5. O. Henry.
6. Lewis Carroll, the pen name of Charles L. Dodgson.
7. Pittman, Newton, and Walton.
8. He was a Persian poet and astronomer who died in 1123 A.D. He was one of eight scientists appointed by the Sultan to reform the calendar and wrote the famous "Rubaiyat".
9. He was the Count of Monte Cristo in Alexandre Dumas' story of the same name.
10. Eugene O'Neill for *Beyond the Horizon, Anna Christie,* and *Strange Interlude.*
11. The wife of Abraham Lincoln.
12. Socrates, whose wife's name, Xantippe, has become synonymous with carping criticism.
13. Peter Minuit.
14. Admiral George Dewey.
15. The first white child born in Virginia.
16. Joel Chandler Harris.
17. Edgar Allan Poe.
18. Charles Kingsley.
19. The circulation of the blood.
20. Hiawatha.
21. Johann Strauss, whose three sons were Johann II, Eduard, and Joseph.
22. This invention is credited to Leonardo da Vinci.
23. Charles Dickens.
24. Paris.
25. Wallis Warfield, who married the Duke of Windsor.

HERE ARE THE QUESTIONS YOU SHOULD HAVE ASKED TO SET II-A

1. How large a population must a town have before it can become a city?
2. What is the difference between a gallon and a galloon?
3. What two well known men have five daughters?
4. What does the word oakum mean?
5. What is buckram?
6. Who is responsible for the phrase "Day by day in every way, I'm getting better and better."?
7. What is the difference between Holbein and Holstein?
8. For what two things was Sir Thomas Lipton noted.
9. Identify the following historical dates: August 1, 1914; April 6, 1917; November 11, 1918.
10. What are the nicknames of these states: Washington, Texas, Vermont, Kentucky, New Hampshire, Connecticut.
11. Where is Ireland Island and for what is it noted?
12. What is the difference between a long and short ton?
13. Into how many periods is a day at sea divided?
14. Why do you see the flash of a distant gun before you hear it?
15. Which are the two brightest stars in the Northern hemisphere?
16. Who was John Paul Jones?
17. What is a soporific?
18. What is the brig of a ship?
19. What was the Singing Memnon?
20. What is nostalgia?
21. What is a windsock?
22. How does frost kill a plant?
23. Where did General Lee offer his sword to General Grant?
24. What part of a mile is 2640 feet?
25. What is philology?

HERE ARE THE QUESTIONS YOU SHOULD HAVE ASKED TO SET II-B

1. What is the difference between a replica and a reproduction?
2. What are the seven wonders of the modern world?
3. Why was an acorn used so frequently on the designs of Colonial furniture?
4. When is the American flag displayed on a large building during its construction?
5. What is a Papal Bull?
6. Between what countries was the battle of Trafalgar fought?
7. What is a grilse?
8. What was the name of the boy who stood on the burning deck?
9. What are antipodes?
10. What is meant by the letters P.B.X. in want-ads?
11. What is meant by "the Roaring Forties"?
12. In the chemical alphabet, what does the letter C represent?
13. What are the two outlets to the Mediterranean Sea?
14. What is the difference between disperse and immerse?
15. How many people does one Congressman represent?
16. What are two meanings for the word flat?

17. What is the difference between an alien and an alienist?
18. What is a dottle?
19. Where would you look for the island of Langerhans?
20. What race of people are known as Creoles?
21. When can't a grasshopper jump?
22. What is the abbreviation of pennyweight?
23. Where is east west, and west east?
24. What is an axiom?
25. What is a sporran?

HERE ARE THE QUESTIONS YOU SHOULD HAVE ASKED TO SET II-C

1. Distinguish between peruke and perique?
2. What is a trivet or tripod?
3. What is a peduncle?
4. According to Einstein what is the fourth dimension?
5. Who was called "the Keeper of the Twenty-four Golden Umbrellas"?
6. What is the Kohinoor?
7. What is a campanile?
8. What is a gibbous moon?
9. How many of the seven wonders of the world are still in existence?
10. What is the difference between a marten and a martin?
11. How many passengers were there aboard the Mayflower?
12. What discovery enabled Nobel to endow the Nobel prize?
13. In Roman numerals what would LXXXIV be?
14. What is the name given to the spot directly opposite to the zenith?
15. What is a baker's peel?
16. What is an overshot?
17. Where is the exact center of North America?
18. Who was the Maid of Orleans?
19. What is a windrow?
20. What is the difference between auricle and oracle?
21. Define paw and paw-paw.
22. The Khyber Pass connects what two countries?
23. Where and what is the Bridge of Sighs?
24. Where did the expression "stone broke" originate?
25. What is the difference between pistol and pistole?

HERE ARE THE QUESTIONS YOU SHOULD HAVE ASKED TO SET II-D

1. What is the name for a field of rice?
2. What American organization has the motto "Be prepared"?
3. When was Shakespeare born, and when did he die?
4. Give two definitions of the word ama.
5. What is a nosologist?
6. Name four animals whose names start with the letter B.
7. What would be the matter with you if you suffered from alopecia?
8. What is the meaning of the phrase "E pluribus unum"?
9. What is the largest National Park in the United States?
10. What was the philosopher's stone?
11. What was the name of the first steamship to cross the Atlantic?
12. Who were the Anzacs?

13. What was the name of the ship on which Lord Nelson died?
14. Who was Frankenstein?
15. Give three meanings for the word kennel.
16. What is the meaning of the word hippopotamus?
17. Where is the Sargasso Sea?
18. What is the motto of the state of Massachusetts?
19. What is a septuagenarian?
20. What is a hippocampus?
21. Name five trees from which paper pulp is made.
22. What is the position of the Massachusetts star in the national flag?
23. How long is a knot, or sea mile?
24. Which is the oldest college in the United States?
25. Is the Bank of England publicly or privately owned?

ANSWERS TO CONUNDRUM QUIZ NUMBER ONE

1. Lansing, Michigan.
2. Five below.
3. They have just had a March of thirty-one days.
4. Sixteen; for (four) better, for worse, for richer, for poorer.
5. The side the son sets on.
6. When he's a little shaver.
7. To a store where they retail spirits.
8. Such a thing had never entered his head before.
9. Because his work makes him sell fish. (Selfish)
10. Because he has only four quarters a month, and he spends them to get full.
11. Banana skins.
12. Because their bills are all over dew. (Over due.)
13. A little before Eve.
14. Both have caused the downfall of man.
15. Because they nose (knows) it all.
16. You can't convict a man without a hearing.
17. The China Clipper.
18. Because six of them always go after tea. (T)
19. Pull out the plug.
20. When the dove brought the green back to Noah.
21. Only a single spring.
22. Jail birds.
23. K-9 (Canine)
24. Everything in life and nothing in tennis.
25. Because it was planted in the spring.

ANSWERS TO CONUNDRUM QUIZ NUMBER TWO

1. When Ruth walked to the well with a pitcher.
2. A quarter to two.
3. It stops and looks round.
4. Because it is always on the lookout for buoys.
5. A lamplighter.
6. Raining cats and dogs.
7. Because there is no parting or dying there.
8. The light headed ones.
9. A hill is an inclined plane, an inclined plane is a slope up, and a slow pup is a lazy dog.
10. Because its capital is always Dublin. (Doubling)
11. You can't hear his waggin'.

12. One eats too long and the other longs to eat.
13. Arkansas; Noah looked out of the Ark and saw.
14. One tongue is enough for any woman.
15. Just as soon as you're better to show that there is no ill feeling.
16. One was made of wood and the other was Maid of Orleans.
17. Goldfish; they travel around the globe every day.
18. Pages.
19. Jonah wasn't on the Ark. Didn't you Noah?
20. Because he's been to sea. (See)
21. Because when purchased it goes not to the buyer but to the cellar. (Seller)
22. Because they are always the longest in bed.
23. Ur-chins.
24. Because it's chin-chilly.
25. A fence.

ANSWERS TO CONUNDRUM QUIZ NUMBER THREE

1. Valley Forge.
2. It's seldom seen after Lent.
3. When he is out of patients.
4. They threw one cigarette overboard and made the raft a cigarette lighter.
5. A pack of cards.
6. Eat the dates on the calendar, drink from the springs in the bed, and open the door with the key of the piano.
7. Cork.
8. The fox and the cock; they had only a brush and comb between them.
9. To keep a check on his stomach.
10. Courtship.
11. Heat, you can catch cold.
12. A cook book.
13. When the cow jumped over the moon.
14. Because if you drop it you don't have to stoop and pick it up.
15. When U and I are one.
16. They both operate with rackets and spend much of their time in courts.
17. Grow, sir. (Grocer)
18. The scissors.
19. When it's been smoked.
20. If it were twelve inches long it would be a foot.
21. The waist of time.
22. When he took a hack at the cherry tree.
23. When it is a toll gate.
24. True, they use a rope.
25. Marriage.

ANSWERS TO CONUNDRUM QUIZ NUMBER FOUR

1. The figure six.
2. Yes—your dignity.
3. A splinter.
4. Our equal.
5. Most people use a tea-spoon.
6. Because it is matchless.
7. The twelve-fifty, because it's ten to one if you catch it.
8. Telling a hair-raising story to a bald-headed man.
9. If you don't C sharp you'll B flat.
10. It was built by Wren.
11. Because it's the scenter.
12. Hailing street cars.

13. Because for every grain they give a peck.
14. Because Noah was sitting on the deck.
15. Because of the sand which is there. (Sandwiches there)
16. A frog, he croaks every night.
17. Coronation, vaccination, assassination, stagnation, procrastination, domination, illumination.
18. Because he always sticks out two feet.
19. A snowflake.
20. One watches cells and the other sells watches.
21. A dollar bill, because when you put it in your pocket you double it, and when you take it out you find it increases. (In creases)
22. Peacocks do not lay eggs, peahens do.
23. Pg. That's pig without an eye. (I)
24. When he is turned into a stable.
25. A river.

ANSWERS TO HISTORY QUIZ NUMBER II-A

1. It is the place where General Robert E. Lee surrendered to General U. S. Grant on April 9, 1865.
2. The Revolution at Cooch's Bridge, Delaware.
3. April 19, 1775.
4. The Magna Chàrta.
5. The Stuarts.
6. The first ten amendments to the Constitution.
7. Because the Merrimac was sinking the North's biggest warships.
8. The Rubicon.
9. Delaware.
10. Confederate Prison in Richmond, Virginia, during the Civil War.
11. The Constitution, commonly known as "Old Ironsides", was launched at the Boston Navy Yard, October 21, 1797. She was reconditioned at the Navy Yard in 1930.
12. Amendment to the Constitution must be proposed by a two-thirds majority of both houses of Congress and approved by three-fourths of the states.
13. The Declaration of Independence.
14. Revolutionary War, 1775; War of 1812; Mexican War, 1848; Civil War, 1861; Spanish War, 1898; World War, 1917. When all these dates are added together the resulting number is 11111.
15. New York, 1785-1790.
16. The oldest son of the king of France. After the Revolution of 1830 the title was abolished.
17. It was a system whereby fugitive slaves were smuggled from the slave states into Canada by northern sympathizers.
18. Twenty-one.
19. Columbus discovered America in 1492; and the Pilgrims landed in 1620.
20. St. George.
21. The Spanish-American War.
22. New Mexico in 1912.
23. The Carthaginians and the Romans before the Christian era.
24. The Tower of London.
25. The seven kingdoms formed in England by the Saxons after they broke down the Roman rule.

ANSWERS TO HISTORY QUIZ NUMBER II-B

1. Montgomery, Alabama.
2. The King of Denmark.
3. First permanent English settlement in North America in Virginia.
4. The Treaty of Ghent.
5. The Revolutionary War.
6. Virginia.
7. The battle of Bennington in the Revolutionary War; the battle of the Wilderness in the Civil War; the battle of Belleau Wood in the World War.
8. Gauls.
9. Under the Washington Elm in Cambridge, Massachusetts.
10. Revolutionary War; War of 1812; Mexican War; Civil War; Spanish-American War, and the World War.
11. The English nation.
12. The Spanish-American War.
13. Savannah, Georgia.
14. Massachusetts.
15. Finland.
16. Charlestown Navy Yard.
17. Corsica, where he was born; Elba, where he was imprisoned; and St. Helena, where he died.
18. The Department of Labor.
19. King Edmund, the Canute.
20. February 15, 1898, in Havana Harbor.
21. The Americans won at Saratoga; the Confederates won at Second Bull Run; the Americans at Manila Bay.
22. Fort Sumter in Charleston, S.C., harbor.
23. The French flag in 1684 under La Salle.
24. In the cathedral of Seville, Spain.
25. In the Third Century, B.C.

ANSWERS TO HISTORY QUIZ NUMBER II-C

1. An office holder who has been defeated for re-election, but whose term of office has not expired.
2. The flag of the Confederate States of America during the Civil War.
3. Casimir Pulaski.
4. England.
5. Virginia.
6. Gavrilo Princep, who shot and killed Archduke Franz Ferdinand in Sarajevo, Serbia in 1914, was sent to prison and died before the end of the war.
7. The Constitution of the United States.
8. Fifteen.
9. Lafayette and Rochambeau from France; Von Steuben and De Kalb from Germany; Pulaski and Kosciuszko from Poland.
10. Yes, in a bottle in the Massachusetts Historical Society Rooms.
11. Pennsylvania.
12. At the battle of Bunker Hill.
13. In 1800, an Act of Congress provided for the removal of the United States government to Washington.
14. Revolutionary War, 1783; War of 1812, 1814; Civil War, 1865; World War, 1918.
15. Cicero (106-43 B.C.) was named "Pater Patria", Latin for "Father of the Country".

16. Italian (Corsican).
17. The term of Napoleon's second reign as Emperor, climaxed by the battle of Waterloo.
18. Jefferson Davis.
19. All North American Indians born within the territorial limits of the United States were given citizenship by an act of Congress, June 2, 1921.
20. The Department of Justice.
21. Six years.
22. The repeal of Prohibition (Eighteenth Amendment).
23. The Romanoffs.
24. At Lookout Mountain overlooking the city of Chattanooga, Tennessee, November 23-25, 1865.
25. Pennsylvania.

ANSWERS TO HISTORY QUIZ NUMBER II-D

1. At Waterloo, the British and Allies defeated the French; at Santiago, the Americans defeated the Spanish; at Sedan, the Germans defeated the French.
2. The Incas.
3. The Russo-Japanese War of 1904 ended with the treaty signed at Portsmouth, N. H., September 5, 1905.
4. France in 1881.
5. Napoleon Bonaparte.
6. From the Manhattans.
7. The Maine with the Spanish-American War; the Monitor with the Civil War; Old Ironsides with the War of 1812.
8. No; it is on Breed's Hill, where the battle was actually fought.
9. It is a federal republic like the United States.
10. "There'll be a hot time in the old town tonight."
11. Alexander the Great; Julius Caesar; The Duke of Wellington.
12. "The die is cast."
13. 342 chests.
14. William Penn; he died when Franklin was 13 years of age.
15. Pompeii.
16. Vermont settlers organized by Ethan Allen, 1775, to defend grantees of New Hampshire against efforts of New York to deprive them of their land.
17. By George Washington, September 18, 1793.
18. The Secretaries of State, the Treasury, War, Navy, Interior; the Postmaster General, and the Attorney General.
19. Disguised as Indians, 58 men boarded three English vessels, and emptied their tea cargoes overboard on December 16, 1773.
20. They stand for the Latin words Rex Imperator, meaning King and Emperor.
21. A financial panic in Wall Street, September 26, 1869.
22. Six: Great Britain, France, Holland, Norway, Chile, and Russia (Old Empire).
23. "I pledge allegiance .... justice for all."
24. France, Spain, Mexico, Republic of Texas, Southern Confederacy, and the United States.
25. British soldiers killed three, and injured many others after they were pelted with snowballs on March 5, 1770.

ANSWERS TO GENERAL QUIZ NUMBER XVII-A

1. Calvin Coolidge, Charles Dawes, Charles Curtis.
2. John O'Groats and Land's End.
3. Old Scrooge's clerk in Dickens's Christmas Carol.
4. In eastern Brazil.
5. Wellington, New Zealand.
6. Boston, Massachusetts.
7. Carson City.
8. Small or diminutive in size.
9. Maine.
10. Tomte; he is a gnome with a tall hat and a long beard.
11. Put it in the barnyard as it's a rooster.
12. Kentucky.
13. The Bay of Bengal.
14. New Jersey.
15. Venice.
16. Rounding the most southern tip of South America, Cape Horn.
17. The Allegheny and the Monongahela.
18. 25,020 miles.
19. They are all mounted military units.
20. The volt was named after the Italian Alessandro Volta. The ampere after the Frenchman Ampere, who contributed to the theory of electricity. The watt after James Watt, the Scottish inventor.
21. An ancient Greek unit of weight and money. In modern Greece it is the unit of currency.
22. Fox, bear, lion, and horse.
23. Sand.
24. Jefferson City.
25. Aloysius.

ANSWERS TO GENERAL QUIZ NUMBER XVII-B

1. The West Indian Islands, excepting the Bahamas.
2. A city in Africa.
3. Georgia.
4. A spray of the palm tree, with twelve shoots on it, was used in Egypt at the time of the winter solstice, as a symbol of the end of the year.
5. That's the technical term for a skunk, so use your own judgment.
6. Jefferson City, Missouri; Carson City, Nevada; Oklahoma City, Oklahoma; Salt Lake City, Utah.
7. "And laying his finger aside of his nose——".
8. Louis XIV, King of France.
9. They are all exactly the same distance, 440 yards.
10. Booth, Emile, Raphael, Gibbs, van Loon.
11. No; Deadwood Dick is a dime novel hero; Deadeye Dick is the villain in the Gilbert and Sullivan operetta H.M.S. Pinafore.
12. It was named after Juno, Roman patron goddess of marriage.
13. Alaskan, Pacific, Mountain, Central, Eastern, Atlantic or Colonial.
14. Vatican City, with an area in square miles of 0.16 and a population in 1936 of about 1000. This is 6,500 people per square mile.
15. A nye.

16. Mississippi, Suwanee, Nile, and Rye.
17. Alaska has over twice the area of Texas.
18. Utah, Iowa, Ohio.
19. Leonardo da Vinci's fresco of the Last Supper, showing thirteen at the table just before the betrayal.
20. Delaware.
21. A person who is in civilian clothes who has a right to wear a uniform.
22. A character in Dickens's Christmas Carol.
23. Brazil with 3,285,319 square miles as opposed to the United States' 3,026,789.
24. Nicaragua, Costa Rica, and El Salvador.
25. James K. Polk.

ANSWERS TO GENERAL QUIZ NUMBER XVII-C

1. Shakespeare, in *Hamlet*, Act II, Scene 2.
2. The Zoo.
3. A popular name given to New Haven, Connecticut.
4. In 1659 the General Court of Massachusetts enacted a law "that anybody found observing Christmas in any way" should be fined five shillings.
5. New York and Vermont.
6. Flour, beer, shoes, molasses.
7. It extends from Buffalo to Albany, a distance of 360 miles.
8. French.
9. This term is applied to the members of the President's cabinet.
10. John Tyler, Zachary Taylor, William Taft.
11. In the Italian Bay of Naples.
12. Men in White, Ruggles of Red Gap, Yellow Jack, Green Light, The Scarlet Pimpernel, the White Angel.
13. Maine.
14. 1874.
15. The entrance to San Francisco harbor.
16. Eve, navy, dandy, Abel, water, go, run, eggs, stripes, ink, roses, carry, bat, bolt.
17. Little town of Bethlehem.
18. They were all vice-presidents of the United States.
19. Pine, fir, spruce, hemlock, holly, mistletoe.
20. Arkansas.
21. Cow, moose, buffalo, elephant, seal.
22. It is named for the Swedish botanist Dahl.
23. That is entered just as an aid to conditioning it.
24. In India the water buffalo is so used.
25. Elephant tusks.

ANSWERS TO GENERAL QUIZ NUMBER XVII-D

1. Slang for a second lieutenant in the army.
2. Three.
3. A circular hall or interior space in a building, especially under a central dome.
4. When a diver is pulled out of the water from a depth so rapidly that the pressure of the air is not gradually equalized a state of paralysis is brought on, this is referred to as the bends.

5. Petrol.
6. Thomas Edison, because we are seldom out of sight or hearing of one or more of his inventions.
7. Ore-gon, Ill-inois, La-Louisiana, Ark-ansas, Mass-achusetts.
8. Free on board; delivered to a carrier free but not including transportation or shipping charges.
9. No, it was abolished in 1899.
10. Seamen stand at attention on each side of the gangway, while a boatswain's mate blows a whistle, known as a pipe, while the officer to be honored comes aboard or departs.
11. Engrave pictures on wood.
12. A successful rebellion is termed a revolution.
13. In Paris in 1740 by Benjamin Franklin.
14. A light cotton fabric used for dresses or curtains.
15. Saw-fish, Pick-erel, Bar-racuda, Steel-head salmon.
16. I beams are all metal.
17. Taxiing indicates the motion of a plane on the ground or water.
18. Only south.
19. It is the vibration of the wings one hears.
20. A solar year is 365 days, 5 hours, 48 minutes, 46 seconds. A calendar year is 365 days.
21. English bull.
22. A Bishop of Rome during the third century who died a martyr February 14, 270 A.D.
23. A forerunner of the piano.
24. An attendant who bears a torch.
25. Peter Pan, from James M. Barrie's play of the same name.

ANSWERS TO GENERAL QUIZ NUMBER XVIII-A

1. One who stuffs and mounts the skins of birds and animals for preservation.
2. Kissing.
3. With a tuxedo in place of a vest.
4. P. T. Barnum.
5. Broadway, running from Bowling Green to Albany, New York.
6. *The Boston Cooking School Cook Book.*
7. John, Eli, Leland.
8. An accessory is something extra; a part is something that replaces something else in the car's original equipment.
9. One cent.
10. Shakespeare's birthplace at Stratford-on-Avon.
11. A small and mean bed.
12. The flag should be displayed at half mast from sunrise to noon, and at full mast from noon to sunset.
13. Men's coats fold to the right while women's coats fold towards the left.
14. Scarab.
15. Raccoon.
16. India, where it has been cultivated for over 2,500 years.
17. Boar, walrus, hippopotamus.
18. Kissing the Blarney stone, which is in Blarney Castle, near Cork, Ireland, is said to make those who kiss it proficient in smooth and flattering talk.
19. A legendary hero of America.
20. White.

21. Twenty-eight years; it can then be renewed for another period of equal length.
22. For its porcelains.
23. "Et tu, Brute!" Meaning "And thou also, Brutus", when they stabbed him.
24. Neap tide.
25. Germany, United States, Great Britain, France.

ANSWERS TO GENERAL QUIZ NUMBER XVIII-B

1. Silver.
2. A thin, almost transparent paper.
3. To protect themselves from the cold.
4. The Persians; the Turks.
5. A spectre ship seen in bad weather about the Cape of Good Hope, and supposed to mean bad luck.
6. The South Pole.
7. You expire.
8. The photographic industry.
9. The Angelus, by Millet.
10. Warmer.
11. December 4, 1932.
12. Navy.
13. So that it won't rust.
14. The Rock of Gibraltar by a little more than 250 feet.
15. Right.
16. Peeling is stripping the skin; paring is cutting it.
17. A petition written with the signatures in a circle so as not to show who first signed it.
18. The set of ropes supporting the mast.
19. A ruminant is a cud-chewing animal. To ruminate is to think or ponder.
20. A song sung by sailors in rhythm to their work.
21. Bigamy refers to a state of having two wives at the same time; digamy means twice married legally.
22. The mouse ran up the clock, Little Bo-Peep lost her sheep, Ding dong bell, pussy's in the well.
23. The first is an evader of the truth; the second a sleight of hand artist.
24. Equality of opportunity for all nations.
25. Velvet is a silk fabric; velveteen is a cotton fabric.

ANSWERS TO GENERAL QUIZ NUMBER XVIII-C

1. A delicate jewel work made with twisted threads, usually of gold or silver.
2. A famous hero of Arabian romance and adventure.
3. Not knowing what you are buying.
4. Niagara Falls, Bison, the Arlington Amphitheater.
5. The art of dancing.
6. Wink your eye, which takes about one-tenth of a second.
7. United Press; Associated Press, International News Service.
8. An Admiral's aide.
9. Buzzard's Bay on the West end, and the Cape Cod Bay on the East.
10. A name given to the game of shuffle-board when played on ship board.

11. A woman of literary tastes or occupation.
12. Washington was a native of Virginia, a truly styled English colony, where the money used was the crown, pound, and shilling. The dollar did not come into use until April 2, 1792.
13. A person who sells drugs and compounds prescriptions.
14. A model or pattern.
15. An organized massacre of a group or class.
16. Aquarius, waterman; pisces, fish; aries, ram; taurus, bull; gemini, twins; cancer, crab; leo, lion; virgo, virgin; libra, scales; scorpio, scorpion; sagittarius, bowman; capricornus, goat.
17. Omnibus.
18. Benzine, water, gasoline, alcohol, soda-water, glycerine.
19. An atheist denies the existence of God; an agnostic neither denies nor affirms.
20. The steel cable that runs along the tops of the center poles to keep them in position.
21. Memphis, Tennessee.
22. Last name.
23. There are twenty-five square miles in a five mile square.
24. Commute is to travel regularly; compute is to reckon, estimate, or number.
25. A squib is a tubular case filled with gunpowder; a squid is a ten armed cuttlefish; a squill is a crustacean.

ANSWERS TO GENERAL QUIZ NUMBER XVIII-D

1. The esophagus is the canal through which food passes to the stomach; a sarcophagus is a stone coffin.
2. Plebeians.
3. Etymology is the study of the origin of words; entomology is the study of insects.
4. One which is not engaged in regular trade, but takes a cargo when offered.
5. California grows about ninety per cent of the almonds grown in the United States.
6. A kind of cloth; a rippled surfaced cotton fabric.
7. Dog house; a gay dog; putting on the dog; dog tired.
8. An encumbrance or mental burden.
9. A device for counting; it is made up of a wire frame on which beads or balls are strung.
10. Forty-four feet.
11. The shutter.
12. All are names of roses.
13. One who deserts his party or cause.
14. It was sheathed in stone and none but King Arthur himself had the power to withdraw it.
15. The horse will eat himself to death; the mule will eat only his fill.
16. To keep his coat buttoned.
17. No, the walker could travel about three times as fast.
18. A fiesta is a religious festival; a fiasco is a complete failure; a fiacre is a hackney coach.
19. A mollusk with a conical shell found on rocks at low tide.

20. "Above thy deep and dreamless sleep the silent stars go by."
21. The headquarters of the London Police.
22. Evolution.
23. Water.
24. Greenwich Village.
25. French: au revoir; German: auf Wiedersehen; Spanish: adios; Hawaiian: aloha noa oai.

ANSWERS TO GENERAL QUIZ NUMBER XIX-A

1. An obsolete, short, muzzle-loading gun with a large mouth.
2. A leech.
3. A brother of a religious order; especially of one of the mendicant orders.
4. A judge.
5. Farming; both from the standpoint of money value and as a source of raw material.
6. Flattered; it means radiant, brilliant, splendid.
7. A parachute.
8. They are delicate sense organs which help the cat to find its way about.
9. All are derivatives of petroleum.
10. A floating bridge, usually made of boats for military purposes.
11. Four hundred and eighty pounds.
12. Train, taxi, tractor, trolley, truck, trireme.
13. Skipper, chief mate, boatswain, able-bodied seaman.
14. Atmospheric pressure.
15. A rash or hazardous financial venture.
16. Because their resin interferes with their efficient conducting of electricity.
17. A dinner, luncheon, or other form of entertainment in which each guest pays his own way.
18. English mailboxes are so called.
19. Orange, lemon, lime, tangerine, grapefruit, kumquat.
20. Raw recruits.
21. An Eskimo's ice house.
22. None.
23. Soapstone.
24. Any United States legal tender note having devices printed on the back in green.
25. Latin.

ANSWERS TO GENERAL QUIZ NUMBER XIX-B

1. The Franks.
2. Sloop, yawl, schooner, brig, bark.
3. A light yellowish brown.
4. A paid servant of northern Africa, usually a camel attendant or guide.
5. Because the air between them serves as an insulation.
6. I don't know, Alaska. (I'll ask her.)
7. A finger wave is set with the fingers and a comb while the hair is wet; a marcel wave is set with an iron while the hair is dry.
8. Five aces.
9. Twenty-four to the quire; five hundred to the ream.
10. Milk.
11. A period of a thousand years.
12. New York, Pennsylvania, Illinois.
13. Because old time salesmen announced themselves by beating on a drum.
14. To date before the true time.
15. The power to act for someone

else, usually the right to vote for
another.
16. Clocks, elevators, and airplanes.
17. Mercury.
18. A housebreaker or thief.
19. A mark put into paper by the
manufacturer.
20. Silk.
21. A small bed which may be pushed
out of sight under a larger bed.
22. Sea gulls.
23. Because this dates back to the
time when barbers were also surgeons and this was the sign of
their craft.
24. It is a definite unit of measure
equal to 1/48 of an inch.
25. Weight is the measure of the
force of gravity.

ANSWERS TO GENERAL QUIZ NUMBER XIX-C

1. It was dug out by swiftly flowing
water.
2. Flag, color, standard, and ensign.
The color is the flag carried by
unmounted units; the standard
refers to the flag carried by
mounted or motorized units; the
ensign is the flag flown from
small boats or ships.
3. At Valladolid, Spain, in 1506.
4. Organic, having once been part of
a tree.
5. 100.
6. Twenty-nine years old.
7. "Are you there?"
8. That he is a baronet.
9. Because the water there had to
be boiled anyway.
10. Constraint by force or fear.
11. A rochet is a linen vestment worn
by bishops and abbots; a rocket
is an aerial firework.
12. An open set of shelves used for
bric-a-brac.
13. An edible shrimplike crustacean.
14. White or blanched pale.
15. About one hundred and twenty.
16. The Eskimo dog.
17. Tungsten.
18. Only as a signal of distress.
19. Throw it away as it is only the
fragment of a broken piece of
pottery.
20. The Pacific is farther east.
21. France.
22. No species of birds now living
are provided with teeth.
23. The Romans.
24. Dayta.
25. Waterloo, in which Napoleon was
defeated.

ANSWER TO GENERAL QUIZ NUMBER XIX-D

1. Fifteen.
2. Six.
3. The principle of a vacuum as a
means of insulation.
4. A benediction.
5. Religious indifference.
6. Pips.
7. Six flat surfaces, eight corners,
twelve edges.
8. Sandhurst.
9. Timbuktu is a trading town of
the French Sudan, on the southern edge of the Sahara Desert.
Because it is the last town before the desert it has come to
mean some far distant place, a
place out of reach of the rest
of the world.

10. A dance.
11. It is a by product from the distillation of turpentine.
12. Old yarn or cloth run through a machine known as a picker. The stock is the same but the fiber much shorter. The term is used to indicate an inferior piece of goods or work.
13. One who distributes Bibles and religious literature.
14. A type of light used in making motion pictures.
15. A fish.
16. Aaron Burr and Alexander Hamilton; Hamilton was killed.
17. Panama.
18. Blonde, brunette, red head, brunette, in that order.
19. Species means a kind or sort; specie is metal money.
20. Adamant, as the word means very hard or determined.
21. Goldfish, canary, swan, peacock.
22. A wide mouthed pitcher.
23. The nightingale.
24. An elephant piling teak in a sludgy, squdgy creek.
25. Never, a barometer does not require winding.

ANSWERS TO DON'T CONFUSE 'EM II-A

1. A tarantella is a lively dance; a tarantula a venomous spider.
2. A gossoon is a young lad and a bassoon a musical instrument.
3. A gourmand is interested in quantity of food, a gourmet in quality.
4. Doggerel is a poor or low form of verse in irregular or comic style.
5. An autocracy is government by one with absolute authority. A democracy is government by the people through elected representatives. A plutocracy is government by the rich.
6. Bi-weekly means every two weeks; bi-monthly means every two months; bi-annually means twice a year.
7. An ossicle is a small bone.
8. A specialist in diseases of the mind.
9. Epistles are letters; apostles are messengers.
10. Here are the answers in order: an American wasp with yellow markings; a nickname for a sailor; a short, loose jacket which is so called because adopted from the jacket worn by Eton students in England; a harness-like contraption to keep violent prisoners under control.
11. Antimony is a hard white element used chiefly in alloys. Antinomy is the contradiction between two laws or principles.
12. Stationary means fixed and stationery means writing materials.
13. Voracity is greediness; veracity is truthfulness.
14. Ingenious is skillful or inventive; ingenuous means frank or innocent.
15. A centaur is a fabulous animal, half horse, half man.
16. The first is a dog trained to protect life or property and the second is a trick of duty two hours in length on ship.
17. A zither is a stringed musical instrument and a zephyr is a gentle breeze, usually used poetically.

18. A hurricane and a cyclone are the same: violent winds; a tornado is a funnel shaped cloud that progresses in a narrow path; it's more violent than a hurricane.

19. A statue is a carved or moulded figure; stature is height; statute is law.

20. An ordnance is artillery and ordinance is a law or rite.

21. A pinnacle is a stone upright ending in a spired point in Gothic architecture. Pinnace is a British vessel with eight banks of oars and sails.

22. A lea is a meadow; lee means the sheltered side.

23. Resin is the raw material from which turpentine is made; rosin is the substance that remains after turpentine is made.

24. No; collusion means a group working together to perpetrate a fraud. A collision is a violent striking together of two bodies in violent fashion.

25. They are opposites; condemnation is censure or blame; while commendation is praise.

ANSWERS TO DON'T CONFUSE 'EM II-B

1. Emanate means to flow out of; emulate to strive to equal or to imitate; emigrate means to go out of a country.

2. A genealogy is the history or descent of a person or family; geology is the study of the earth, especially rocks.

3. A dory is a flat bottomed boat; a lory is a type of parrot; a Tory is a member of the Loyalist party or favoring the crown.

4. Cribbage is a card game.

5. An armadillo is a small burrowing animal of South America; a peccadillo is a slight offense or petty fault.

6. The first means to build up, the other to tear down.

7. Hetty Green was a capitalist who died in 1916. Paris green is an arsenate used as a pigment and an insecticide. Bowling green is a section of lower Manhattan and a town in Kentucky.

8. A red cap is a porter, a madcap is an irresponsible person, foolscap is a large sheet of writing paper, a percussion cap is used to set off explosives, and the cap and bells were the ancient insignia of the court jester or fool.

9. Pathos is the quality in human experience which excites feelings of pity or sympathy; bathos is false pathos, a comedown or an anticlimax.

10. An oculist is an eye doctor while an optician is one who makes or sells optical instruments.

11. A caret is a mark indicating an omission; a carat is a measure of weight used to measure precious stones.

12. No; a prodigy is something out of the usual course of nature; a protegee is one under the care and protection of another.

13. A husband is a woman's marital mate; a husbandman is a tiller of the soil.

14. A ewe is a female sheep; a ewer is a pitcher or water jar.

15. A jurist is a judge and a juror is a member of the jury.
16. An asteroid is a small planet and an asterisk is a mark used in printing.
17. A stethoscope is a doctor's instrument used in testing the heart and lungs; a stereoscope is an old time device for looking at pictures; a periscope is a device for seeing around a corner, used in submarines.
18. A metropolis is the chief city of a country or state; a necropolis is the city of the dead, or, more commonly, a cemetery; the Acropolis is the citadel of Athens.
19. A mantel is a shelf, usually above a fireplace; a mantle is a cape or cloak.
20. An auger is an instrument or tool for boring holes; an augur is one who foretells the future.
21. The humerus is the bone of the upper arm.
22. A raconteur is an expert teller of tales.
23. A paragon is an example or model of perfection.
24. A somnambulist walks in his sleep while a somniloquist talks in his sleep.
25. An anecdote is a short narrative of an entertaining character; an antidote is a remedy for a poison.

ANSWERS TO DON'T CONFUSE 'EM SET NUMBER II-C

1. A talisman is a charm and a talesman is a person added to a jury.
2. Carton is a pasteboard box or the white disk within the bullseye of a target while a cartoon is a caricature or sketch for a fresco or mosaic.
3. Abode is a place of continued residence or a dwelling; adobe is unburnt brick dried in the sun, used for building purposes in Central America and Mexico.
4. Celestial means heavenly; a celesta is a percussion musical instrument.
5. When a person leaves his own country he is an emigrant, when a person enters a foreign country he is an immigrant.
6. Avenge is to punish on behalf of another; revenge is to punish on one's own behalf.
7. It's a metal pin split lengthwise. and used to fasten a nut or bolt to a shaft to keep it from slipping off.
8. A rip is a tear. Riprap is a foundation of loose stones.
9. A fiesta is a festival holiday and a siesta is a short midday sleep or rest.
10. An antiseptic is something which arrests the growth of micro-organisms; a germicide destroys micro-organisms; an anaesthetic is capable of local or general insensibility.
11. A nostrum is a quack medicine while a rostrum is a stage or platform for public speaking.
12. Rusticate means to spend a period of time in the country.
13. A stork is a large bird and a stoic is a person indifferent alike to pain or pleasure.

14. A mandrill is a variety of West African baboon.
15. The art of kissing.
16. To hobnob is to associate with in a familiar manner; to kowtow is to bow before or to act subserviently; a pow wow is an Indian gathering or, more commonly, a conference.
17. Associate them with these things in this order: embroidery, drawing, music, and the United States Military Academy.
18. A navvy is a laborer on public works.
19. A barnacle is a small sea animal and a binnacle is a box for a ship's compass.
20. A titmouse is a small bird with gray, black and white plumage.
21. Antimony is a metal; one of the elements.
22. A chateau is a castle or manor house while a plateau is a broad elevated tract of flat land.
23. A burro is a donkey.
24. French doors are doors used as a partition and usually of glass; stevedores are dock laborers, and humidors are jars for preserving tobacco.
25. A ballad is a short narrative poem, or popular song; a ballet is a theatrical exhibition acted chiefly in dancing; a ballot is a little ticket used in voting or the art of voting by putting a ticket into a box.

ANSWERS TO DON'T CONFUSE 'EM SET NUMBER II-D

1. Misanthropy, meaning a hatred of mankind.
2. Canon is a law or rule; cannon is a large gun.
3. Ante means before and anti means against.
4. There is no difference, they are all egg shaped.
5. Etymology is the study of words.
6. The first is readily communicable without contact; the second is transmitted by contact.
7. A coiffeur is a male hair-dresser; a coiffure is a manner of dressing the hair.
8. Chiropody is treatment of the feet; chirography is the judgment of character by handwriting.
9. A faker is a swindler and a fakir is a Mohammedan priest.
10. A lama is a Buddhist priest of Tibet and a llama is a South American beast of burden.
11. Goods from a wrecked ship found floating in the sea is flotsam; jetsam refers to goods which have been cast from a ship in distress to lighten its load, or such goods when washed ashore.
12. Indite means to write or dictate; indict means to charge with a crime.
13. Celanese is a dress fabric and is vegetable in origin. Pekingese is a breed of dog and is, of course, animal. Manganese is a mineral.
14. A caddie is an attendant who carries a golf player's clubs; a caddy is a small box or can for holding tea.
15. Conscription is compulsory military or naval service. Description is an account of anything in words or writing.
16. Monogamy—marriage to only one wife at a time. Polyandry

—having more than one husband at a time. Polygamy—having more than one wife at the same time.

17. A waif is a homeless wanderer; a wafer is a thin disc, as of candy, bread or metal; a waiver is a voluntary surrender of a right or privilege.
18. Ham is cured pork or an amateur radio enthusiast; a hamlet is a very small village.
19. A benedict is a newly married man.
20. Bisect means to cut into two equal parts; dissect means to cut into pieces.
21. A Shaker is a member of a religious sect; a shako is a high military hat.
22. A whetstone is a stone for sharpening edged tools; a grindstone is a flat, circular stone mounted so that it may be rotated for sharpening edged tools; a lodestone is a natural magnet; a rhinestone is a paste gem, usually made to imitate diamonds.
23. A travelogue is a travel talk given with illustrated slides. The decalogue is the ten commandments. An analogue is that which corresponds to some other thing. A catalogue is a list of names or articles arranged in a methodical manner.
24. One which rolls out from under a larger bed.
25. Yes. An aviator is one who flies an airplane and "sky pilot" means a minister.

ANSWERS TO TRAVEL QUIZ NUMBER II-A

1. Colorado.
2. Yukon, Mackenzie and St. Lawrence Rivers.
3. Tennessee, eight: Kentucky, Virginia, North Carolina, Mississippi, Alabama, Georgia, Arkansas, Missouri.
4. Hongkong is an island, the city on the island is Victoria.
5. Pennsylvania.
6. Sacramento.
7. Constantinople.
8. North.
9. Pago Pago; Manila; San Juan; Juneau.
10. Asia.
11. Phoenix.
12. France.
13. Mountain range in California.
14. Damascus, Syria. St. Augustine Florida.
15. Russia.
16. Austin, Texas; Pierre, South Dakota; Columbus, Ohio; Lincoln, Nebraska; Augusta, Maine; Raleigh, North Carolina; Jackson, Mississippi; Montgomery, Alabama; Helena, Montana.
17. Lake Michigan.
18. North Channel.
19. The Rio Grande.
20. Spain.
21. Buenos Aires, Argentina.
22. Maine has more water than Rhode Island has land.
23. In the St. Lawrence River.
24. Virginia; Elizabeth was known as the Virgin Queen.
25. It is regarded as the swiftest river in the world.

ANSWERS TO TRAVEL QUIZ NUMBER II-B

1. The English Channel.
2. In the eastern Pyrenees, between Spain and France.
3. Northern Russia; China; Eastern ridge of the Appalachians in the United States; South Africa.
4. Minneapolis and St. Paul, Minnesota.
5. Oslo.
6. No, Salem is.
7. New York, New Jersey, North Carolina, South Carolina, Rhode Island, North Dakota, South Dakota, New Hampshire, New Mexico, West Virginia.
8. Birmingham.
9. Strait, Bay or River, Sea or River, Ocean, Sea, Sound, Sea or River, Sea or Channel.
10. Australia.
11. Crawford, Dixville, Pinkham, Franconia, Grafton, and White Mountains Notch.
12. New South Wales, Australia.
13. Portland, Maine and Portland, Oregon.
14. The Adriatic Sea.
15. Germany, Italy, Germany.
16. Ottawa.
17. Spain.
18. Marseilles.
19. No; Amundsen did.
20. St. John is in New Brunswick, and St. Johns is in Newfoundland.
21. Bronx, Brooklyn, Queens, Manhattan, Richmond.
22. The Jordan River.
23. The Pacific Ocean.
24. The Hudson River.
25. Alberta, British Columbia, Manitoba, New Brunswick, Nova Scotia, Ontario, Prince Edward Island, Quebec, Saskatchewan.

ANSWERS TO TRAVEL QUIZ NUMBER II-C

1. 178 feet. 14 feet out of the perpendicular.
2. Burma, British India.
3. New York, Ohio, Illinois.
4. Spain.
5. Wyoming.
6. Its ruins and rock tombs.
7. North.
8. Bolivia, Brazil, Argentina, Chile, Colombia, Guiana, Ecuador, Paraguay, Peru, Uruguay, Venezuela.
9. International Bridge.
10. Grand Pré, Nova Scotia.
11. Utah, Colorado, Arizona, and New Mexico.
12. East River.
13. Maine (May); Minnesota (Minna); Delaware (Della); Idaho (Ida).
14. In the Irish Sea. It is a separate British island.
15. Cuba is touched by the Atlantic Ocean, the Gulf of Mexico and the Caribbean Sea.
16. Japan.
17. In Kittery, Maine.
18. Off the coast of Venezuela, South America.
19. Sofia.
20. 4: Idaho, Iowa, Indiana, Illinois.
21. There is no such place; it was a fabulous city of great wealth, supposedly located somewhere in South America, which Pizarro's

338

lieutenant Orellana pretended to have discovered.
22. Florida.
23. Georgia.
24. In Australia.
25. Austin, Texas; Augusta, Maine; Albany, New York; Atlanta, Georgia; Annapolis, Maryland.

ANSWERS TO TRAVEL QUIZ NUMBER II-D

1. Agra, India; Paris, France; Moscow, Russia; Cork, Ireland.
2. Buenos Aires.
3. Kansas City, Kansas, and Kansas City, Missouri.
4. Hibernia.
5. The Lassen Volcano in northern California.
6. Boston, Massachusetts.
7. South Carolina; Massachusetts; New York; Vermont.
8. Switzerland; India; Vermont; South America.
9. Texas, Idaho, Maine.
10. Vermont.
11. Minnesota, Wisconsin, Iowa, Illinois, Missouri, Kentucky, Tennessee, Arkansas, Mississippi and Louisiana.
12. Mont Blanc.
13. Yes.
14. Brazil.
15. Atlantic Ocean.
16. It is an old name for China.
17. The Severn.
18. Elbrus, in the Caucasians.
19. Cuba.
20. The Rocky Mountain watershed.
21. The Adriatic.
22. New Hampshire, Vermont, Maine.
23. Provincetown, Massachusetts. Looking west you can see no land, so the sun appears to set in the Atlantic ocean.
24. It has been estimated that Shakespeare never made a continuous journey as far as a round trip from Boston to New York.
25. Quebec, Canada.

ANSWERS TO MUSIC QUIZ NUMBER II-A

1. Ocarina.
2. "Where the foe's haughty host in dread silence reposes." From the "Star-Spangled Banner."
3. For its productions of Gilbert and Sullivan operettas.
4. "Wind of the western sea."
5. In Scituate, Massachusetts, on the old Lawson estate.
6. Very soft.
7. "To the land of my dreams."
8. Swan song, from the tradition that a swan sings melodiously when it is about to die.
9. None.
10. It is part of the third stanza of "Yankee Doodle".
11. "Blue Moon"; "Yellow Rose of Texas"; "Red Sails in the Sunset"; "Wearing of the Green"; "Rose of Tralee".
12. He was married to Cosima, daughter of Franz Liszt.
13. They all mean the same thing.
14. "Rigoletto" by Giuseppe Verdi.
15. A scale in music which proceeds by halftones or semitones.
16. A band has no stringed instruments.
17. There are twelve verses. The

chorus is: "Yankee Doodle keep it up, Yankee Doodle dandy, Mind the music and the step, And with the girls be handy."

18. It is a keyboard musical instrument consisting of a series of steel plates struck by small hammers and producing soft bell-like tones. It was invented by Mustel of Paris in 1886.

19. Wagner.

20. Tempo is the rate of speed at which a musical composition is to be played. Time is rhythmical division.

21. A Northerner; he was born in Pittsburgh, Pa.

22. "Upon the seat of a bicycle built for two."

23. "Carmen."

24. Both; the novel by Anatole France, and the opera by Jules Massenet.

25. Piano, organ, harp, traps.

ANSWERS TO MUSIC QUIZ NUMBER II-B

1. The kettledrum.
2. Very loud; fast; sing.
3. Gilbert and Sullivan's "H.M.S. Pinafore"; the character is Sir Joseph Porter.
4. None.
5. "Dixie".
6. Alice Blue Gown; Sweet Alice, Ben Bolt; Alice, where art thou?
7. Joe.
8. Charles Francois Gounod.
9. "Show Boat" by Jerome Kern.
10. Annie Laurie.
11. Sir Harry Lauder.
12. Victor Herbert.
13. Play it; it is an old musical instrument, having three strings. It is played with a bow.
14. "Down on the Farm"; "Old McDonald had a Farm"; "The Old Gray Mare"; "In the Shade of the Old Apple Tree"; "Those Barnyard Blues".
15. A tinkling sound, like bells.
16. A pretentious fellow, a fop or a dandy.
17. "Drums in My Heart"; "Piccolo Pete"; "Lady, Play Your Mandolin"; "Ukulele Lady"; "Sam, the Old Accordion Man"; "Two Guitars"; "When Mother Played the Organ"; "The Man with the Mandolin".
18. A spinet is an obsolete small form of harpsichord.
19. Irving Berlin.
20. No; violins were not known until at least 1500 years after Nero lived.
21. Cornet, clarinet, concertina, cymbals.
22. "The Blue Danube"; "Tales from the Vienna Woods"; "Artists' Life"; "Southern Roses"; "Voices of Spring".
23. "The daring young man on the flying trapeze."
24. Oscar Strauss.
25. The manager.

MUSIC QUIZ NUMBER II-C

1. Overtones.
2. Small brooks.
3. A stage coach.
4. They are the three little maids from school in Gilbert and Sullivan's "the Mikado".

5. "The *gold* of her hair, and the *blue* of her eyes."
6. A musical instrument resembling a banjo.
7. Rouget de Lisle, in 1792.
8. A melody sung by Venetian gondoliers.
9. Eight diatonic degrees in music.
10. The Aeolian harp.
11. Ludwig van Beethoven.
12. The Blue Danube.
13. The bagpipe.
14. Trombone, trumpet, tuba, triangle.
15. "How dear to my heart are the scenes of my childhood."
16. "Tales of Hoffman" and "Cleopatra".
17. Sweet Alice, in "Ben Bolt".
18. "Blue Skies"; "Am I Blue"?; "Blue Moon"; "My Blue Heaven".
19. The defense of Fort McHenry, Baltimore, Maryland, in the war of 1812.
20. Sally.
21. Play it. A vina is an East Indian musical instrument.
22. A musical instrument.
23. "Blue Bells of Scotland"; "Song of India"; "Come Back to Erin".
24. Samuel Woodworth, born in Scituate, Massachusetts.
25. The piano.

MUSIC QUIZ NUMBER II-D

1. "Moonlight and Roses"; "Mexicali Rose"; "Yellow Rose of Texas"; "Only a Rose"; "Tulip Time"; "A Little White Gardenia".
2. Nelly Bly.
3. "Thy woods and templed hills".
4. Xylophone.
5. "Tea for Two"; "Turkey in the Straw"; "In the Shade of the Old Apple Tree"; "Yes, We Have No Bananas".
6. A musical instrument.
7. "Stars in Your Eyes"; "East Side of Heaven"; "Sing Out the News"; "The Boys from Syracuse".
8. "Little Gray Home in the West"; "There's a Home in Wyoming"; "Home, Sweet Home"; "Home on the Range"; "I'll Take You Home Again, Kathleen"; "Keep the Home Fires Burning".
9. The opera is "Carmen" written by Georges Bizet in French.
10. "Missouri Waltz"; "Beautiful Ohio"; "My Old Kentucky Home"; "California, Here I Come"; "Marching through Georgia".
11. "Kiss me again"; "Kiss in the Dark"; "Between a Kiss and a Sigh"; "Kiss Waltz".
12. A 3 stringed, lutelike musical instrument.
13. The one who plays the kettledrums.
14. "Old Gray Bonnet;" "Dem Golden Slippers"; "Alice Blue Gown".
15. "The Last Rose of Summer".
16. "Annie Doesn't Live Here Any More"; "Annie Laurie"; "I Must See Annie Tonight". (Know 'Annie' more?)
17. Play briskly.
18. Rudy Vallee's Connecticut Yankees; Guy Lombardo's Royal Canadians; Fred Waring's Pennsylvanians.

19. He was a prisoner on board a British warship off Fort Mc-Henry, Baltimore.
20. "Heaven Can Wait"; "Pennies from Heaven"; "I Never Knew Heaven Could Speak".
21. In the last stanza of the Star-Spangled Banner".
22. "The Blue Danube Waltz"; "Beautiful Ohio"; "Swanee River".
23. 1814.
24. Discord.
25. Toscanini. He is a conductor, the others are pianists.

ANSWERS TO SUPER QUIZ II-A

1. An egg laying mammal; the porcupine ant-eater.
2. Pelota or jai-alai, originally played in the country of the Basques in the Pyrenees Mountains.
3. The floor or sawdust put down for the performers to work on.
4. Ophiology is the scientific study of serpents; ophthalmology is the science of eye treatment.
5. A medieval garment worn under a suit of armor.
6. It's a pick for a stringed instrument such as the mandolin.
7. It's the amount of light you'd get on a page of print held one foot away from an ordinary candle.
8. It's the water line on a ship.
9. Filtrum.
10. It travels the opposite way from the sun.
11. A Laplander's traveling sled or sleigh.
12. Rip-rap is broken stones loosely thrown together as a foundation as in deep water.
13. The helve.
14. Stockinet is an elastic textile fabric; a stockade is an enclosure for cattle, or a fortress.
15. Air weighs fifteen pounds a square inch.
16. No; a mandrake is a common woodland plant; a mandrill is a large and ferocious baboon of West Africa.
17. A game of ninepins.
18. Centrifugal force is a force which tends to impel a thing outward, away from the center of rotation; centripetal force is the opposite, tending to force an object towards the center of rotation.
19. An instrument with a rubber edge for cleaning windows and decks by scraping the water from them.
20. A post or bar which divides the panes of glass in a Gothic window.
21. It is a group of different atoms.
22. They are bonds, like United States government bonds.
23. The tipple.
24. Bezel.
25. A Turkish open pavilion or summer house.

ANSWERS TO SUPER QUIZ NUMBER II-B

1. A coal mine.
2. A unit for measurement of sound.
3. The shaven part of the head of an ecclesiastic.
4. Extinct means abolished or out of existence. Instinct is the impulse operating without the aid of instruction or experience.

5. Trying to form a square equivalent in area to a given circle mathematically.
6. It was an ancient galley having two banks or tiers of oars.
7. A stock is a share in a business, and a bond is a loan, but they both pay dividends, or at least, should.
8. The hangman's noose.
9. Fifty-three years.
10. One twentieth.
11. You'd have a case of blood poisoning.
12. It is the *bell* of the clock in the tower of the Houses of Parliament, in London.
13. An hygrometer is an instrument for measuring the degree of moisture in the atmosphere. An hydrometer is an instrument to determine the specific gravity of fluids.

14. It is a type of tapestry.
15. Busbies.
16. The power required to lift 33,000 pounds one foot in one minute.
17. Red cedar.
18. She is supposed to be enlightening the world and therefore was made to face the world.
19. Iron pyrites.
20. An Italian, Count Alessandro Volta, a noted physicist.
21. Gutenberg.
22. Scandinavian.
23. A concert in which each performer plays a different tune. It is sometimes called a Dutch Melody when vocal efforts only are used.
24. To determine the degree of intelligence of the person tested.
25. One existing for the relief of the poor.

ANSWERS TO SUPER QUIZ NUMBER II-C

1. A tropical tree used in making pipes.
2. A penguin cannot fly.
3. A snake, the most dangerous and poisonous of the viper family.
4. A large grassy area in a tropical country.
5. It is a shawl-like arrangement slung over the shoulders of a woman and usually used to carry a baby in; it is quite common in foreign countries.
6. You would be going fishing; a barn-door-skate is a salt water fish.
7. The Permanent Court of International Justice.
8. It is an instrument for measuring the power and properties of the sun's rays.

9. The installment plan.
10. Cement; the sack is tied, filled from the bottom and then sewed up.
11. The Imperial gallon contains one fourth, namely one quart, more than the standard gallon.
12. A person equally at home in any part of the world.
13. A statement of self-evident truth.
14. It's an instrument used to determine parallel straight lines.
15. The parrot.
16. Duncan Phyfe was a famous American cabinet maker of the early Federal period. He lived from 1768 to 1854.
17. Thomas Alva Edison in 1914.
18. There were one hundred and twenty men in the expedition of

whom ninety were members of the crew.

19. The hot water would heat the cold because there is energy in heat and in cold there is none.
20. An optical illusion.
21. A ship travelling eastward is lighter because of the earth's eastward rotation.
22. The strip of stars better known as the milky way; hence the word galaxy has come to mean an assemblage of brilliant persons or things.
23. A sun dial.
24. Scandinavian books containing the northern mythology.
25. The amount of energy needed to lift a pound one foot.

ANSWERS TO SUPER QUIZ II-D

1. A Treasury note is a demand note issued by the United States Treasury while a bank note is a promissory note issued by a legally authorized bank, and forming part of the country's currency.
2. It was the name of the fashionable promenade of Vienna, in old Vienna.
3. You'd be in a dory with whaling men in it being pulled over the waves by a wounded whale which had been harpooned.
4. Shorthand.
5. A bull manipulates to force the market up; a bear to force it down.
6. Forty-eight feet.
7. An explosive powder of high power.
8. One hundred and twenty-eight cubic feet. (A cord of wood is 8 x 4 x 4)
9. Kelp or the ashes of burnt seaweed.
10. A worm, commonly known as the angle worm, which comes out of the earth usually at night.
11. It is a process which protects milk from harmful bacteria through heating it not less than 142 degrees Fahrenheit for thirty minutes.
12. A person afflicted with mental unsoundness, accompanied by delusions.
13. Mica.
14. At Runnymede, June 15, 1215.
15. Lombard Street.
16. A spy or stool pigeon employed by the police.
17. A maple orchard, where sugar is tapped and refined maple sugar is made.
18. Fly's wings vibrate 330 times a second; the bee's 190 times.
19. A hand of playing cards without a picture card.
20. It is Xenophon's story of the "March of the Ten Thousand".
21. Lucrezia Borgia and Catherine de Medici.
22. Isaiah Sellers, a Mississippi river pilot whom Clemens knew as the "Patriarch of the Craft".
23. Aurora Australis.
24. Tar, pitch, and turpentine.
25. A sword or mace bearer; also an official who has the care of the interior of an English cathedral.